LABORATORY TECHNIQUES
IN
ZOOLOGY

ROY MAHONEY, A.I.S.T.

Chief Technician, Zoology Department,
University College, London

WASHINGTON
BUTTERWORTHS
1966

Suggested U.D.C. number: 591·08

Printed in Great Britain by R. J. Acford Ltd., Industrial Estate,
Chichester, Sussex

76811

CONTENTS

v

PREFACE

During the past decade, teachers of zoological techniques, including myself, have been unable to obtain a textbook which could be used as a basis for a teaching syllabus. It is hoped that this book will fill the gap, and be found useful not only to students and teachers of the combined City and Guilds of London Institute and Institute of Science Technology course, but also to other workers who are interested in the practical side of zoology.

This book is the result of a collection of techniques made during the past twenty years. Many of the techniques have been tried and tested by either myself or by one of my close associates. The first chapter—Phylum Technology—is arranged according to a system devised by R. H. Harris, a system which has proved itself during the many years of teaching by both he and myself. Many of the techniques have one or more modifications, but the method given is that favoured by the author. This does not mean that other modifications should not be tried. Due to lack of space, the section on microscopes has been deliberately abbreviated and includes only the basic principles of compound and phase-contrast microscopes. Similarly, some other small sections of the combined C. & G./I.S.T. syllabuses, such as electrophoresis and chromatography have been omitted. Excellent textbooks on these techniques are already available.

References to the numerous techniques have been given wherever possible, but in many cases the origins are obscure. I hope that I will be forgiven for any omission.

I would like to thank Mr. C. Atherton and Mr. B. Brooker for producing the excellent photographs, Dr. D. H. Tompsett for his advice on corrosion techniques, Miss B. Shirra for her help regarding neurological staining methods, Mr. R. H. Harris for his technical advice and encouragement, my own technical assistants for their efforts, and last, but not least, my wife Sheila for her patience and encouragement.

R. MAHONEY

Billericay,
1965

PHYLUM TECHNOLOGY

TAXONOMY

By studying the anatomy of adult animals, together with their embryological development, zoologists are able to arrange the immense number of animals into some sort of plan. Those which have many similarities will be more closely linked than others which have few similarities. The part of zoological work which deals with this sort of planning is known as Taxonomy, Classification or Systematics. The scheme of classification will be more easily followed if one considers it from its starting place, the individual species.

SPECIES: A species are animals which interbreed freely with one another, and which are essentially similar in all details of their anatomy (excepting sexual differences); e.g., stoats.

GENUS (plural, GENERA): Species which are similar in most respects are grouped together as a genus; e.g., stoats, weasel, pole cat, mink, and ferret.

SCIENTIFIC NAME: The scientific name of an animal is formed by combining its generic name and its specific name. The first letter of the generic name is always capitalized; e.g., *Mustela erminea*, the 'stoat' or 'ermine'. This system of combining the genus with the specific name is known as the Binomial System of Nomenclature. It was first devised by the Swedish naturalist Linnaeus in the middle of the eighteenth century. Strictly, the scientific name is followed directly by the name of the zoologist who first described the species and gave it its first scientific name; e.g., *Mustela erminea* Linnaeus or *Mustela erminea* L. Also, the year in which the species was first named is added and is set off by a comma or parentheses; e.g., *Mustela erminea* Linnaeus, 1758. If, at a later date, a species is transferred to another genus from one with which it was originally linked, parentheses are placed around the original describer.

VARIETY: There are often minor variations between members of a particular species, and when sufficiently distinct, these differing animals are called varieties. They are particularly noticeable among domestic animals.

SUBSPECIES: When distinct varieties inhabit definite geographical areas they are usually referred to as subspecies, the subspecific name following immediately after the specific name; e.g., *Mustela erminea stablis* Barrett-Hamilton, 1904, the British mainland 'stoat', and *Mustela erminea ricinae* Miller, 1907, the Islay and Jura 'stoat'.

SUBGENUS: A genus may include species which, although not differing sufficiently to warrant a separate genus of their own, and which perhaps fall into natural groups within the genus, are given subgeneric names, one of which must be the same as that of the genus; e.g., *Sciurus* (*Parasciurus*) *niger* is a species of the subgenus *Parasciurus* in the genus *Sciurus*. Note that the subgeneric name is placed after the genus and is in parentheses. It has become the practice to place the old generic name in parentheses after the new generic name with an intervening equals sign; e.g., *Acinonyx* (= Cynailurus). This practice is not, however, strictly correct, and care should be taken to see that confusion does not occur between old generic names and subgenera.

FAMILY: A family comprises those genera which bear certain degrees of resemblance. The family name must be derived from the genus which has been fixed as typical, and must end in the suffix *-idae*. The typical genus from which the family name is derived is known as the type genus.

ORDER: In a similar way, those families which bear some degree of resemblance are linked together to form an order.

CLASS: Again, orders which show major similarities are placed together in a class.

PHYLUM: A phylum comprises classes which have the same general anatomical structure.

The taxonomic divisions given above are the major ones, but in practice there are several other divisions which are commonly used. The subdivisions are generally prefixed with 'super' for a higher division and 'sub' for a lower one; e.g., subphylum, subclass and superfamily. There are certain agreed endings for many of these divisional names: they are

> Superfamily ends in *-oidea*; e.g., Canoidea
> Family ends in *-idae*; e.g., Canidae
> Subfamily ends in *-inae*; e.g., Caninae

There are also proper endings for two other subdivisions of subfamilies, these are TRIBE which ends in *-ini*, and SUBTRIBE which ends in *-ina*.

2

A complete list of the taxonomic divisions is given below (Simpson, 1945).

Kingdom
  Phylum
    Subphylum
      Superclass
        Class
          Subclass
            Infraclass
              Cohort
                Superorder
                Order
                  Suborder
                    Infraorder
                      Superfamily
                      Family
                        Subfamily
                        Tribe
                          Subtribe
                          Genus
                            Subgenus
                            Species
                            Subspecies

Other divisions such as infrafamily, supertribe, or supergenus, may be added to this list if necessary.

Modern taxonomists usually divide the animal kingdom into twenty-six phyla belonging to two separate subkingdoms.

Subkingdom PROTOZOA: acellular animals.
  Phylum PROTOZOA.

Subkingdom METAZOA: the metazoa are multicellular animals, the cells of which are all working in concert so as to perform the functions of one individual. The cells may lose their boundaries in the adult state.

(1) MESOZOA: multicellular animals composed of an outer layer of somatic cells and interior reproductive cells.
  Phylum MESOZOA.

(2) PARAZOA: multicellular animals which show only incipient tissue formation. There are no organ systems, and the internal cells are of different kinds. No mouth or digestive tract. The animals are porous with one to many internal cavities lined by choanocytes or 'collar-cells'.
  Phylum PORIFERA.

3

(3) EUMETAZOA: animals which have a more complex structure with the cells forming proper tissue and organs. They have a mouth and a digestive tract (except when they have been lost by parasitic degeneration). Only a small proportion of the interior cells are used for reproduction. The body is not porous and there are no body cavities lined with choanocytes.

(*a*) Eumetazoa showing radial, biradial, or radio-bilateral symmetry. Tentacles bearing nematocysts usually surround the mouth. No rows of ciliated plates.
Phylum CNIDARIA.

(*b*) Eumetazoa with biradial symmetry. If tentacles are present they do not surround the mouth, and may bear lasso cells and not nematocysts. Eight radial rows of ciliated plates (ctenes) are present.
Phylum CTENOPHORA.

(*c*) Eumetazoa with bilateral symmetry or with secondary radial symmetry. Organs are developed, and there is usually well-developed mesoderm derived from the endoderm. Usually with body spaces other than the digestive cavity. An anus is generally present.

All remaining phyla of the animal kingdom belong to the bilateria. They are:

Phylum PLATYHELMINTHES: anus absent.

Acoelomates

Phylum NEMERTINA: anus present.

The acoelomates have the region between the body wall and the digestive tract filled with mesenchyme.

Phylum ENTOPROCTA: intestine looped.

Pseudocoelomates

Phylum ASCHELMINTHES: intestine more or less straight.

Phylum ACANTHOCEPHALA: no intestine.

The pseudocoelomates have a space between the body wall and digestive tract, but this is not a true coelom but a remnant of the blastocoel and it is therefore called a pseudocoel. An anus is always present.

The remaining bilateria are all coelomates, i.e., they have a true coelom. They usually have a well-developed entomesoderm. They

4

can be roughly divided into those with a lophophore and those without a lophophore.

Phylum ECTOPROCTA or POLYZOA

With lophophore—Phylum PHORONIDA

Phylum BRACHIOPODA

A lophophore is a circular or crescentic or double, spirally coiled ridge, bearing ciliated tentacles.

Without lophophore
- Phylum MOLLUSCA
- Phylum SIPUNCULIDA
- Phylum ANNELIDA
- Phylum ONYCHOPHORA
- Phylum TARDIGRADA
- Phylum PENTASTOMIDA
- Phylum ARTHROPODA
- Phylum ECHINODERMATA
- Phylum CHAETOGNATHA
- Phylum POGONOPHORA
- Phylum HEMICHORDATA
- Phylum CHORDATA

This scheme omits Phylum ARCHAEOCYATHA, which were reef-forming, sponge-like organisms but are now totally extinct.

PHYLUM PROTOZOA

The protozoa are acellular animals (a few are regarded as plants) without tissues or organs. Protozoa exist singly or in colonies, and except for a very few instances such a colony will be formed from components which are all identical, except when they are engaged in reproductive activities. It is for this reason that the colonial forms cannot be confused with metazoans.

Class Mastigophora, the 'flagellates'. The locomotory organelles are flagella, which may persist throughout life, or appear intermittently, or may only appear in young stages.

Subclass Phytomastigophorea. This subclass is usually dealt with by botanists who regard this group as plants. Chloroplasts are usually present, but they may be colourless and are placed in this subclass because they are obviously related to chloroplast-bearing forms. Examples of this subclass are *Ochromonas, Chilomonas, Volvox, Euglena, Ceratium*, and *Noctiluca*.

Subclass Zoomastigophorea. Without chloroplasts. Some examples are *Histomonas, Trypanosoma, Leishmania, Trichomonas, Trichonympha*, and *Opalina*.

Class Sarcodina. The locomotory organelles are pseudopodia.

Subclass Rhizopodea. Without axopodia. Some examples are *Amoeba, Entamoeba, Difflugia, Arcella, Elphidium, Globigerina*, and *Physarum*.

Subclass Actinpodea. Axopodia (ray-like, stiffened pseudopodia) are

5

present. Examples are *Actinosphaerium, Acanthometra*. The first example belongs to the order Heliozoida 'sun animalcules' and the second example belongs to the order Radiolarida or 'radiolarians'.

Class Sporozoa. Obvious locomotory organelles are lacking; all members of this class are parasitic and form spores. Some examples are *Monocystis, Gregarina, Plasmodium, Babesia* and *Eimeria*.

Class Ciliata, the 'ciliates'. Locomotory organelles are cilia. Two types of nucleus are present in ciliates, micronucleus and macronucleus. Some examples are *Prorodon, Balantidium, Colpoda, Tetrahymena, Paramecium, Acineta, Vorticella, Carchesium, Spirostomum, Stentor, Nyctotherus, Tintinnopsis, Euplotes* and *Stylonychia*.

CULTURAL METHODS
Amoeba

Cover to a depth of $\frac{1}{2}$ in. the bottom of some sterile Petri-dishes, with either boiled rain-water or Chalkley's medium. The pH in either case should be adjusted to between 5·8 and 6·0. Into this solution place boiled wheat grains (about 2 to every 25 ml.). After several days a mould-like growth of *Colpidia* should form around each wheat grain. This is the food source.

Obtain some living *Amoeba*, either from an established culture or by collection. *Amoeba* are frequently obtained from the surface of mud and decaying leaves at the bottom of ponds and slow streams. Some species are found on *Sphagnum* moss or in soil.

Inoculate the medium with some living *Amoeba*, making a note of the date when they are added. Subculture every month, or before, should the culture become infected with moulds or other micro-organisms. Periodically inspect the culture with the aid of a micro-scope. It is a healthy sign if fission is taking place. If the *Amoeba* are all at the top or the bottom of the culture medium, this is usually a sign of contamination and the *Amoebae* should be subcultured. The cultures should be kept at a temperature of about 18°C and out of direct sunlight.

Chalkley's Medium
Stock solution:

Sodium chloride	.. 20 g
Potassium chloride	.. 0·8 g
Calcium chloride	.. 1·2 g
Glass redistilled water	made up to 1 l.

To prepare the medium: dilute 5 ml. of stock solution with 995 ml. of glass redistilled water. If extra food is required, further *Colpidia* should be cultured.

Soil amoebae are easily obtained and cultivated in the following way: soak some soil in water for 1–2 weeks; then with a wire loop remove some of the surface scum. Streak this scum on to the surface of an agar plate (0·1 per cent peptone, 1·5 per cent agar). As bacteria multiply, any cysts of *soil amoebae* which are present hatch out and feed on the bacteria leaving clear patches in the streaks. The bacteria take about 1–7 days to develop into a thick culture.

Paramecium

The method of Wichterman (1953) using either hay or lettuce infusions gives excellent results.

(*a*) Hay infusion: boil 6 g of cut timothy hay (spikes and stems cut into 1 in. lengths) in 1 l. of water for 20 min; cover flask-opening with a well-fitting beaker and boil for a further 15 min. Leave covered to stand for 24 h and then inoculate with *Paramecium*. This method does well for all species except *P. aurelia* and *P. bursaria* (these are better kept on a more dilute infusion using 4 g of hay per litre instead of 6 g). Maintain for long periods by adding a few pieces of boiled hay about once a month.

(*b*) Lettuce infusion: separate the clean leaves of a lettuce and dry them slowly until they are crisp and brown in a warm oven. Grind in a pestle and mortar; the resultant dried powder will keep for a long period in a stoppered bottle. Add 1·5 g of the dried lettuce to 1 l. of boiling distilled water and allow to boil for 5 min. Filter while hot into smaller (250 ml.) flasks and autoclave. Leave in stoppered flasks overnight and the medium is then ready for use. Sealed flasks of the medium will keep for long periods. Mix 2 parts of the medium with 1 part distilled water to obtain the correct working strength. An excess of $CaCO_3$ may be added to bring the pH to 7·2.

All species will grow in this medium except *P. calkinsi* and *P. woodruffi*, and it is especially good for *P. bursaria*. *P. calkinsi* and *P. woodruffi* from brackish water require a mixture of sea-water. Wichterman successfully used 2 parts filtered sea-water with 3 parts hay or lettuce infusion.

The following notes on culture methods for algae and protozoa were kindly supplied by The Botany School, Cambridge.

SOIL + WATER CULTURES

In many cases the best growth of algae or protozoa for morphological purposes is achieved by the soil-plus-water method.

The basic medium E is made up as follows: put about 1 or 2 cm³ of a good calcareous garden loam in the bottom of a test tube or jar. Carefully add about 7–10 ml. of water (tap-water is usually satisfactory). Plug or cover the vessel and steam for 1 h on two

7

consecutive days. Allow to stand a further day before inoculating. The pH should then be about 7·4.

Stand cultures of photosynthetic forms in a window avoiding direct sunshine. A room temperature of 18°–22°C is usually best for all these cultures. Extra light may be given from filament or fluorescent lamps.

The following are among the most useful varients of E.

M: using a calcareous clay soil in place of the garden loam.

$E +$ Ca: a speck (about 2 per cent of the soil volume) of $CaCO_3$ is placed beneath the soil. Recommended for volvocales.

NH_4E: NH_4M: a speck (about 2 per cent of the soil volume) of $NH_4.Mg.PO_4$ is placed beneath the soil. The latter varient is recommended for *Euglena*.

P; $P + E$: peats of various kinds with or without soil are used to produce media of various pH values and of various nutrient contents.

$St M$; $St E$: a speck of starch placed beneath the soil. The former varient is recommended for *Astasia* and *Polytoma*.

$Gr E +$ Ca: a pearl barley grain added with the $CaCO_3$ below the soil in a test tube culture. Recommended for *Paramecium aurelia* and *P. caudatum*, also *Spirostomum* and *Colpidium*.

$W E$: a wheat grain per test tube placed beneath the soil.

Any of these media may be made up with sea-water at a quarter, half or full strength.

SOIL EXTRACT CULTURES

Many algae and some protozoa grow very well in soil extract cultures and are free from the detritus which can be a disadvantage in the case of soil + water cultures. Earlier exhaustion of nutrients is, however, a possible disadvantage with the soil extract cultures.

The basic medium e is prepared as follows: put some good garden loam in a vessel; add water until the volume of supernatant water is twice that of the soil. Heat in a steamer for 3 h, allow the soil to settle and then strain the supernatant liquid through muslin. Add a little (about 2 per cent of the volume of extract) preservative*. This stock solution can be kept for several months.

To make the medium, use 10 per cent of the extract in glass-distilled or deionized water; put it into culture vessels and autoclave (bring up to 20 lb./in.^{2} and remove heat).

---

* Preservative: *o*-chlorobenzene ..   ..   1 part
             ethylene dichloride   ..   1 part
             n-butyl chloride ..   ..   2 parts

This preservative is *very poisonous* and great care must be taken not to inhale the vapour. All traces of the preservative are removed during the autoclaving process.

8

It is best to make a number of stock soil extracts of different pH values and from soils of different organic contents. These are then mixed in various proportions according to experience. The pH is measured the day after the medium has been made up.

The following are the most useful varients of *e*:

e + *s* : Soil extract	..	..	..	10 per cent
KNO₃ ..	..	..	..	0·02 per cent
K₂HPO₄	..	..	..	0·002 per cent
MgSO₄.7H₂O ..	..	..	0·002 per cent

Recommended for *Paramecium bursaria*. *B.E.e* + *s*: this is *e* + *s* with 0·1 per cent of beef extract. Only to be used with bacteria-free cultures.

OTHER EASILY OBTAINED PROTOZOA
(after Mackinnon and Hawes, 1961)

Cephaline gregarines are readily obtained from mealworms, which are sold by pet shops as food for amphibians and reptiles. Mealworms are the larvae of the beetle *Tenebrio molitor*, and contain four cephaline gregarines, the first three of those listed being the most common: *Gregarina cuneata* Stein; *G. polymorpha* Hammerschmidt; *G. steini* Berndt; *Steinina ovalis* Léger and Dubosq.

Lightly anaesthetize the larva, cut off the head, and at the posterior end make two oblique cuts through the body wall, taking care not to

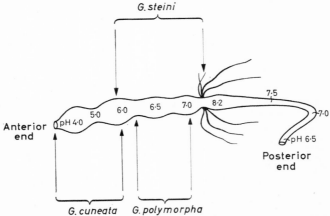

Figure 1.1. Approximate distribution of three gregarines in the gut of a mealworm larva (after Göhre, 1943)

cut the gut. Pull away the hind end with the gut attached to it. Float into Ringer's solution or invertebrate saline and remove any adherent fat. The three commonest species live in definite regions of the gut (see *Figure 1.1*).

Cut away the hind gut, and cut the mid-gut into two to separate the first species from the last two species. Tease fragments in a drop of invertebrate saline on a slide. Apply a No. 0 coverslip and examine under a microscope fitted with a high-power objective.

Gregarina blattarum v. Siebold is frequently found in the mid-gut of cockroaches of the following genera: *Periplaneta americana*; *Blatta orientalis*; *Blattella germanica*.

METHODS FOR EXAMINING PROTOZOA
A. IN THE LIVING STATE

The following methods are recommended:

(*i*) Use a hanging drop preparation, i.e. put one drop of a thick culture on to the under surface of a coverslip and hold this above a glass slide by means of a ring of plasticine or other support.

(*ii*) Put a drop of thick culture on a slide, and cover with a coverslip held apart from the slide by a hair.

Whichever method is used, the protozoa should be examined with a high-power microscope or, better still, with a phase contrast microscope. It may be necessary to slow down fast-moving protozoa, and this is easily done by mixing the drop of culture with a drop of 2 per cent aqueous methyl cellulose. (Methyl cellulose takes about 24 h to dissolve in cold water. The mixture should not be heated.)

Vital staining methods

(*i*) Brilliant Cresyl Blue. A basic dye staining many structures, including the skeletal apparatus of astomate ciliates. The stock solution is 1 per cent in absolute alcohol. Dilute 10 times for use, place a drop on a slide, allow the alcohol to evaporate, add a drop of culture and a coverslip, sealing the edge with melted vaseline. Leave to stain for 5–30 min.

(*ii*) Janus Green B. This stains mitochondria. Use like brilliant cresyl blue or use in dilutions from 1:10,000 to 1:200,000.

(*iii*) Neutral Red. This stains vacuoles, and is used at dilutions of 1:10,000 or like brilliant cresyl blue. It is an indicator and food vacuoles are first coloured red, then orange and finally yellow as they pass from acid to alkaline reactions.

Demonstration of digestion in Paramecium

This is easily carried out by the following method: concentrate some of the *Paramecium* culture, and add this to some milk which has been stained with a few grains of Congo red. Put aside for two hours.

Upon examination, the process of digestion is clearly demonstrated. The ingested red fat globules turn blue at first (due to acid secretion into the food vacuole) and then through shades of purple to red (due to alkaline secretion).

Fixation methods

(*i*) *Free-living protozoa*

A drop of the culture should be concentrated by centrifugation. Pipette off some of the protozoa with as little water as possible. Allow to stand in the pipette for about one minute to enable the protozoa to relax, then eject rapidly into a few millilitres of Schaudinn's fluid + acetic acid. Allow to fix for 15 min. By alternately centrifuging and replacing the fluid with ascending grades of alcohol dehydrate the protozoa. Smear some slides with glycerol-albumen, and pick up some of the dehydrated protozoa in a pipette and allow them to fall on to the prepared slides from a height of 1 in. The protozoa should then be securely attached to the slide which should be immediately placed into absolute alcohol. The slides are then ready for staining.

(*ii*) *Sedentary protozoa*, e.g. *Vorticella*

It is often better to allow sedentary forms to attach themselves to slides or coverslips. This is done by placing a rack of clean slides or coverslips into a thick culture of the protozoa and leaving it there for several days. After this time several should be attached. Flood the slides suddenly with Schaudinn's fluid + acetic acid, and leave to fix for 15 min., then transfer to 70 per cent alcohol.

(*iii*) *Parasitic protozoa*

(*a*) *Monocystis* may be prepared by smearing a small portion of seminal vesicle of an earthworm on to a clean slide, and fixing in either Schaudinn's fluid + acetic acid or in equal parts of absolute alcohol and ether.

(*b*) *Opalina* and *Nyctotherus* may be obtained from infected frogs by emptying the rectal contents into a small Petri-dish containing some invertebrate saline. Examine the fluid with a microscope to confirm the presence of the parasites. If present, pipette some of them on to a slide, allow the slide to partially dry and then plunge into Schaudinn's fluid + acetic acid, allow to fix for 15 min.

(*c*) *Trypanosoma* and *Plasmodium* and all other protozoan parasites which live in blood are easily prepared by smearing the infected blood

11

on to clean slides and staining as for blood smears using Leishman's or Giemsa's stain.

Staining methods

(*i*) *Naked protozoa*

(*a*) *Alcoholic iron haematoxylin method*—This is an excellent technique for many protozoa. The method is as follows:

Wash the slide in 70 per cent alcohol, then mordant for 10 min in 1 per cent iron alum in 70 per cent alcohol. Wash in 70 per cent alcohol, stain in 1 per cent haematin in 70 per cent alcohol for 10 min. Wash in 70 per cent alcohol, then differentiate under a microscope with 1 per cent iron alum in 70 per cent alcohol. Dehydrate through 90 per cent alcohol and absolute alcohol, clear in cedarwood oil, then xylene, and finally mount in Canada balsam, or Green Euparal. If a counterstain is required, Orange G (saturated solution in 90 per cent alcohol) may be used.

(*b*) *Romanowsky stains, e.g. Leishman's and Giemsa's stains*—These give excellent results with protozoa contained in blood smears (see page 186).

(*ii*) *Shelled protozoa*, e.g. Foraminifera

Fix in 5 per cent formalin in sea-water, and then dissolve away the shell in weak acid (acid alcohol is suitable). When this has been carried out, wash the foraminiferans in 70 per cent alcohol to remove the acid, and then stain by any desired method. Borax carmine, Mayer's paracarmine and alcoholic iron haematoxylin give excellent results (see page 249, and also page 195 for use of chelating agents).

SPECIAL STAINING METHODS

Feulgen's test for deoxyribonucleic acid (DNA)

This test for DNA is very easily applied to protozoa which have been attached to slides. The method is described on page 253. Very small nuclei or those with little DNA may resist the Feulgen reaction or the result may be very pale. Such difficult subjects, e.g. *Trypanosomids* and *limax amoebae*, should be stained with one of the following methods:

Delamater's Azur A or Thionine

(*a*) Fix in Schaudinn's fixative + acetic acid; (*b*) Hydrolyse as for Feulgen's test; (*c*) Rinse and stain for 2–10 h in one of the following: (*i*) thionine—to 10 ml. of 0·25 per cent aqueous solution thionine add, 15 min before use, 1 drop of thionyl chloride. Nuclei are stained intensely, cytoplasm a pale violet. (*ii*) Azur A: add 2 drops of thionyl chloride to 10 ml. of 0·25 per cent aqueous solution. Azur A, again

12

15 min before use. This stains the nuclei only; (*d*) After Azur A stain the cytoplasm lightly with Chromotrope 2R; (*e*) Dehydrate, clear and mount.

Too much thionyl chloride causes precipitation in either stain. Huebschmann (1952) made the following good modification. Make up the stain as follows:

2 per cent aqueous Azur A	10 ml.
N/1 hydrochloric acid	0·6 ml.
10 per cent potassium metabisulphite solution	0·6 ml.

Stain for 30–60 min. If overstained, differentiate in 70–96 per cent alcohol.

Delamater's Basic Fuchsin

(*a*) Fix in Schaudinn's fixative + acetic acid; (*b*) Hydrolyse for 5 min at room temperature, 5 min at 60°C and a further 5 min at room temperature in N/1 hydrochloric acid; (*c*) Give three rinses in distilled water; (*d*) Mordant for 4 min in 2 per cent formalin; (*e*) Wash in distilled water, then stain for 15 min in 0·5 per cent basic fuchsin in 0·04 N hydrochloric acid (the solution is made by adding 0·2 ml. N/1 HCl to 5 ml. of 0·5 per cent basic fuchsin); (*f*) Wash in distilled water; (*g*) Dehydrate and simultaneously destain the cytoplasm in the graded alcohols; (*h*) Clear in xylene, and mount in Canada balsam.

DEMONSTRATION OF FLAGELLAE
Lugol's Iodine

Irrigate the organisms with a drop of Lugol's iodine. After a few seconds the animals will die but their flagellae should be clearly demonstrated. For permanent preparations the following method is recommended:

Couch's Modification of Loeffler's Stain

(*a*) Mount the concentrated protozoa in a small drop of water; (*b*) Fix in the vapour of osmium tetroxide and allow to dry; (*c*) Heat gently in the following mordant for ½–1 min:

20 per cent tannic acid (aqueous solution) ..	10 parts
Ferrous sulphate (saturated aqueous solution)	5 parts
Basic fuchsin (saturated solution in 95 per cent alcohol)	1 part

The mixture should be filtered before use; (*d*) Rinse in water; (*e*) Stain in alkaline Gentian violet in anilin water. This is prepared by shaking up 5 ml. anilin oil in 95 ml. of distilled water, and dissolving 4 g Gentian violet in this solution. Make alkaline with 1 or 2 drops

13

of sodium hydroxide solution. Filter just before use. Warm gently in this stain for 1–2 min, wash in water, dry and mount.

SILVER IMPREGNATION METHODS

Silver impregnation is frequently used on ciliates and flagellates. It provides clear black-and-white maps of the kinetosomatic distribution in ciliates. In flagellates, it shows up the flagellae, and some other organellae.

(1) *The Chatton-Lwoff Technique for Ciliates*

An improved modification by Professor J. Corliss (1953).

(*a*) Fix in Champy's fluid for 1–3 min (osmium tetroxide vapour may be used as an alternative).

(*b*) Wash twice in Da Fano's fixative and then leave in a third change for several hours. Specimens may be stored in this for several weeks. Da Fano's fixative is:

Cobalt nitrate	1 g
Sodium chloride..	1 g
40 per cent formaldehyde	10 ml.
Distillled water	90 ml.

(Use sea-water in place of distilled water and omit the sodium chloride for marine organisms.)

(*c*) Concentrate the organisms by letting them settle or by centrifugation. Place one drop of them on to a warm slide. Add 1 drop of warm (35–45°C) saline gelatin and mix with the tip of a warm needle. Draw off the excess fluid so as to leave the specimens grouped in a thin layer of gelatin. Do not inject bubbles into the gelatin, but perform the operation briskly. Saline gelatin is:

Powdered gelatin	10 g
Sodium chloride..	0·05 g
Distilled water	100 ml.

Store in a refrigerator until required.

(*d*) Place the slide into a moist chamber (e.g., Petri-dish with a wet filter paper) and put it in the refrigerator or on ice for about 2 min while the gelatin sets. Place in cold 3 per cent silver nitrate (5–10°C) and keep it cold to prevent the gelatin from melting, and dark to prevent premature reduction of the silver; the best place for this is the refrigerator. Keep it there for 10–20 min depending on the organism.

(*e*) Flush with cold distilled water and place in a white-bottomed dish (or glass vessel standing on a filter paper) containing cold distilled water to a depth of 3–4 cm. Expose to light. Sunlight will do, or the cheapest kind of ultraviolet health lamp. The exposure time, usually 20–30 min, is determined for the material by trial. The preparation must be kept cold.

(*f*) Remove to 70 per cent alcohol, dehydrate, clear in xylene, and mount in Canada balsam.

N.B. Any preparations which are too black at the end of stage (*d*) may be toned under a microscope by covering with a drop of 1 per cent gold chloride. Have ready a large beaker of cold distilled water so that the toning may be instantly stopped at the desired time; the gold chloride may act very rapidly.

(2) *Horvath's Formol-silver Method*

For ciliate fibrillar systems, cilia and trichocysts, and also flagellate pellicular systems: (*a*) Concentrate the organisms by centrifugation. Decant the supernatant fluid and suspend the animals in a few millilitres of tap-water; (*b*) Into 1 ml. of 40 per cent formaldehyde squirt 1–4 ml. of the concentrated culture, and mix well; (*c*) After 1 min centrifuge and decant, and immediately add 1 per cent (or stronger) silver nitrate solution; (*d*) After 3–4 min, centrifuge and decant as much as possible. Add 2–3 ml. of 1 per cent sodium hydroxide solution; (*e*) Shake continuously for 2 min and then centrifuge; (*f*) Wash and centrifuge first in distilled water and then in 30, 50, and 70 per cent alcohol; (*g*) Then add a few drops of 90 per cent alcohol and pour into a tube with a little glycerol–alcohol (80 per cent alcohol + equal volume of glycerol); (*h*) Mount in glycerol–alcohol.

N.B. The longer the reagents react (especially the formalin), the greater the deposit of silver.

The greater the proportion of culture to formalin, the more the deeper structures (neuronemes, endoplasmic boundaries, contractile vacuoles, etc.) take up the silver.

The greater the proportion of formalin to the culture, the greater the prominence of the lattice.

(3) *Bodian Protargol (Protein-silver) Method for Protozoa*

This technique was originally developed for vertebrate nervous tissue but has been successfully used, especially for flagellates, in proto-zoology. The preliminaries are:

(*A*) Preparation of the stain. *The protargol must be of good quality*. Make a 1 per cent solution by sprinkling it on to the surface of distilled water in a beaker, without heating, stirring or otherwise disturbing, until the solution is complete. Prepare fresh before use.

(*B*) The solution is used in the presence of copper. Have ready snips of copper wire cut into lengths weighing 0·5 g. They are eventually added to the protargol solution in the quantity of 5 g to every 100 ml. of solution.

15

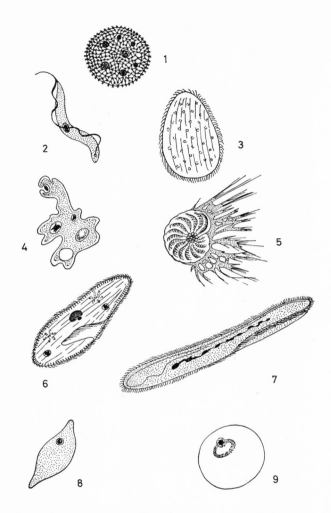

Figure 1.2. Some examples of protozoans: 1. *Volvox*, a phytomastigophoran; 2. *Trypanosoma*, a zoomastigophoran; 3. *Opalina*, a zoomastigophoran; 4. *Amoeba*, a sarcodinan; 5. *Elphidium*, a foraminiferan; 6. *Paramecium*, a ciliate; 7. *Spirostomum*, a ciliate; 8. *Monocystis*, trophozoite stage of a sporozoan; 9. *Plasmodium*, malarial parasite in a red blood cell

(*C*) The protozoa must be fixed in Hollande's or Bouin's fluid. Hollande's fluid is:

Copper acetate, neutral..	..	..	..	2·5 g
Picric acid	.. ..	..	..	..	4 g
40 per cent formaldehyde	..	..	..	10 ml.
Glacial acetic acid	..	..	..	1·5 ml.
Distilled water ..	..	..	..	..	100 ml.

Dissolve the copper acetate in a mortar in cold water. Add picric acid little by little. This mixture keeps. Add the formalin and acetic just before use.

(*D*) Bleach if necessary, and especially if the material has been stored for a long time in alcohol after fixation. The bleaching method is: (*i*) Take to water; (*ii*) Transfer to 0·5 per cent potassium permanganate (aqueous solution) for 5 min; (*iii*) Wash in distilled water, and transfer to 5 per cent oxalic acid for 5 min. Then wash in several changes of distilled water.

The impregnation method can now be carried out: (*a*) Place copper wire up to the amount needed in a dish, pour in the protargol solution and soak coverslip preparations in it for 2–3 days. Incubate resistant material at 37°C. Change the solution on the second day (most coverslip preparations can be handled in 10 ml. of solution, which requires a single 0·5 g length of wire); (*b*) Wash in distilled water; (*c*) Reduce in 1 per cent hydroquinone in 5 per cent sodium sulphite, for 5–10 min. A weaker solution may give better results; (*d*) Wash in several changes of distilled water; (*e*) Tone in 1 per cent gold chloride for 4–5 min; (*f*) Wash in distilled water; (*g*) Place in 2 per cent oxalic acid until the preparation is purple, usually about 3 min; (*h*) Wash well in distilled water then transfer to 5 per cent sodium thiosulphate for 5–10 min; (*i*) Wash in several changes of distilled water, dehydrate, clear and mount.

EMBEDDING METHOD FOR SECTIONING OF PROTOZOA

(*a*) Fix the protozoa, and wash with distilled water. If an alcoholic fixative is used it will be necessary to bring the organisms to water gradually by centrifugation.

(*b*) Prepare a block of agar and cut a small cavity in its upper surface. Into this cavity pipette the concentrated, fixed protozoans and then remove the supernatant fluid. Seal the cavity with warm agar.

(*c*) Cut the block into shape and embed it in the usual way in paraffin wax.

N.B. It helps if the protozoa are lightly stained with haematoxylin or some other easily removable stain so that they are easily seen during

17

the operation. Large protozoa such as *Opalina* and *Spirostomum* may be orientated in the agar with a warm needle under a dissecting microscope.

EXTRACTION OF FORAMINIFERA FROM FORAMINIFEROUS ROCK
(after Johnson, J. C., 1935)

(*i*) Crush small pieces of the rock, and put the fragments into a cloth bag. Immerse in water and knead. The resultant milky fluid is poured away, and the bag is re-immersed in the water. It is then kneaded again, changing the water regularly until the water remains clear.

(*ii*) The bag containing the washed fragments of rock is now boiled for 1–2 h in a strong aqueous solution of sodium bicarbonate. It is then washed in running water for several minutes. Only the foraminifera should remain.

EXTRACTION OF RADIOLARIA FROM RADIOLARIAN ROCK
(after Johnson, J. C., 1935)

(*i*) Boil small pieces of the rock in a solution of 4 oz. washing soda in 1 pint of water, for 30 min.

(*ii*) Decant about nine-tenths of the water and gently crush the remaining mass. Add the decanted solution again and continue alternative boiling and crushing until all the earth is well broken up.

(*iii*) Radiolaria will meanwhile have floated off in the decanted solution. Stir this well, then allow the radiolaria to settle.

(*iv*) When they have settled, pour away the solution above them and discard it. The radiolaria should then be boiled for a further ten min in a fresh solution of washing soda.

(*v*) Finally, put the sediment into a jar with about $\frac{1}{2}$ oz. water to which has been added $\frac{1}{2}$ teaspoonful of sodium bicarbonate. When the sodium bicarbonate has dissolved, add carefully 1 oz. concentrated sulphuric acid. This will liberate any radiolaria which are still trapped in the earth, and will clean all of them. Wash well in several changes of running water, then store in distilled water.

PHYLUM MESOZOA

The Mesozoa are endoparasites that during at least some part of the life-cycle are constructed from one or more reproductive cells which are enclosed by a layer of cells known as the syncytium. The life-cycles of the Mesozoa are complicated and involve alternation of sexual and asexual generations. They are common parasites in the nephridia of some cephalopods, particularly squid and octopus. The total number of cells is usually less than 25, and the ordinary form of the animal is a minute ciliated worm-like animal, 6 to 7 mm in length.

PHYLUM PORIFERA

There appear to be no published techniques for members of this phylum, but good results could no doubt be obtained if they are treated like parasitic protozoa, as regards preparation of permanent mounts.

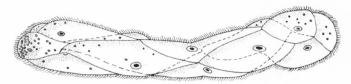

Figure 1.3. A Mesozoan: Nematogen of *Pseudicyema truncatum*, from *Sepia* (after Whitman, 1882, by courtesy of McGraw-Hill Book Co., Inc.)

PHYLUM PORIFERA

The Porifera or 'sponges' are asymmetrical or radially symmetrical metazoa which are without organs, mouth or nervous tissue. The entire body is permeated with minute pores, canals and chambers through which flows a current of water. One or more of the internal chambers is lined with choanocytes or 'collar-cells'. The incurrent openings are known as ostia, and the excurrent openings are known as oscula. The ostia are always much smaller than the one or more oscula. All adult porifera are sessile, and except for members of the family Spongillidae are all marine.

Class Calcarea, the calcareous sponges. The skeleton is composed of separate calcareous spicules, which may be one-, three-, or four-rayed. Examples of this class are: *Leucosolenia, Clathrina, Sycon* and *Grantia.*

Class Hexactinellida, the glass sponges. The skeleton is composed of triaxon (6-rayed) siliceous spicules or some modification of the triaxon form, which may be separate or united into a network. Examples are *Euplectella* and *Hyalonema.*

Class Demospongiae. The skeleton is composed of siliceous spicules or horny fibres or both.

Subclass Tetractinellida. The spicules are tetraxon in form which are typically 4-rayed. There are no horny fibres of spongin. Examples are *Geodia* and *Thenea.*

Subclass Myxospongida. Sponges of simple structure with no spicules.

Subclass Monaxonida. The larger spicules are monaxial (single-rayed) Spongin may or may not be present. This subclass contains the freshwater family of sponges, *Spongillidae.* These reproduce asexually by the formation of gemmules. Examples are *Ephydatia* and *Spongilla.*

Subclass Keratosa, the horny sponges. The skeleton is composed of horny fibres of spongin, and contain no siliceous spicules. This subclass contains the family *Spongiidae,* which includes the 'bath sponges', *Euspongia* and *Hippospongia.*

CULTURAL METHODS

Small marine sponges, e.g. *Sycon, Grantia* or *Leucosolenia—* These may survive for a few weeks if kept in circulating, well aerated sea-water kept at about 10°C.

19

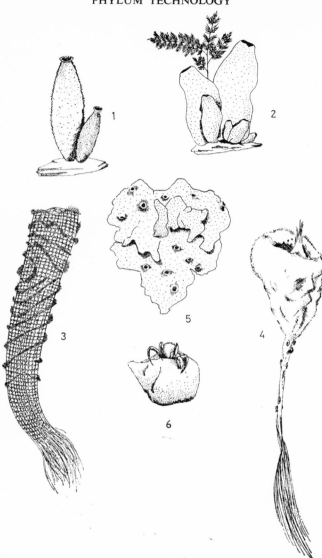

Figure 1.4. Some examples of Porifera: 1. *Sycon coronatum,* a calcareous sponge; 2. *Grantia compressa,* a calcareous sponge; 3. Dry silicious skeleton of *Euplectella aspergillum,* a hexactinellid sponge; 4. Dry siliceous skeleton of *Hyalonema,* a hexactinellid sponge; 5. *Halichondria panicea,* an encrusting monaxonid sponge; 6. A 'hermit-crab' inhabiting *Suberites,* a monaxonid sponge

PHYLUM CNIDARIA

Freshwater sponges, e.g. *Spongilla* and *Ephydatia*—These should be obtained in late summer or autumn, and will often survive for a week or so if kept in an aerated aquarium filled with pond-water. It is advisable to use water from the same source as the sponge. If this is not possible use dechlorinated tap-water that has been standing for a few days. Gemmules are easily collected and may be put into dishes of pond-water, and kept in the dark at 20°C. If the floor of the dish is lined with clean glass slides, young sponges will attach themselves to these and after 10 days' growth they should be transferred to a balanced aquarium. They may grow for several weeks, but rarely survive for a longer time.

FIXATION AND PRESERVATION

Aqueous fixatives should be avoided at all costs, as these frequently cause sponges to macerate. If the material is to be used for histological preparations, fixation in alcoholic Bouin gives excellent results:

80 per cent alcohol	150 ml.
40 per cent formaldehyde solution	60 ml.
Glacial acetic acid	15 ml.
Picric acid	1 g

Alternatively, when museum preparations are required, it is sufficient to preserve sponges in 90 per cent alcohol, after preliminary fixation in absolute alcohol for 24h.

SPICULE EXTRACTION

The identification of most sponges is carried out by microscopic examination of the spicules. To obtain the spicules, boil a small piece of sponge in 10 per cent aqueous potassium hydroxide solution until it disintegrates. Allow the spicules to settle, pour off the supernatant fluid, and rinse with distilled water. Pour away this water, and repeat the washing several times, taking care to allow the spicules to settle each time. Wash and store the spicules in 70 per cent alcohol. If permanent preparations are required, then wash several times with absolute alcohol, and then twice with xylene. Finally pipette the spicules on to a glass slide and mount in Canada balsam. Calcareous sponges may be identified by treating a small portion of the prepared spicules with dilute hydrochloric acid, which will cause them to dissolve if calcareous.

PHYLUM CNIDARIA

Until the last few years this phylum and the phylum Ctenophora were grouped together and called phylum Coelenterata. Nowadays, they are generally considered to be two distinct phyla. The Cnidaria are solitary

21

or colonial, sedentary or free-living, aquatic, diploblastic (being formed from a cellular endoderm and ectoderm separated from each other by a structureless mesogloea) animals. They are fundamentally of radial symmetry. The mouth is generally surrounded by a number of tentacles which are armed with nematocysts. The body cavity is known as the enteron and opens only through the mouth. The enteron is frequently subdivided by mesenteries or may take the form of numerous canals. There is a simple network of a nervous system. The life-cycle frequently shows alternation between an asexual hydroid and sexual medusoid generation.

Class Hydrozoa. Solitary or colonial cnidarians, typically showing alternation between asexual hydroid and sexual medusoid generations. Either generation may be suppressed. The hydranth is without mesenteries and the medusa is supplied with a velum (muscular swimming organ) and with gonads developed on the ectoderm which are discharged directly into the water.

Order Hydroida. The hydroid generation well developed. Examples are *Hydra* (with no medusoid stage), *Bouganvillea, Tubularia, Obelia* and *Clytia*.

Order Milleporina, 'stinging corals', consist of a hydroid colony occupying the surface layer of a massive, porous calcareous skeleton. Medusae are formed in special cavities, and when they are freed they are devoid of mouth, digestive system and tentacles. An example is *Millepora*.

Order Siphonophora. Consist of free-floating or swimming colonies of many types of hydroid and medusoid individuals attached to a stem or disc. The upper end of the colony may consist of one or more swimming-bells or a float (pneumatophore). Examples are *Muggiaea, Physalia* 'Portuguese man-o'-war', and *Velella*.

Class Scyphozoa (Scyphomedusae), the 'jelly-fishes'. The medusae are usually free-swimming, but a few are attached by an aboral stalk. There is no velum. Gonads are developed on the endoderm. The hydroid stage is frequently absent, but if present it consists of a scyphistoma. This gives rise to ephyra larvae by transverse fission, and these in turn develop into mature medusae. The scyphozoa are exclusively marine. Some examples are *Haliclystus, Aurelia,* and *Pelagia*.

Class Anthozoa. Members of this class exist only as polyps, the medusoid generation being completely suppressed. They exhibit hexamerous (6-rayed), octomerous (8-rayed), or polymerous (many-rayed) radial symmetry. The oral end of the polyp is expanded into an oral disc, and the gastrovascular cavity is divided by septa which bear nematocysts. Gonads are developed on the endoderm. The anthozoa may be solitary or colonial, but they are all marine.

Subclass Alcyonaria (Octocorallia). Polyps have eight tentacles and eight complete septa. They are all colonial, and have an endoskeleton of spicules. This subclass is divided into several orders, the most important being the following:

Order Alcyonacea; e.g., *Alcyonium* 'dead man's fingers'.
Order Coenothecalia; e.g., *Heliopora* 'blue coral'.
Order Gorgonacea, 'horny corals', 'gorgonians' or 'sea-fans'.
Order Pennatulacea, 'sea-pens' and 'sea-pansies'.

Subclass Zoantharia (Hexacorallia). Polyps have their tentacles usually arranged in multiples of six; they may be solitary or colonial. If a skeleton is present it is not composed of loose spicules. This subclass is divided into several orders, the most important being the following:

Order Actiniaria, 'sea-anemones'. The skeleton is absent; e.g. *Actinia, Anemonia, Taelia.*

Order Madreporaria, 'true corals'. These corals are responsible for the formation of the extensive coral reefs. The skeleton is calcareous.

Order Antipatharia, 'black corals'. If present, the skeleton is black.

Order Cerianthharia. Long, solitary anemone-like animals, without a pedal disc, and with numerous tentacles arranged in two whorls. The septa are also numerous. An example is *Cerianthus.*

CULTURAL METHODS

(1) HYDROZOA. *Hydra.* These are easily maintained in aquaria filled with water, obtained from the same source as the *Hydra*, if possible. On no account should they be put into tap-water. The aquaria should be stocked with a good supply of *Elodea canadensis* in order to oxygenate the water. Feed daily with a number of small crustacea (e.g., *Daphnia*), and remove any accumulation of bottom debris at regular intervals. The temperature of the water should be maintained near to 20°C. In winter, if the temperature drops below 10°C, they may disappear, but will often survive as winter eggs, and reappear in the spring. Avoid direct sunlight.

(2) SCYPHOZOA. *Aurelia* (Scyphistoma stage). The scyphistoma of Aurelia may be maintained in aerated sea-water in shallow dishes, and fed with ground shrimp or particles of meat. The water should be changed after feeding. The temperature should be maintained at 10°C.

(3) ANTHOZOA. Only sea-anemones are easily cultured. They should be kept in well-aerated sea-water at 10°C. In summer, if no refrigeration is available, the temperature of the water may be kept down by passing a spiral of thin-walled glass tubing, through which cold water circulates along the length of the aquarium. Loss of water is kept to a minimum by fitting the tank with a glass lid, and any water loss made good with glass-distilled water. Feed directly on to the tentacles once a week with a small piece of fresh liver, heart or pieces of *Mytilus* or cleaned earthworm.

FIXATION AND PRESERVATION
Hydrozoa

Hydra—These should be placed in a small container full of water, and narcotized by the addition of a few crystals of menthol to the surface of the water. When fully narcotized, the fluid should be pipetted off, and a warm solution of Bouin's fixative pipetted on to the specimens, squirting the fluid from the base of the animal to the tentacles. After a few minutes transfer the specimens to a fresh

23

solution of Bouin's fluid. After 24 h the specimens should be transferred to 70 per cent alcohol in which they may be stored.

Alternatively, Heidenhain's 'Susa' may be used in a similar way, but the specimens must then be treated with iodine followed by sodium thiosulphate. Another recommended fixative is corrosive-acetic (a few drops of 10 per cent acetic acid are added to saturated aqueous mercuric chloride solution immediately before use).

All other hydroids—These should be narcotized by the use of menthol, magnesium sulphate, magnesiun chloride,or chloral hydrate, and fixed in a similar way to that described for *Hydra*.

Medusae of Hydroids—Place into a small glass crystallizing dish containing some water and narcotize with stovaine, or menthol. When narcotized, draw off the water, and replace with 5 per cent formalin (made up with sea-water if marine).

Siphonophora—Some species benefit from being narcotized with menthol before being fixed. The fixation methods to be used vary with the various groups of siphonophores (Wagstaffe and Fidler, 1957).

(*i*) Calyconectae. Fix in a saturated solution of picric acid, then transfer to 5 per cent formalin, then gradually increase the concentration of the formalin to 10 per cent.

(*ii*) Physonectae. Plunge carefully into a saturated aqueous solution of mercuric chloride, and when dead, add a quantity of Flemming's fluid, and leave to fix for 24 h. Then add alcohol gradually until the alcoholic content of the mixture is 70 per cent. This resultant solution is recommended for storage of the animals.

(*iii*) Cystonectae. Fix in a mixture of 95 parts saturated aqueous mercuric chloride solution and 5 parts glacial acetic acid. When dead transfer to 0·5 per cent chromic acid solution for $1\frac{1}{2}$ h, and then transfer to 30 per cent alcohol for $\frac{1}{2}$ h, 50 per cent alcohol for 1 h, finally storing in 70 per cent alcohol.

(*iv*) Disconectae. Fix in a saturated solution of picric acid or mercuric chloride, and when dead add a small quantity of chromic acid and leave to act for $\frac{1}{2}$ h. If picric acid was used, remove to 30 per cent alcohol for 2 h, 50 per cent alcohol for 1 h, then store in 70 per cent alcohol. If mercuric chloride was used, wash well in running water, then transfer through 30 per cent and 50 per cent alcohols to 70 per cent alcohol for storage.

Scyphozoa

It is not usually necessary to narcotize scyphozoans, but should it be required menthol may be used. Fixation should be carried out by placing the medusae mouth upwards in a vessel containing 5 per cent sea-water formalin. After 10 min, and if the specimen is to be mounted as an exhibit, sufficient 5 per cent picric acid solution, to just colour the formalin, may be added. Stir occasionally over a period of 24 h, during which time add formalin to bring its concentration up to 10 per cent.

Hydratuba and scyphistoma—These stages should be fixed in any of the methods recommended for hydroids.

Anthozoa

(*i*) *Alcyonaria*—Narcotize by the addition of menthol crystals to the water containing the animals, then kill in hot saturated aqueous mercuric chloride solution. After treating the specimens with iodine, followed by sodium thiosulphate, they should be stored in 70 per cent alcohol.

(*ii*) *Zoantharia*—Most of the Zoantharia are highly contractile, and great care must be taken to ensure that they are properly narcotized before being fixed. The usual method is as follows: allow the animals to extend in a vessel of sea-water, then add some crystals of menthol to the water, and leave them overnight, or place them in the dark for 12 h. Then without leaving the animals uncovered with water, pipette off as much of the water as possible, then flood with 10 per cent formalin. If possible, pipette some of the fixative into the mouth. When dead, transfer to fresh 10 per cent formalin, in which they may be stored. For some species menthol is not very successful and causes the animals to macerate, and in these cases, magnesium sulphate should be tried. Another, often successful, method is to place the animals in a container half-full of sea-water, allow them to extend, then place the container into a freezing chamber of a refrigerator or deep-freeze. When frozen solid, remove from the container, chip off as much of the surrounding ice as possible, and plunge into 10 per cent formalin. When dead, transfer to fresh 10 per cent formalin.

SPECIAL PREPARATIONS
The Preparation of Nematocysts and Spirocysts

(1) Squash a small piece of tentacle, acrohagus or acontium, of a sea-anemone between two clean slides or cover-glasses. Alternatively, to get detached and discharged nematocysts on to a slide, touch a tentacle on to a glass slide which has been coated with a thin layer of saliva; (2) Fix the squash in Schaudinn's fixative for 10 min; (3) Rinse in water, then treat with Lugol's iodine for 1 min;

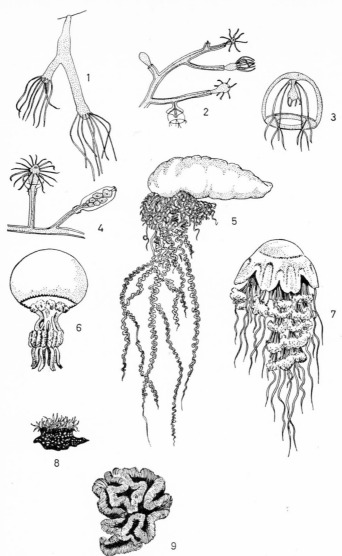

Figure 1.5. Some examples of cnidarians: 1. *Hydra*, a budding animal—gymnoblast hydrozoan; 2. *Bouganvillea*, a portion of colony—gymnoblast; 3. *Bouganvillea*, a medusa—anthomedusan (from Bullough, 1950, by courtesy of Macmillan & Co. Ltd.); 4. *Obelia*, a portion of colony—calyptoblast hydrozoan; 5. *Physalia*, an entire colony—siphonophore (after Barrett and Yonge, 1958); 6. *Rhizostoma octopus*, a scyphozoan (after Barrett and Yonge, 1958); 7. *Chrysaora isosceles*, a scyphozoan; 8. *Actinia equina*, an actinarian anthozoan; 9. A coral stripped of its living tissue—madreporarian

26

(4) Rinse in water, then remove iodine with 2 per cent sodium thio-sulphate; (5) Rinse in water, then for spirocysts stain in 1 per cent acid fuchsin for 5–10 min, or for nematocysts stain in 1 per cent methyl violet for 5 min; (6) Rinse in 70 per cent alcohol for a few seconds, then in 90 per cent alcohol for a few seconds, then finally complete the dehydration in absolute alcohol for a few seconds; (7) Clear in xylene and mount in neutral Canada balsam.

TEMPORARY PREPARATION OF NEMATOCYSTS OF HYDRA

A simple method of demonstrating nematocysts of *Hydra* which the student can carry out is as follows: place a living *Hydra* on a glass slide in a drop of pond-water, and cover it with a coverslip. With a pipette apply one drop of 0·5 per cent methylene blue solution to one edge of the coverslip, and draw it underneath by touching the water at the opposite side with a piece of filter paper. This procedure should be carried out under a microscope. After a few seconds the nematocysts will stain a bright blue colour, and many will be discharged; some may even become completely detached.

PHYLUM CTENOPHORA

Until the last few years the Ctenophora were usually treated as a separate subphylum of the phylum Coelenterata, the other subphylum being the Cnidaria. The ctenophores are all solitary, free-living animals, which are biradially symmetrical and also diploblastic, the mesogloea being very highly developed. There are no nematocysts present, but instead unique lasso cells are developed. Exclusively marine, the ctenophores are usually of planktonic habit, though a few creep on the sea-bed. There are two classes of ctenophores, those with tentacles and those without.

Class Tentaculata. Tentacles are present. Examples from this class include *Pleurobrachia, Hormiphora, Callianira, Lampetia, Boliopsis, Mnemiopsis, Cestum, Velamen, Coeloplana* and *Ctenoplana.*

Class Nuda. Tentacles are absent. Members of this class are all of conical form, and have a very wide mouth and pharynx. An example from this class is *Beroë.*

KILLING AND PRESERVATION

Ctenophora are difficult to preserve well, and some species require special methods. The best general method appears to be the following (Wagstaffe and Fidler, 1957): transfer the specimens from sea-water to chromic-osmic mixture, taking great care not to damage the individuals. Chromic—osmic consists of:

1 per cent chromic acid solution	.. ..	100 ml.
1 per cent osmium tetroxide solution..	..	2 ml.

The specimens should be left in this mixture for 15–60 min, then taken very slowly through 30, 40, 50, 60 and 70 per cent alcohols. They should be stored in 70 per cent alcohol.

Beroë ovata—These require some support during the fixation procedure; this may be carried out by selecting a glass tube of suitable dimensions (of sufficient diameter to keep the animal extended when placed into the mouth), and placing the open end of the tube into the mouth, keeping sufficient air in the tube to keep the animal afloat. After the animal has been in 70 per cent alcohol for two days the specimen will be hard enough to withstand the tube being withdrawn.

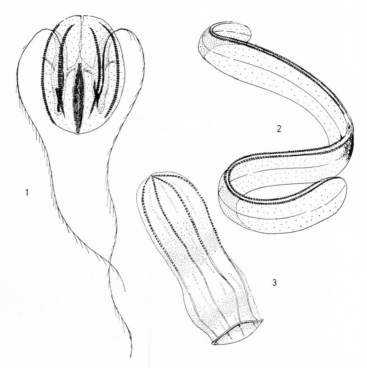

Figure 1.6. Three examples of Ctenophora: 1. *Pleurobrachia*; 2. *Cestum*; 3. *Beroë*

Beroë forskalii—The following method has been recommended: kill the animal in a mixture of 100 ml. copper sulphate (1 per cent aqueous solution) and 10 ml. mercuric chloride (saturated aqueous solution); after a few minutes transfer to chromic-osmic mixture for 1 h, then treat with the graded alcohols to 70 per cent alcohol, in which it should be stored. This procedure is carried out without inserting a tube into the mouth.

Bolina—These specimens should be killed by immersing them in Flemming's fluid:

1 per cent chromic acid solution	150 ml.
2 per cent osmium tetroxide solution.. ..	40 ml.
Glacial acetic acid	10 ml.

Leave for one hour to fix, then transfer to 30 per cent alcohol, and by gradual stages to 70 per cent alcohol, in which they should be stored.

Callianira—These may be killed as for *Beroë forskalii*, but should be hardened in the following solution after fixation:

Concentrated sulphuric acid	10 ml.
Mercuric chloride (saturated aqueous solution)	10 ml.
Chromic acid (0·5 per cent aqueous solution)	10 ml.

Cestum veneris—These should be killed in the following manner. Place the animals in a dish containing a small quantity of water, and add a relatively large quantity of the following mixture:

1 per cent chromic acid solution	100 ml.
Glacial acetic acid	5 ml.

After 10 min, the animals should be washed carefully in fresh water and then gradually taken through grades of alcohol to 70 per cent alcohol, in which they may be stored.

N.B. For all species of Ctenophora, 70 per cent alcohol is the recommended storing medium. Solutions of formaldehyde should be avoided.

PHYLUM PLATYHELMINTHES

The Platyhelminthes are bilaterally symmetrical, triploblastic animals, with a well-developed mesodermal parenchyma. They are commonly referred to as 'flatworms' due to the fact that they are all flattened dorso-ventrally. They are acoelomate and have no skeleton, but spines and hooks are produced in some forms. The gut when present has a mouth but no anus. They are not metamerically segmented but budding by transverse fission occurs in Turbellaria and by strobilation in Cestoda. There is no blood system and no respiratory system. The nervous system shows some degree of centralization, having 'cerebral' ganglia, and lateral and/or dorsal and ventral longitudinal nerve trunks. The excretory system is protonephridial with flame bulbs. The reproductive system is complex, and nearly always hermaphrodite. Fertilization is internal. Usually some form of asexual reproduction occurs. The Platyhelminthes are free living in the sea, or in freshwater or damp situations, or they may be commensal or parasitic.

Class Turbellaria. The majority of turbellarians are free living in water or damp soil, but a few are commensal or parasitic. Usually of leaf-like or oval shape, with a glandular and often ciliated epidermis. They are never strobilated, and never develop hooks. The intestine may be simple

29

or branched or even absent as in the Acoela. The life-cycle is simple.

Order Acoela. All marine; with a mouth and pharynx, but no intestine; digestion takes place by means of phagocytic parenchyma cells. Examples are *Convoluta* and *Ectocotyle*.

Order Rhabdocoela. Live in fresh water, the sea, or in damp places; a few are commensal or parasitic; the intestine is a straight simple sac. Examples are *Stenostomum* and *Macrostomum*.

Order Tricladida. Live in fresh water, the sea, or in damp places; a few are marine commensals; the intestine has three main branches. Examples are *Bdelloura, Gunda, Planaria, Dendrocoelum, Geoplana* and *Polycelis*.

Order Polycladida. Members are marine, some commensal; the intestine has numerous ramifying caecae. An example is *Leptoplana*.

Class Trematoda, the 'flukes'. All adult trematodes are parasitic, but their larvae may be free living. Adults are of leaf-like shape, and are never strobilated; adults have a thick cuticle without cilia; one or more suckers are present, and frequently hooks are also present; gut has a mouth, pharynx and an intestine which is usually forked; life-cycle is usually complex; the trematodes have great powers of reproduction, both asexual and sexual.

Order Monogenea. Life-cycle is simple, and is confined to one aquatic host; monogeneans are usually ectoparasitic and have large posterior adhesive suckers, often equipped with hooks. Examples are *Polystoma, Gyrodactylus, Entobdella*, and *Diplozoon*.

Order Digenea. Life-cycle is complex involving two or more hosts (one intermediate host which is always a mollusc, and a primary host which is always a vertebrate). Usually both oral and ventral suckers are present, without hooks. Examples are *Fasciola, Opisthorchis, Paragonimus* and *Schistosoma*.

Class Cestoidea. Endoparasites both as adults and as larvae; usually they are ribbon shaped and strobilated; adults have a thick cuticle, without cilia; suckers or bothria are present; hooks are often possessed; the gut is entirely absent; there are no sense organs, and the nervous system is but poorly developed. The life-cycle is complex usually involving one, two or three hosts. They have great powers of reproduction, both sexual and asexual.

Subclass Cestodaria. Adults live in the intestines or body cavity of fish and their body is not divided into proglottids; there is only one set of reproductive organs. Examples are *Gyrocotyle* and *Amphilina*.

Subclass Cestoda, the 'tapeworms'. Adults live in the intestines of vertebrates, and their bodies are usually ribbon like and are divided into numerous proglottids, each with a set of reproductive organs; bothria or suckers are confined to the head.

Order Pseudophyllidea. Adults live in intestines of vertebrates. The scolex is equipped with two bothria; the adult develops operculate eggs which liberate ciliated 'coracidia' larvae; there are two intermediate hosts for a procercoid and a plerocercoid larva. Examples are *Diphyllobothrium* and *Schistocephalus*.

Order Tetrarhynchidea. Adults live in the intestines of selachian fish; the scolex is provided with two or four bothria and four armed eversible proboscides; procercoid and plerocercoid larvae develop in two intermediate hosts. Examples are *Haplobothrium, Otobothrium* and *Grillotia*.

PHYLUM PLATYHELMINTHES

Order Cyclophyllidea. Adults live in the intestines of reptiles, birds and mammals; the scolex is provided with four muscular suckers and often with a rostellum which may bear hooks. The larva is a cysticercus, a coenurus, or a hydatid cyst in one intermediate host. Examples are *Dipylidium, Taenia* and *Echinococcus.*

CULTURAL METHODS

Only the Turbellaria are easily cultured. Planarians may be collected from beneath stones, in fast-flowing streams, or trapped in a glass

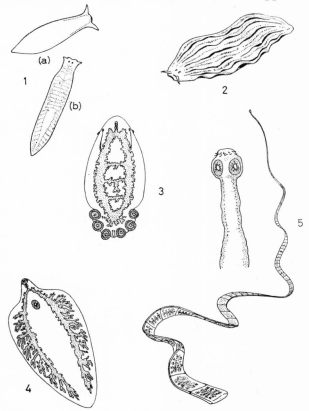

Figure 1.7. Some examples of Platyhelminthes: 1 (a) *Polycelis cornuta,* and (b) *Dendrocoelum lacteum*—two triclad turbellarians; 2. *Prostheceraeus vittatus,* a marine polyclad turbellarian (after Barrett and Yonge, 1958); 3. *Polystoma,* a monogenetic trematode (from Bullough, 1950, by courtesy of Macmillan & Co. Ltd.); 4. *Fasciola hepatica,* 'liver fluke'—a digenetic trematode (after Bullough, 1950); 5. *Taenia solium,* 'tapeworm'—a cestode (showing scolex enlarged)

jar baited with a piece of raw beef, liver, or freshly killed earthworm. They will survive in aquaria if fed occasionally with living *Tubifex* or *Enchytraeus*, or a piece of fresh liver. Any dead food should be removed before it has time to foul the water, as planarians will not tolerate contaminated water.

The culture of trematodes and cestodes *in vitro* has been tried, but with little success. More information may be obtained from the following books: *The Biology of the Trematoda*, Ben Dawes, Cambridge University Press; *Culture Methods for Invertebrate Animals*, Needham, Dover Publications.

FIXATION METHODS

Turbellaria should be starved for a few days to eliminate the gut contents. They are then placed into a Petri-dish containing the minimum amount of water to just cover them. Fill the dish with 1 per cent nitric acid and after a few seconds when the animals are extended, pour away the fluid and replace with Gilson's fixative, which is prepared as follows:

Mercuric chloride	5 g
80 per cent nitric acid	4 ml.
Glacial acetic acid	1 ml.
95 per cent alcohol	15 ml.
Distilled water	220 ml.

Allow this mixture to stand for 3 days before filtering. An alternative method of relaxing Turbellaria is to add a few crystals of menthol to the water containing them. Whichever method is employed, the fixation is completed with the animal being gently compressed between two glass slides. Fix for 24 h and then, if necessary, bleach with Mayer's chlorine solution (see page 196). Store the animals in 70 per cent alcohol after treating them for a few minutes with iodine solution to remove the mercury deposit.

M. E. Lavoie, in *Turtox News*, recommends fixing Polyclads in F.A.A.

Absolute alcohol	90 parts
Glacial acetic acid	5 parts
40 per cent formaldehyde solution	5 parts

The solution is heated then poured over the relaxed worms. The relaxation is carried out by exposing the worms to freezing temperatures just prior to fixation.

Trematodes must first of all be cleaned, by rinsing in several changes of isotonic saline, or preferably by shaking them vigorously in a tube containing some saline. Replace with clean saline and continue shaking to relax the worms. Pour away the saline and replace with a fixative and continue shaking for a further few minutes. Alternatively the worm may be gently compressed between two slides and then plunged into fixative. Suitable fixatives are: saturated aqueous solution of mercuric chloride, 10 per cent formalin, Helly's fluid, and Bouin's solution.

Small specimens and larval stages should be placed into a tube, and the top covered with fine muslin. This tube can then be easily emptied by inversion, and filled by submerging it in the required fluid without any danger of losing the specimens.

Cestodes must also be washed free of debris which generally clings to them. The rinsing should be done with isotonic saline. Large cestodes should be wrapped around a strip of glass or a bottle and secured to this with a piece of nylon monofilament, then completely immersed in 1 per cent chromic acid. When dead, fix in formol-acetic-alcohol for 24 h. This is prepared as follows:

40 per cent formaldehyde solution	6 parts
Glacial acetic acid	1 part
95 per cent alcohol	20 parts
Distilled water	40 parts

When fixed, transfer to 50 per cent alcohol, and give several changes of this solution before finally storing in formol-alcohol.

70 per cent alcohol	95 ml.
40 per cent formaldehyde solution	5 ml.
Neutralized with borax	

Good results have also been obtained by fixing in a saturated solution of mercuric chloride for 12 h, and then transferring to Lugol's iodine for 1 h, and, after rinsing several times in 70 per cent alcohol, finally storing in 70 per cent alcohol.

C. A. Ristroph (1934) recommends fixation in the following mixture:

40 per cent formaldehyde solution	10 parts
95 per cent alcohol	25 parts
Glacial acetic acid	5 parts
Glycerol	10 parts
Distilled water	50 parts

Fix for 12 h then transfer the worms to 35 per cent alcohol for a further 4 h. Then transfer to 50 per cent alcohol for a few hours before transferring to 70 per cent alcohol, in which the specimens may be stored. Staining with Mayer's hydrochloric acid carmine gives a good clear differentiation. This is prepared as follows:

Carmine	4 g
Water	15 ml.
Concentrated hydrochloric acid	30 drops

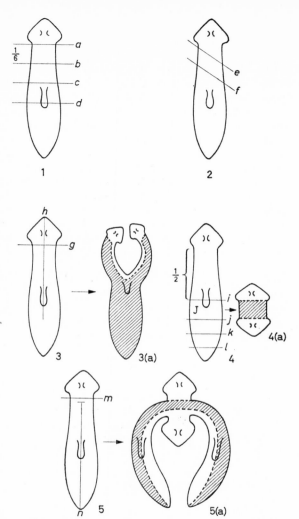

Figure 1.8. Some suggested operation cuts (from Hamburger, 1942, by courtesy of The Univ. Chicago Press): 1. Transverse cuts at *a*, *b*, *c*, and *d*. Distance apart about one-sixth of body length; 2. Oblique cuts at *e* and *f*; 3. Partial sagittal cut at *h* and complete transverse cut at *g*; 3 (a). Resultant formation of *duplicitas anterior* by cuts at *g* and *h*; 4. Transverse sections at *i*, *j*, *k*, *l* and *J* pieces become bipolar; 4 (a). Resultant bipolar form by cutting at *i* and *j*; 5. Complete transverse cut at *m*, and partial sagittal cut at *n*; 5 (a). Resultant *duplicitas cruciata* by cuts at *m* and *n*. [The shaded areas in 3 (a), 4 (a), and 5 (a) indicate old tissue, and the unshaded areas in these diagrams indicate regenerated tissue]

Boil until the carmine is dissolved then add 95 ml. of 85 per cent alcohol, filter and neutralize with ammonia as closely as possible to the point of precipitation without allowing the carmine actually to precipitate. A dilution of 10 per cent of the above mixture in slightly acidified 70 per cent alcohol is used to stain the worms. Overstain, then differentiate in acid alcohol. Dehydrate slowly with graded alcohols, then clear in methyl salicylate.

RECOMMENDED STAINING METHODS
If properly fixed, it is a relatively simple matter to prepare paraffin sections of Platyhelminthes. Staining may be carried out using any desired method. Two recommended methods are: (*i*) Ehrlich's haematoxylin and eosin; (*ii*) Masson's trichrome technique.

On the other hand it is more difficult to prepare well-stained wholemounts of Platyhelminthes (for full methods see page 247–251).

Recommended methods for Turbellaria and Trematodes are: (*i*) Heidenhain's iron haematoxylin; (*ii*) Modified Ehrlich's haematoxylin using iron alum; (*iii*) Gower's carmine.

Recommended methods for Cestodes are: (*i*) Mayer's haemalum; (*ii*) Modified Ehrlich's haematoxylin using iron alum; (*iii*) Mayer's hydrochloric acid carmine.

EXPERIMENTS TO SHOW REGENERATION OF PLANARIANS
Planarians show remarkable powers of regeneration and some interesting experiments can be carried out in the laboratory by following the instructions below.

Starve the animals for one week prior to the operations. For each individual experiment select 8–10 healthy specimens of a uniform size. A low power binocular dissecting microscope must be used when actually performing the operations. The cuts may be made with a sharp razor blade. Prepare several Petri-dishes, containing fresh pond-water or tap-water which has stood for several days and has been aerated, and another dish for discarded pieces of planarians.

Before commencing the actual experiments, practise some operation cuts on other specimens. The selected animal is placed in a drop of water on a clean slide and allowed to extend. The cut is then made in the desired plane; it must be made perpendicular to the slide and not obliquely.

Label each Petri-dish which will contain an operated planarian, and also make a diagram of the animal and indicate the position of the cuts.

Perform the various operations and transfer each of the animals to an individual Petri-dish. Discard all the unwanted pieces of animal material at once. Do not feed the operated animals until regeneration is complete (about 8–14 days). Keep the animals in a cool, dark place, or cover the dishes containing the regenerating animals with an inverted cardboard box.

Inspect the animals every second or third day. Discard all dead specimens. On the previously prepared diagrams indicate the border line of old and new tissue. For a long period of time the new regenerating tissue will remain unpigmented, and is therefore easily distinguished from the old tissue. The first appearance of eye-spots and pharynx should be particularly noted. Some suggestions for operation cuts are given in *Figure 1.8* (after Hamburger, 1942).

PHYLUM NEMERTINA (= RHYNCHOCOELA)

The nemertines are also known as nemerteans and 'ribbon worms'. They are acoelomate bilaterally symmetrical animals with an anus. A circulatory system is present, and they have a unique eversible proboscis which is enclosed in a tubular cavity (the rhynchocoel). This rhynchocoel is situated dorsal to the gut. Nemertines are elongated worms, usually with cylindrical bodies, but sometimes they are somewhat flattened. The body surface is covered with a glandular, ciliated epidermis. Protonephridia are present. There is a nervous system consisting of a brain and a pair of lateral nerve cords. The sexes are usually separate (dioecious). In some cases a free-swimming larva is produced, and this is called a pilidium larva. The majority of nemertines are free-living marine animals, but a few are commensal, while others live in freshwater and terrestrial habitats. About 550 species are known.

Subclass Anopla. In this subclass the mouth is situated posterior to the brain, and the central nervous system is situated beneath the epidermis or among the muscle layers of the body wall. The proboscis is unarmed.

Order Palaeonemertini. The dermis is gelatinous, and the body-wall musculature consists of two or three layers; if there are three layers of musculature the innermost layer is circular. An example is *Tubulanus*.

Order Heteronemertini. The body-wall musculature is always three-layered, the innermost layer being longitudinal; the dermis is fibrous. An example is *Lineus*.

Subclass Enopla. In this subclass the mouth is anterior to the brain, and the central nervous system is situated internal to the body-wall musculature. The proboscis may be armed.

Order Hoplonemertini. The proboscis is armed with one or more stylets, and the intestine is straight with paired diverticula. An example is *Amphiporus*.

Order Bdellomorpha or Bdellonemertini. The proboscis is unarmed and the intestine is sinuous and has no diverticula. There is a posterior adhesive disc. Members are commensal. An example is *Malacobdella*, commensal in *Pholas*.

CULTURAL METHODS

Individuals of small littoral species are sometimes easily maintained in marine aquaria. They are essentially carnivorous, and may feed on small annelids, but they will often survive for a year or more without food, living on their own body reserves. Asexual reproduction may occur while fasting, but sexual reproduction does not occur

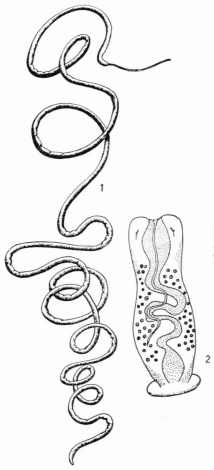

Figure 1.9. Two examples of nemer-teans: 1. *Lineus longissimus*, a heteronemertine; 2. *Malacobdella*, a commensal bdellonemertine from the mantle cavity of certain bivalves, notably *Pholas*

under such conditions. The bottom of the aquarium should be covered with a layer of pebbles and sand mixed with a little mud. The temperature should be kept below 15°C.

Freshwater species may survive in small aquaria if they are provided with minute crustacea, nematodes, turbellaria, and other suitable animals for food. The water must be free from bacterial decomposition. Dead animals must be removed as soon as they are seen. Temperature should be maintained about 20°C.

Terrestrial species may be kept in the moist soil of potted plants such as ferns and moisture-loving tropical plants, which are kept in a heated greenhouse.

Further information may be obtained from: *Culture Methods for Invertebrate Animals*, Needham, Dover Publications.

KILLING AND PRESERVATION METHODS

The nemerteans should always be narcotized before fixation. Marine species should be narcotized in 7 per cent magnesium chloride solution, or by the gradual addition of 14 per cent magnesium chloride solution to an equal quantity of water containing the animals. If the proboscis is required in the everted position, it may be necessary to hold the posterior part of the animal with a pair of forceps, and with a second pair of forceps gently squeeze the anterior part moving the forceps gradually towards the mouth.

The gradual addition of magnesium chloride to water containing the animals is recommended for the narcotization of freshwater and terrestrial nemerteans. When relaxed, small nemerteans should be introduced into lengths of glass tubing of a suitable diameter, and then the tube containing the worm placed horizontally in a dish of fixative. Recommended fixatives are Heidenhain's 'Susa', and saturated mercuric chloride solution. After fixing for 12 h, the worms should be transferred to 70 per cent alcohol containing some iodine. After a few hours transfer the animals to fresh 70 per cent alcohol and store until required.

Paraffin sections are easily prepared from nemerteans killed and fixed by this method. Staining with Masson's trichrome technique shows clearly the arrangement of the muscle layers in the body wall.

Whole-mount preparations of such nemerteans as *Malacobdella* and *Pelagonemertes* are clearly stained by using the rapid iron-Ehrlich's haematoxylin or Heidenhain's iron haematoxylin, or anthracene blue techniques.

PHYLUM ENTOPROCTA

Although the entoprocts possess a body cavity other than the gut cavity, it is not a true coelom and is therefore termed a pseudocoelom. The entoprocts are solitary, or colonial, stalked sessile pseudocoelomate animals. There is a circlet of ciliated tentacles at the distal end of the animal. The digestive tract is looped, and both the mouth and the anus open inside the circlet of tentacles. The rounded oval mass of the body is known as the calyx and this contains all of the visceral organs. The calyx itself is borne on a slender stalk. The base of the stalk is attached to some animal or object. A few entoprocts are hermaphrodite, but the great majority are dioecious. Eggs develop into a trochophore type of larva and these in turn develop into the adult form. Except for the genus *Urnatella*, all entoprocts are marine. About 60 species of entoprocta are known. Although widely distributed, they are usually only found in small numbers.

Examples are *Loxosoma*, *Loxocalyx*, *Pedicellina*, *Myosoma*, *Chitaspis* and *Urnatella*.

CULTURAL METHODS

There appears to be little published information on the culture of entoprocts. The food of entoprocts consists of diatoms, desmids, protozoans and other similar small organisms.

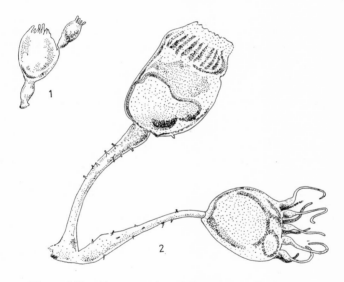

Figure 1.10.   Two examples of Entoprocta: 1. Loxosoma;
2. Pedicellina

KILLING AND PRESERVATION METHODS

Entoprocts must always be narcotized before being killed. This should be done by the addition of menthol crystals to the surface of the water containing the animals. Alternatively add 1 per cent stovaine (amyl chlorohydrin) solution, or add 1 per cent β-eucaine hydrochloride to the water.

When the individual zooids no longer respond to being touched with a needle, draw off most of the water, and replace with 5 per cent formalin. After a few minutes replace with a fresh quantity of 5 per cent formalin. Store in 5 per cent formalin, or pass slowly through 30 per cent and 50 per cent alcohols, and store in 70 per cent alcohol.

PHYLUM ASCHELMINTHES (NEMATHELMINTHES)

Until recently the classes which constitute the phylum Aschelminthes were nearly all regarded as separate phyla. This is because, in spite of the fact that the relationship between these classes is looser than is the case with classes of most other phyla, the evidences of relationship are so specific that they cannot be ignored. The six classes of this phylum are; Rotifera, Gastrotricha, Kinorhyncha, Nematoda, Nematomorpha and Priapulida. For convenience, they will be dealt with in this chapter in the same manner as are the rest of the phyla.

The Aschelminthes are pseudocoelomate animals which are mostly wormlike in shape. These bilaterally symmetrical animals are unsegmented or occasionally superficially segmented and the body is covered with a cuticle. The digestive tract is usually straight, though it may be curved, and lacks a definite muscular wall (except in the Priapulida). The anus is always well posterior to the mouth. Respiratory and circulatory systems are absent. The sexes are separate and the reproductive systems are relatively simple in structure. Predominately aquatic animals, the Aschelminthes inhabit fresh water and sea-water, though many nematodes are terrestrial. This phylum includes free-living, epizoic, and parasitic forms.

CLASS ROTIFERA

The rotifers or 'wheel animalcules' are common aquatic Aschelminthes. The anterior end of a rotifer is modified into a corona (a ciliary organ). This may be developed into two trochal discs. The beating cilia move so as to give the appearance of a rotating wheel, hence the common name 'wheel animalcules'. The pharynx is provided with internal jaws, the structure of which is of taxonomic importance. A pair of flame-bulb protonephridia are present. The rotifers are commonly found and about 1,500 species have been described. There are three orders of rotifers. They are:

Order Seisonacea. Rotifers of this order are of very elongated shape and have a long neck region. They are marine and epizoic. The corona is only slightly developed.

Order Bdelloidea. The anterior end is retractile, and the corona has two trochal discs or has been reduced from such a condition. Free swimming or creeping, they are provided with more than two pedal glands, and the foot is often equipped with more than two toes, and with spurs. Males are wanting. Reproduction is by parthenogenesis.

Order Ploima. The corona of these free-swimming rotifers is normal, and the foot when present is equipped with two toes and two pedal glands.

KILLING AND PRESERVATION METHODS

For those engaged upon any serious work with rotifers, the methods given by Hanley (1949) and those published by Wagstaffe and Fidler (1957) will be invaluable. Below are a few techniques which will give reasonable results with the majority of rotifers.

As with protozoa and many other small animals, rotifers should be examined in the living state whenever possible. A phase-contrast microscope will prove of great value. Vital staining may be carried out, using dilute solution of any vital stain (a solution of 1 part in 50,000 neutral red solution is recommended). The animals may be slowed down by mixing the drop of water containing them with a drop of 2 per cent methyl cellulose solution. Due to the fact that some contraction occurs after killing, the rotifers should always be identified while living. Those species which are identified by the characteristics of their firm loricae should be killed without previous narcotization so that the body will contract and not obscure the lorica. Killing may be carried out in 5 or 10 per cent formalin.

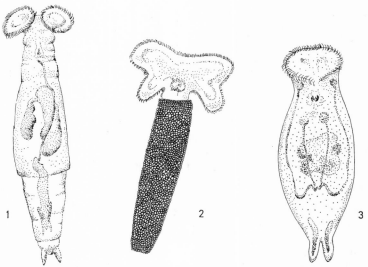

Figure 1.11. Three examples of Rotifera: 1. *Philodina*; 2. *Floscularia*; 3. *Hydatina*

Soft-bodied forms should always be narcotized before killing, and a set of trophi should also be prepared, as an examination of them will be necessary for accurate identification. A rapid method of narcotizing rotifers is to mix every millilitre of culture with 3–10 drops of the following solution:

2 per cent benzamine hydrochloride solution..	3 parts
Water	6 parts
Pure cellosolve (ethylene glycol mono-ethyl ether)	1 part

An alternative method is to add a few drops of the following mixture to the culture solution:

Eucaine hydrochloride ..	..	..	..	1 g
90 per cent alcohol	..	..	..	10 ml.
Distilled water ..	..	..	..	10 ml.

Some rotifers, e.g. *Rhizota*, may be killed by placing one or two drops of a cold culture in a watch glass, and suddenly flooding it with hot water, then immediately transferring them to 10 per cent formalin. Fixation may be carried out by using one of the following methods:

(1) Add one drop of both 1 per cent aqueous osmium tetroxide solution and 1 per cent chloroplatinic acid solution to each millilitre of narcotized culture, and leave for a few minutes. Centrifuge, then pipette off as much of the fixing solution as possible and replace it with water. Centrifuge, pipette off the water, and wash again. Repeat the washing several times. Store if necessary in 5 per cent formalin.

(2) Add to a few drops of concentrated, narcotized culture a few millilitres of Fol's picro-chromic acid fixative. This consists of:

Picric acid (saturated aqueous solution)	..			10 parts
Chromic acid (1 per cent solution chromic trioxide)	..	..	..	25 parts
Distilled water ..	..	..	..	65 parts

(3) Add to a few drops of concentrated, narcotized culture a few millilitres of a saturated aqueous solution of mercuric chloride (about 7 per cent). After this fixative it will be necessary to treat the fixed rotifers with iodine, and remove the iodine with 2 per cent sodium thiosulphate solution.

(4) Add to a few drops of concentrated, narcotized culture a few millilitres of 10 per cent formalin.

It is important to remember that fixation should be carried out before the cilia actually cease beating, but after the animals have become sufficiently narcotized so as to prevent them from contracting when touched. The final storage solution for rotifers should be 2·5 per cent formalin.

THE PREPARATION OF TROPHI

The trophi is the masticatory apparatus which is attached to the inner wall of the pharynx or mastax (the term mastax is used as synonymous with trophi by many authors). Each trophi consists of seven main pieces which are hard and cuticularized. They occur in several different types that are correlated with different modes of feeding.

The rotifers should be heated in 10 per cent aqueous sodium hydroxide solution for a few minutes. Experience is necessary to determine the length of time required. Over-maceration can cause dissociation of the components of the trophi. Having macerated sufficiently, pour the mixture into a small dish or watch glass, and draw off the fluid by means of a pipette. Wash the trophi with several changes of water. It may be necessary to clear any remaining tissue mechanically, for which a feather will be a suitable cleaning implement. When clean, flood with 2·5 per cent formalin, and prepare a fluid mount of the trophi. This is carried out by first of all making a cell, using a slide turntable, from 'Murrayite', 'Glyceel', gold size, or other suitable cement. When the cell has dried, pipette the trophi into the cell, then fill the cell to excess with 2·5 per cent formalin. Remove any air bubbles which may be present, then carefully add a coverslip, ensuring that no air is trapped. Blot away any excess fluid, then using the turntable seal the cell with three or more coats of 'Glyceel' or 'Murrayite', allowing each coat to dry before applying the next.

CLASS GASTROTRICHA

This class of Aschelminthes consists of microscopic aquatic animals. There is no corona, but cilia are present on limited areas of the body. The cuticle is unsegmented, and there are often spines, scales and plates present. There are from 2 to many adhesive tubes present. These insignificant animals comprise about 1,500 known species. They are usually grouped into two separate orders.

Order Macrodasyoidea. These are marine gastrotrichs, which have a number of adhesive tubes situated along the body. They are all hermaphroditic.

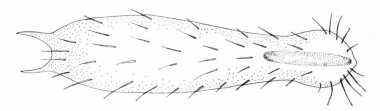

Figure 1.12. An example of Gastrotricha: Chaetonotus

Order Chaetonotoidea. Although a few are marine, the majority of this order live in freshwater habitats. Their adhesive tubes are limited to the posterior end, and are two or four in number. They only occur as parthenogenetic females, the males being entirely wanting.

CULTURAL METHODS

Packard (1959) states that many specimens of *Lepidoderma squamatum* were reared in a 0·1 per cent malted milk solution for a period of 22 months. Half a gram of Horlick's malted milk was dissolved in 500 ml. of clear water from a spring-fed river tributary, usually unfiltered, and boiled for 5 min. This was left exposed for 24 h before being used. Animals were raised in rectangular, covered refrigerator dishes in quantity lots and in depression slides singly or in mass. When once a culture was started, a small amount of fresh solution was added daily to keep up a supply of animals. Excess fluid was drawn off to prevent overflowing.

Lepidoderma concinnum, and a species of *Chaetonotus*, were also raised in the same medium for several weeks.

CLASS KINORHYNCHA OR ECHINODERA

Devoid of cilia, but more or less spiny, the kinorhynchs are microscopic Aschelminthes which dwell entirely in the sea. The cuticle is superficially segmented into thirteen, or sometimes into fourteen, segments. The spiny anterior end of the animal is invaginable into the following segments, and it is these more posterior segments which form a lid over the anterior end, when it is invaginated. Sexes are separate. This is a small insignificant class consisting of about 100 known species.

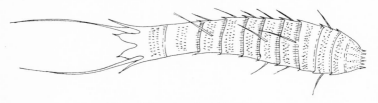

Figure 1.13. A typical kinorhynch

CULTURAL METHODS

Little seems to have been published about methods for the culture of Kinorhyncha. No doubt the best method to employ would be to maintain the culture in a marine aquarium. As the Kinorhyncha have benthonic habits and live among slime and mud, or less often among algae, the aquarium should be supplied with a quantity of suitable mud. The species that live among algae feed on diatoms, while the others feed on fine detritus and bottom material. In laboratory cultures, kinorhynchs have been known to live for half a year to more than one year.

CLASS NEMATODA

Nematodes or 'round worms' as they are commonly called are aquatic, terrestrial or parasitic worm-like Aschelminthes. The body of a nematode is generally cylindrical and circular in cross-section, hence the common

44

name. The cuticle which is tough, making fixation difficult, is usually smooth, but may be ringed and have bristles. Cilia are entirely absent. The epidermis is divided by four or more longitudinal chords, and arranged between these chords are the sections of subepidermal muscles which consist solely of longitudinal fibres. There is a simple nervous system with a brain in the form of a circumenteric ring with attached ganglia. The sexes are usually separate, but parthenogenesis and hermaphroditism also occurs. Although this class is very large, the technician rarely needs a knowledge of its taxonomy as the usual fixation and staining methods are applicable to all species.

THE COLLECTION OF NEMATODES FROM SOIL AND PLANT MATERIAL

Although there are numerous modifications of this method (see Goodey, 1963), the following will enable sufficient nematodes to be extracted for class use with the minimum amount of trouble. The method is the Baermann funnel technique. Set up the apparatus as shown in *Figure 1.14*, with the soil or plant material contained in muslin bags. After leaving the filled bags to remain partly submerged in the water for several hours, open the spring clip and allow a small quantity of the water to run out into a watch glass or small test tube.

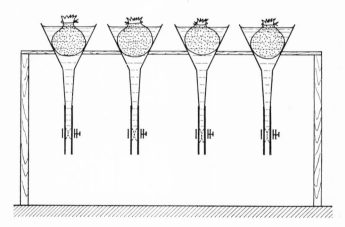

Figure 1.14. Baermann funnel method for extracting nematodes from soil or plant material

Allow the nematodes to settle and pipette off the supernatant fluid. The nematode which is most frequently dissected due to its large size is *Ascaris lumbricoides var. suis,* which lives in the intestines of the pig. Usually obtained from slaughterhouses. Parasitic nematodes

45

can frequently be obtained from the guts of animals which are being dissected.

CULTURAL METHODS FOR *RHABDITIS*

Free-living nematodes such as *Rhabditis* are commonly present in soil, and from the soil they find their way into the nephridia of the more posterior segments of earthworms. To obtain a rich supply of *Rhabditis*, half fill a number of Petri-dishes with some damp soil, and add to the soil some pieces of chopped earthworm. Best results are obtained if the posterior portions of the worms are used. Replace the lids of the Petri-dishes, and set aside in a cool place for two or three days. Provided that the soil has been kept damp, a rich supply of nematodes should be covering the putrefying pieces of earthworm. They may be transferred to a watch glass containing water, and then examined, or they may be added to a few Petri-dishes containing a sloppy, nutrient agar mixture (about 1 per cent). If they are only to be kept for a few more days the nematodes should develop and survive. They are easily visible in the agar when examined under a microscope, and the agar prevents them from moving rapidly.

KILLING AND FIXATION METHODS

Larval nematodes may sometimes be successfully narcotized by pipetting them into an equal volume of a solution of Lugol's iodine diluted with 10 volumes of distilled water.

Anaesthetization of nematodes may be carried out by the following method (Goodey, 1963). Add two drops of dichloro-ethyl ether to 50 ml. of water in a stoppered bottle. Shake well, and allow the mixture to settle. This solution will keep nematodes anaesthetized for some time and allow them to be studied under a microscope. They usually recover when put back into fresh water, or they may be fixed.

Before fixing nematodes they should be washed free from any attached debris. It is preferable to kill the animals in an extended condition, and this can be achieved by using heat. Small specimens should be put into a test tube with as little water as possible, and the tube lowered into a water bath maintained at 65°C. Agitate gently and the worms will extend as heat-rigor occurs. Large nematodes such as *Ascaris* should be killed in an extended condition by holding each end of the animal in a pair of blunt wooden forceps, and plunging it into a bath of hot fixative.

There are numerous fixatives recommended for nematodes, and two of them are listed below:

(1) TAF (Courtney, Polley and Miller, 1955):

40 per cent formaldehyde solution.. ..	7 ml.
Triethanolamine	2 ml.
Distilled water	91 ml.

(2) Formalin-acetic (Seinhorst, 1962):

40 per cent formaldehyde solution.. ..	10 ml.
Glacial acetic acid	1 or 0·5 ml.
Distilled water	up to 100 ml.

THE PREPARATION OF WHOLE-MOUNTS OF NEMATODES

(1) The glycerol-ethanol method of Seinhorst, 1959 gives excellent results with many nematodes. The nematodes are transferred from the formol-acetic fixative, to a small dish containing about 0·5 ml. of the following mixture:

96 per cent ethanol	20 parts
Glycerol	1 part
Distilled water	79 parts

Place the container in a closed glass vessel (a desiccator is ideal) containing an excess (about one-tenth the volume of the vessel) of 96 per cent ethanol. Leave the container in this saturated atmosphere for at least 12 h at about 37°C. This will remove most of the water from the container and leave the specimens in a mixture of ethanol and glycerol. Fill the container with a mixture of 95 parts of 96 per cent ethanol and 5 parts of glycerol and place it in a partly closed dish at 40°C until the ethanol has evaporated. After several hours the nematodes will be in pure glycerol, and can be mounted in glycerol. When mounting in glycerol, the coverslip should be supported by three small pieces of glass fibre, each with a diameter slightly greater than the diameter of the nematode. Warm the coverslip before applying and fix the coverslip in position with three or four drops of 'Glyceel' or 'Zut'. Allow the adhesive to dry, then ring the coverslip with 'Glyceel' or 'Zut' using a turntable. 'Glyceel' ('Zut' in U.S.A.) is sold by G. T. Gurr Ltd., 136, New Kings Road, London, S.W.6.

(2) Another useful method of producing whole-mount preparations of nematodes is the lactophenol method of Franklin and Goodey, 1949. The method is as follows: add sufficient 0·0025 per cent cotton blue lactophenol to a cavity slide to fill the cavity, and place it on a hotplate at 60°C until the lactophenol becomes hot. When hot, transfer to it nematodes which have been fixed for at least 12 h in formol-acetic. Leave the nematodes in the tinted lactophenol until

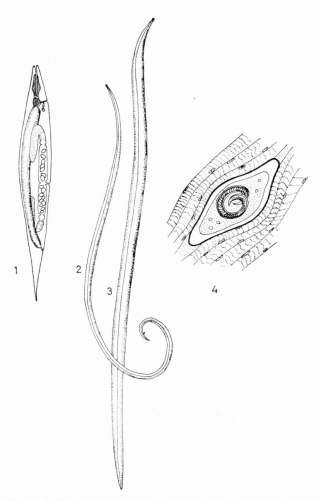

Figure 1.15. Some examples of Nematoda: 1. *Rhabditis,* female seen from right side (from Bullough, 1950, by courtesy of Macmillan & Co. Ltd.); 2. *Ascaris lumbricoides,* male from small intestine of pig; 3. *Ascaris lumbricoides,* female from small intestine of pig; 4. *Trichinella spiralis,* encysted in muscle (from Bullough, 1950, by courtesy of Macmillan & Co. Ltd.)

they are sufficiently stained. Some species of nematodes require a more concentrated staining mixture such as 0·01 per cent cotton blue.

Take care to avoid the lactophenol becoming syrupy due to excessive heating. Lactophenol is prepared in the following way:

Phenol (liquid)	..	..	..	..	.. 500 ml.
Lactic acid	..	..	..	..	.. 500 ml.
Glycerol ..	..	..	..	..	.. 1 l.
Distilled water	..	..	..	..	.. 500 ml.

The cotton blue (water soluble aniline blue) is dissolved in the distilled water before being mixed with the other ingredients.

THE PREPARATION OF PARAFFIN SECTION OF NEMATODES

Transverse sections of large nematodes such as *Ascaris lumbricoides* are frequently required, and these are easily prepared in the following way: cut the nematode into half-inch long pieces and fix these in Zenker's fixative. Leave to fix overnight, then wash the pieces of worm in running water for 24 h. Dehydrate via the usual grades of alcohol, clear in chloroform or cedarwood oil, and embed in paraffin wax in the usual way. Paraffin sections of such material will give brilliant results with such stains as Ehrlich's haematoxylin and eosin, Mallory's triple stain and Masson's trichrome.

Paraffin sections of small nematodes may be prepared after the specimens have been fixed by any of the aforementioned methods, but when the specimens are very small it may be necessary to embed the fixed nematodes in a small block of agar-agar and then process and embed this block in paraffin wax. It will also facilitate the handling of very small nematodes if they are lightly stained with a bright stain such as acid fuchsin after they have been fixed. This can easily be washed out of the sections should it not be required.

CLASS NEMATOMORPHA (GORDIACEA)

Extremely long and slender worms, of cylindrical shape, the nematomorphs are all parasitic as juveniles, and free living as adults. The cuticle is smooth and shows no ringing. There are no lateral epidermal chords as in Nematoda, and the nervous system consists of a small brain and a mid-ventral nerve cord. The nervous system is intimately situated with the epidermis.

Figure 1.16. Nematomorpha: Gordius aquaticus, male

There is no differentiated pharynx, and the ends of the digestive tract often show some degeneration in adult forms. The sexes are always separate. This class of Aschelminthes is usually grouped into two orders.

Order Gordioidea. Freshwater nematomorphs, which have their parasitic phase in terrestrial or aquatic arthropods. The cuticle is devoid of bristles.

Order Nectonematoidea. Marine nematomorphs, which have their parasitic phase in crustaceans. There is a double row of bristles.

There appear to be no published cultural methods for representatives of this class.

KILLING AND PRESERVATION METHODS

Nematomorphs should be killed and fixed as for Acanthocephala, i.e. in warm (about 50°C) corrosive-acetic (see page 52).

CLASS PRIAPULIDA

Priapulids were until recent years always included in the phylum Annelida. But they are now generally recognized as Aschelminthes. They are all marine, and are of a cylindrical shape. Warty in appearance, there is an introversible presoma, and a superficially segmented trunk. The digestive tract is more or less straight with a terminal mouth and anus. The posterior end of members of the genus *Priapulus* bears one or two warty appendages, but these are absent in the genus *Halicryptus*. There appear to be only three known species of Priapulida: *Priapulus bicaudatus*, with two caudal appendages, *Priapulus caudatus*, with one caudal appendage, and *Halicryptus spinulosus*, with no caudal appendage.

Priapulids are found living buried in soft bottoms of littoral zones of the colder seas from the intertidal zone down to about 500 metres. They do not form secretion-lined tubes.

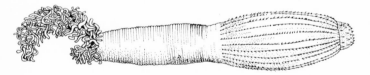

Figure 1.17. Priapulida: Priapulus caudatus

CULTURAL METHODS

There is little published information concerning the culture of priapulids, but Lang (1948) states that the animals are highly predaceous, and will attack such forms as polychaet worms, and other priapulids, with their teeth and swallow them whole. Naturally, only slowly moving prey can be seized. It appears that their need for food is small, as they have been maintained for considerable lengths of time in marine aquaria, and studies of their burrows have been made by keeping priapulids in an artificial translucent slime made of agar-agar (Langeloh, 1936).

KILLING AND PRESERVATION METHODS

Priapulids should be narcotized before killing, by placing them into a 7 per cent solution of magnesium chloride in distilled water. When narcotized, transfer the specimens to Bouin's fluid or 5 per cent formalin in sea-water. If fixed in the former solution, the specimen should be transferred after 24 h to 50 per cent alcohol for one hour, and then transferred to 70 per cent alcohol, in which it may be stored. Alternatively, the specimens may be stored in 5 per cent formalin.

PHYLUM ACANTHOCEPHALA

The Acanthocephala are commonly known as 'spiny-headed worms' because of the presence, at the anterior end, of an invaginable proboscis which is armed with hooks. At first glance they can be easily mistaken for nematodes. These pseudocoelomate bilaterally symmetrical worms have no digestive tract and are all entoparasites, infesting the digestive tracts of various vertebrate hosts, mainly fish, birds, and mammals. The eggs develop, in the body of the female worm, into larvae which require an intermediate host. This host is always an arthropod, and usually an insect, an isopod or an amphipod. There are about 500 described species.

CULTURAL METHODS

Experiments on survival of *Neoechinorhynchus emydis* in artificial media have been made by Gettier (1942) and Van Cleave and Ross (1944). Survival up to 20 days was obtained in 0·5 per cent sodium chloride plus a little calcium chloride. However, this solution was somewhat hypotonic, and a better medium was found to be 0·85 per cent sodium chloride.

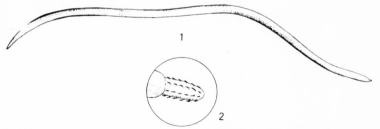

Figure 1.18.   Acanthocephala: 1. *Echinorhynchus*;   2. Anterior end of *Echinorhynchus*, much enlarged

KILLING AND PRESERVATION METHODS

Acanthocephala may be killed in warm (about 50°C) corrosive-acetic. This fixative is prepared in the following way:

| Mercuric chloride (saturated aqueous solution) | 3 parts |
| Glacial acetic acid .. .. | 1 part |

Leave to fix for 30 min, then transfer the specimen to iodized alcohol. Change this solution several times, then store if required in 70 per cent alcohol.

Another method which gives good results with small specimens is to kill and fix the worm in 5 per cent acetic acid in 5 per cent formalin for 24 h. Prolonged staining in Ehrlich's haematoxylin (24 h), followed by careful differentiation, will often give excellent results.

PHYLUM SIPUNCULIDA

Many workers still include this phylum of animals in the phylum Annelida. The sipunculids are wormlike marine animals which live a sedentary existence. The most striking feature is the slender introvert at the anterior

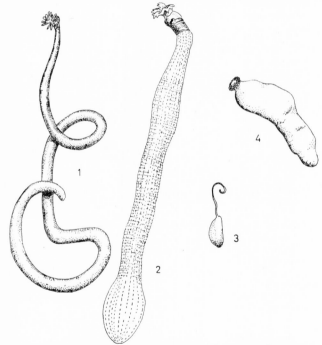

Figure 1.19. Some examples of Sipunculida: 1. Dendrostoma; 2. Sipunculus; 3. Phascolosoma; 4. Cloeosiphon

end, which is continually and rapidly run in and out. The sipunculids are unsegmented, and have a terminal mouth which is frequently surrounded by tentacles. The digestive tract is recurved and opens on the introvert or at the anterior end of the trunk. The nervous system is similar to that of annelids. Sexes are separate. About 250 species have been described, but there are only about 13 genera. Examples are: *Sipunculus, Aspidosiphon,* and *Phascolion.*

CULTURAL METHODS

Common littoral species survive well under laboratory conditions. Hérubel (1907) stated that species of *Golfingia* and *Sipunculus* would live in good condition for months in tanks at Roscoff; but different species vary in resistance and tend to die in other than natural substrates.

Little is known of the feeding habits of sipunculids, but what little is known indicates that diatoms constitute a major part of the diet.

KILLING AND PRESERVATION METHODS

Narcotization should always be carried out before fixation. This may be done by transferring the sipunculids to 7 per cent magnesium chloride solution in distilled water. When narcotized, transfer the animals to a dish containing 5 per cent formalin. Fix for at least 24 h, then store if required in a fresh change of 5 per cent formalin. Alternatively store in formol-alcohol (5 per cent formalin in 70 per cent alcohol).

PHYLUM PHORONIDA

The phylum Phoronida is the first of the three coelomate phyla which possess a lophophore. A lophophore is an extension of the body consisting of ciliated tentacles which embraces the mouth but not the anus. The phoronids are tube-dwelling, wormlike coelomates with a lophophore which is horseshoe shaped. The digestive tract is recurved and the anus opens near to the mouth but outside the lophophore. There is a closed blood circulatory system. The tube in which the animal lives is of its own secretion. Phoronids are hermaphrodite, and the eggs which are liberated (though in some species they may be retained in special brood pouches) develop into a characteristic actinotrocha larva. This in turn develops into the adult form. These marine animals are found in most seas other than polar and sub-polar. They dwell only in the upper littoral zone. Two genera are known, *Phoronis* and *Phoronopsis*, and contain between them about 15 known species.

CULTURAL METHODS

MacGinitie (1959), in describing a method for rearing the larvae of the echiuroid, *Urechis caupo*, states that this method has also been used with success for the rearing of larvae of *Phoronopsis viridis*, as well as the polychaete *Halosydna brevisetosa*, the tectibranch mollusc, *Tethys californicus*, and various sand dollars and sea-urchins.

The method is as follows: if the animals are to be used for only a short period of time they may be left at the bottom of an aquarium with a good supply of running sea-water. Eggs and sperms are collected from the gonopores, and these eggs are placed into finger bowls containing filtered sea-water to a depth of $\frac{3}{4}$ in. Sperm is introduced with a clean glass pipette, and mixed well with the sea-water. Use a minimum amount of sperm. The fertilized eggs should

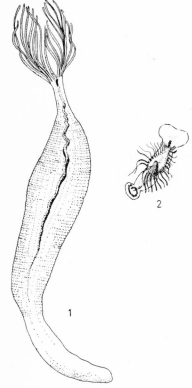

Figure 1.20. Phoronida: 1. Phoronis;
2. Actinotrocha larva of Phoronis

be covered and left to develop for 18–24 h. Then distribute the larvae into a large number of similar finger bowls, with approximately 50 to each bowl. Discard any damaged or abnormal larvae. Put glass covers on the bowls and set them in a cool place. From this time on the larvae should be inspected every day when they are fed with a few drops of diatom culture. Change to fresh filtered sea-water about once each week. The writer is unable to say which species of diatoms were used, but several types were used with success. Possibly *Nitzschia* could be used. The culture of *Nitzschia* is described on page 171. The sea-water should be uncontaminated, and should be kept at as low a temperature as possible, preferably just below that of the sea-water where the animals were obtained. Guard against any sudden change in temperature. Never overfeed with diatoms, make sure that the larvae are eating the diatoms faster than the diatoms are able to reproduce. Each day just after feeding gently aerate the sea-water containing the larvae.

KILLING AND PRESERVATION METHODS

Phoronids should be narcotized prior to fixation. This may be done by transferring the specimens to 7 per cent magnesium chloride solution in distilled water. When completely narcotized, the solution should be drawn off and immediately replaced with formol-alcohol. After 24 h, store in a fresh change of fixative.

PHYLUM ECTOPROCTA

This is the second of the three coelomate phyla which possess a lophophore. This phylum and the phylum Entoprocta constitute the old group known as the Polyzoa or Bryozoa. The common name for members of this phylum is 'moss animals'. The ectoprocts are microscopic sessile coelomates which are colonial and are permanently attached inside exoskeletal cases or gelatinous structures of their own secretion. They are coelomates and possess a circular or cresentic lophophore. The digestive tract is recurved and the anus opens near to the mouth. There is no circulatory system. The colony usually develops by asexual division of an original zooid which developed from a sexually produced larva. Although a few ectoproct colonies are motile, they are usually attached to some submerged object, such as a shell or a frond of sea-weed. The majority of ectoprocts are hermaphroditic. Confusion between ectoprocts and hydroids can be avoided by microscopic examination of the ciliated tentacles of ectoprocts. Marine species can also be distinguished by the fact that the zooids live in box- or vase-like cases, each provided with an orifice through which the lophophore can project.

The ectoprocts are very common marine animals, and are almost entirely restricted to the littoral zone, although some have been taken from deep waters. The phylactolaemata is limited to freshwater forms, and its members exist in relatively few numbers.

Class Gymnolaemata. The lophophore is circular in shape and there is no direct communication between the zooids. With very few exceptions members of this class are marine.

Order Ctenostomata. The zoecia (the cases in which the zooids live) are not calcified, but are chitinous. The orifice of the zoecium has a collar-like closing mechanism. No ovicells or avicularia are produced. Two examples are *Bowerbankia* and *Alcyonidium*.

Order Cheilostomata. The zoecia are box-like and the orifice is closed by means of a hinged lid (operculum). Brood pouches in the form of ovicells are frequently present. Avicularia or vibracula or both may be present. Examples are *Membranipora*, *Flustra*, *Bugula*, *Retepora* and *Cellepora*.

Order Cyclostomata. Zoecia are completely calcified. The orifice has no operculum, and no avicularia are present. Although brood pouches may be present they are not in the form of an ovicell. Examples are *Crisia* and *Tubulipora*.

Class Phylactolaemata. The lophophore is of horseshoe shape (with one exception, when it is circular). The coeloms of the zooids are continuous. Never calcified. Dwell exclusively in freshwater. Examples are *Fredericella*, *Plumatella*, *Lophopus*, *Pectinatella* and *Cristatella*.

CULTURAL METHODS

(1) MARINE ECTOPROCTS

B. H. Grave (1959) reports that the American species of *Bugula*, *B. flabellata* and *B. turrita* are easily maintained for a length of time sufficient for the complete life history to be studied. The breeding season at Woods Hole, Massachusetts, extends from 1st June to 1st November. The larvae are given off by the parent colonies at dawn. To obtain them in abundance, sexually mature colonies should be collected late in the afternoon and placed in a dish of sea-water. These are left overnight near a window. Larvae issue from the colonies early in the morning and continue to be liberated from 5–10 a.m. They promptly swim to the lighted side of the dish, where they may be picked up by a pipette and transferred to fresh sea-water for further study. Although at first they show a positive response to light, they soon change and show a negative response. Still later they make permanent attachments to the sides of the dish and proceed to develop into colonies. The larva requires no food, but as soon as an attachment occurs the dish should be placed in running sea-water to secure food and aeration for the developing colony.

The swimming stage of the larva is about six hours in duration. The first individual of the colony becomes a complete feeding polypide within 2 days, and a colony of eight is established in 1 week if conditions are favourable. The colonies under natural conditions bud rapidly, and become sexually mature in 1 month. They continue to grow for approximately 3 months. Colonies established late in summer live over winter.

The larvae of *B. turrita* may be liberated in the afternoon.

(2) FRESHWATER ECTOPROCTS (PHYLACTOLAEMATA)

All observers have commented on the difficulty of maintaining phylactolaemate colonies in the laboratory. Generally it is necessary to use natural or conditioned water, to eliminate enemies, to prevent accumulation of debris on the colonies, and to provide an abundance of food without adding enough to foul the water. Even at best, it is generally considered to be necessary to give frequent changes of medium and diet or transfer the colonies to fresh culture dishes.

Food which is successful with one species is frequently rejected by other species. Brandwein (1938) added minute protozoans (*Chilomonas, Colpidium*) to cultures of *Pectinatella magnifica* grown in finger bowls containing an agar layer with imbedded wheat grains overlain by a mixture of natural water and very dilute balanced salt solution; but frequent subculturing was necessary. Brandwein noted that *Pectinatella* would eat *Paramecium, Arcella, Blepharisma*, and rotifers.

Most phylactolaemates show a preference for more or less shaded situations. *Cristatella* is usually found living on the underside of leaves of the water-lily *Nymphaea*. The majority of phylactolaemate colonies are found on submerged vegetation, especially that extending out into clear water, away from bottom accumulations.

Bullough (1950) states that although well-grown colonies usually die quickly when brought into the laboratory, freshwater ectoprocts are more easily cultured than are marine ectoprocts. The best way is to collect the statoblasts in late summer and autumn, either by catching with a fine mesh net those floating on the surface of a pond, or by letting an old colony die and disintegrate until the statoblasts float free. Until they are required they can be kept dormant in some cold place. When brought into the warmth (about 20°C) they hatch in about a month. Each statoblast then quickly develops into a single zooid, and small colonies may be grown by adding *Euglena* or *Paramecium* cultures, dried and powdered *Elodea*, or even malted milk. However, for an examination of the internal structure the newly hatched single zooids are best, since they have not yet secreted gelatinous zooecia.

Small colonies of *Plumatella* have been maintained for long periods of time in balanced aquaria, both tropical and cold-water.

KILLING AND PRESERVATION METHODS

For all ectoprocts narcotization is recommended before fixation. Single zooids or colonies should be kept quiet in a small volume of water and allowed to expand their tentacles. Then add a few crystals of menthol, stovaine or β-eucaine hydrochloride. The last mentioned is particularly recommended for freshwater forms. When the individual zooids no longer react when touched with a needle, draw off the water and replace it with 5 per cent formalin, or alternatively add sufficient 40 per cent formaldehyde solution to the water containing the relaxed animals until the concentration is 5 per cent. Ectoprocts may be stored in fresh 5 per cent formalin or taken through 30 per cent and 50 per cent alcohol, and stored in 70 per cent alcohol.

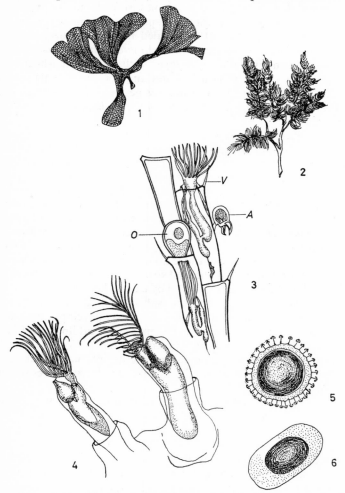

Figure 1.21. Some examples of ectoprocta: 1. *Flustra*, a piece of colony, calcified; 2. *Bugula*, a small branching colony; 3. *Bugula*, part of colony, showing a pair of zooids (one expanded), an ovicell (*O*), a vibraculum (*V*) and an avicularium (*A*), (from Bullough, 1950, by courtesy of Macmillan & Co. Ltd.); 4. *Lophopus*, part of colony (from a stained preparation); 5. Statoblast of *Cristatella*; 6. Statoblast of *Plumatella*

Statoblasts should be fixed with hot (60°C) saturated mercuric chloride solution for 2–3 min. Then rinse thoroughly in 70 per cent iodized alcohol, and transfer to 90 per cent alcohol for 8 h. They may be cleared in euparal essence, and mounted in euparal.

Recommended staining methods for whole-mount preparations of ectoprocts are: borax-carmine, Mayer's paracarmine, anthracene blue, Ehrlich's haematoxylin. To obtain flat preparations it may be necessary to bind small portions of the colony between two glass slides, prior to fixing. If this is done, a thin spacer should also be inserted at each end of the slides so that the specimen is not damaged.

For good preparations of statoblasts the following method is recommended by Wagstaffe and Fidler (1957). Heat the statoblasts in 10 per cent caustic soda solution for 10 min or so, then wash them in glacial acetic acid. Carefully puncture them with a fine needle to release their contents. Wash again in two changes of glacial acetic acid and stain in acid fuchsin dissolved in glacial acetic acid. Such preparations should be washed in glacial acetic acid, transferred to slightly acidulated clove oil and mounted in euparal.

The same authors also recommend the following method for preparations of larvae. If desired, narcotize as above and fix in hot (60°C) Bouin's fluid, then wash in several changes of 70 per cent alcohol to remove all the picric acid, then stain by any of the methods recommended above for whole-mount preparations.

PHYLUM BRACHIOPODA

This is the last of the three coelomate phyla, the members of which possess a lophophore. They are easily distinguished from the other two phyla by the bilaterally symmetrical bivalve shell in which the animal is enclosed. This shell is attached directly or by means of a stalk (pedicle). The two valves of the shell are lined by the mantle extension of the body wall. There is an open type of circulatory system. The valves of brachiopods can be distinguished from those of lamellibranch molluscs by the fact that they are dorsal and ventral in position while in the latter they are lateral, and although the valves are bilaterally symmetrical they are usually very dissimilar. Eggs are sometimes brooded in pouches of the mantle but are usually liberated, as are sperms, into the open sea. Exclusively marine, brachiopods occur in all seas from the intertidal zone to great depths. Although once abundant from Palaeozoic to Mesozoic times, there are only about 250 known species.

Class Ecardines (Inarticulata). Brachiopods which have their valves held together by muscles alone, there being no hinge. There is no internal skeletal support for the lophophore. An anus is present in members of this class.

Order Atremata. The shell contains calcium phosphate. Both valves help in providing passage for the pedicle. The only living family is the Lingulidae with the genera *Lingula* and *Glottidia*.

Order Neotremata. The notch allowing passage for the pedicle is confined to the ventral valve. There are only two existing families of this order, family Discinidae whose members have shells containing calcium phosphate, and family Craniidae, whose members' shells contain calcium carbonate.

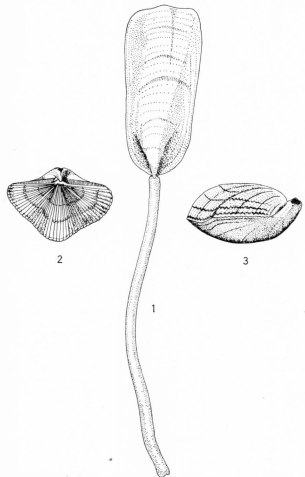

Figure 1.22. Three examples of Brachiopoda: 1. *Lingula* (Order Ecardines); 2. *Spirifera*, an extinct brachiopod (Order Testicardines) [after B.M.(N.H.) publication]; 3. *Magellania* (= Waldheimia) (Order Testicardines)

Class Testicardines (Articulata). Brachiopods which have the valves connected by means of a tooth and socket hinge apparatus. The mineral content of the shell is mainly calcium carbonate. The lophophore is provided with an internal skeletal support. There is no anus present in members of this class.

CULTURAL METHODS

Various authors have commented on the hardiness of brachiopods in laboratory cultures. *Lacazella mediterranea* survived for 6 weeks (Lacaze-Duthiers, 1861); Joubin (1886) kept *Crania anomala* for over 14 months; a Japanese species of *Lingula* and *Glottidia pyramidata* were kept for 6 months by Morse (1902). However, Cloud (1948) could not keep *Terebratulina septentrionalis* even a few days and failed to transport them from Maine to Cape Cod.

The food consists of minute organisms, especially diatoms. Lingulids are more general feeders, the diet consisting of diatoms, dinoflagellates, foraminiferans, radiolarians, mollusc larvae, small crustaceans, annelids, vegetable matter, and mud and sand.

KILLING AND PRESERVATION METHODS

The shell of brachiopods is generally thin and fragile, and the muscles which control the valves of the shell are powerful, hence it is essential that the brachiopods be fixed so that the valves remain gaping. This may be done in the following way: on dredging the brachiopods, transfer them to a dish of sea-water and leave them to settle for about 30 min. Then gradually add 96 per cent alcohol, until the concentration has reached approximately 5 per cent. Leave to narcotize for some time, then when the shell valves open easily insert a chip of wood and immediately transfer the specimen to 70 per cent alcohol. The brachiopods should be stored in a fresh change of 70 per cent alcohol.

TECHNIQUE FOR EXPOSING THE LOOP

Gentle maceration is the technique involved. Elliott (1955) recommends the following method.

Maceration needs special care owing to the very delicate shelly brachial skeleton which is completely embedded in the fleshy lophophore. It is essential that the process be gentle. In the case of dried or spirit preserved specimens, which are tougher than fresh specimens, immersion in tap-water for 7–10 days should, if ineffective, be followed by the addition of a small quantity of bacterial fluid, made by leaving a small piece of meat or fish in a little water for several days. When the lophophore tissue becomes soft, and small fragments fall away, it may be teased free of the loop with a fine camel-hair brush. A needle should only be employed with great care, and it is then really better to subject the specimen to further maceration. The process is completed by several washes in changes of fresh water, and one of very weak disinfectant, if considered necessary, for large specimens. In drying, the brachial skeleton often breaks, and dry specimens should be examined for this defect before maceration.

PHYLUM MOLLUSCA

Mollusca are coelomates which have a body that is not metamerically segmented, and the body regionated into a distinct head, a muscular foot and a visceral mass. The gut is liable to torsion, so much so that the anus may be directed forward. Typically, the nervous system consists of a circumoesophageal ring frequently concentrated into cerebral and pleural ganglia. Pedal and visceral ganglia are joined to this ring. Often there are sense organs present and these may be elaborate. There is a partly open well-developed blood vascular system which consists of a heart, arteries and veins communicating with the haemocoel. Frequently there arises from the dorsal side of the body an extension, the mantle, which may secrete a calcareous shell. The space between the mantle and the body is known as the mantle cavity and into this cavity there is situated the urinary and genital papillae, the anus, and typically the ctenidia. Although in many molluscs the ctenidia play the part of gills, in other molluscs their function is not mainly respiratory, and other organs may be developed for this function. In many cases the fertilized egg develops into a trochophore larva and this in turn develops into a veliger before developing into an adult. A structure which is of great taxonomic importance is frequently present in the buccal cavity. This is the radula.

Class Amphineura, the 'chitons'. The mantle secretes calcareous spicules which may fuse to form plates. Examples are, *Lepidopleurus*, *Tonicella*, and *Lepidochitona*.

Class Gastropoda, the 'univalves'. The body is bilaterally symmetrical, with a well-developed head bearing tentacles, eyes and a radula. The visceral hump is frequently coiled, always undergoing counter-clockwise torsion through 180 degrees, and often undergoing some detorsion. Typically there is a mantle secreting a single shell; members may or may not have a pelagic larval stage.

Order Prosobranchia (Streptoneura). Members undergo torsion, but not detorsion. The heart is always posterior to the ctenidia. The shell is usually well developed and the sexes are separate. Almost all members of this order are marine. Examples are *Haliotis*, 'ormers', *Osilinus*, 'top shells', *Patella*, 'limpets', *Littorina*, 'winkles', *Crepidula*, 'slipper limpets', *Pterotrachea*, and *Nassarius* 'dog whelks'.

Order Opisthobranchia (Euthyneura). Some detorsion has usually occurred, and the shell is reduced or absent. This order includes *Aplysia*, 'sea hares', and the nudibranchs which include such genera as *Archidoris*, *Tritonia*, and *Doto*.

Order Pulmonata (Euthyneura). A shell is usually present, but an operculum is never developed. The mantle wall acts as a lung and there are no ctenidia. There are two suborders: (*a*) Basommatophora, which have eyes situated at the base of a single pair of tentacles—this suborder includes *Limnaea* 'pond snails', and *Planorbis* 'ram's horn snails', and (*b*) Stylommatophora, which have eyes situated at the tips of the posterior of two pairs of invaginable tentacles—this suborder includes *Helix*, the true 'snails', and *Limax*, a genus of 'slugs'.

Class Scaphopoda, 'elephant tusk shells'. The shell is an external curved tube, open at both ends and shaped like an elephant's tusk. The shell is wider anteriorly. The commonest genus is *Dentalium*.

Class Lamellibranchia, 'bivalves'. The shell consists of two valves which are usually connected by a hinge. The body is laterally compressed, and the foot is tongue shaped. Two ctenidia are present and these are usually complex and well-developed.

Order Prosobranchia. Contains such genera as *Nucula* and *Solenomya*.

Order Filibranchia. This large order contains such genera as *Arca*, 'ark shells', *Mytilus*, 'mussels', *Pecten*, 'scallops', and *Ostrea*, 'oysters'.

Order Eulamellibranchia. This is another large order, and contains such genera as *Unio*, *Anodonta*, *Margatifera*, all 'freshwater mussels', *Cardium*, 'cockles', *Tridacna*, 'giant clams', *Ensis*, 'razor shells', *Pholas*, 'piddock', *Teredo*, 'ship worms', and *Brechites* (= *Aspergillum*) 'pepper-pot shells'.

Order Septibranchia. A small order which includes the genus *Cuspidaria*.

Class Cephalopoda, 'head-footed molluscs'. The body of cephalopods is bilaterally symmetrical, and the posterior part of the foot forms an exit funnel from the mantle cavity. The shell, when present, may be internal or external, and may be chambered. The head is well developed and surrounded by circumoral tentacles. The eyes are particularly well developed, and a radula is present as well as a horny beak. There are one or two pairs of ctenidia in the mantle cavity. The eggs of cephalopods contain yolk.

Subclass Nautiloidea. The shell is external and chambered, and there are two pairs of ctenidia. The tentacular arms are numerous and are without suckers. There is no ink sac, and the siphuncle is centrally situated. Includes the genus *Nautilus*, 'pearly nautilus'.

Subclass Ammonoidea. This totally extinct subclass contains the well-known fossil ammonites, which were similar in many ways to the nautiloids, but their siphuncle was situated marginally.

Subclass Coleoidea. This is the largest subclass and contains three orders. With one exception, *Argonauta*, the shell is internal when present, but may be reduced or absent. The shell when external is never chambered. One pair of ctenidia is present. The tentacles bear suckers.

Order Decapoda. There are 10 tentacles present, usually of two kinds. This order is divided into three suborders: (*a*) Belemnoidea, which comprises the extinct 'belemnites'; (*b*) Sepioidea, which contains such genera as *Spirula*, *Sepia*, 'cuttlefish', and *Sepiola*, 'little cuttles', and (*c*) Teuthoidea, which contains the genera *Loligo*, *Histioteuthis* and *Ommatostrephes*.

Order Vampyromorpha, contains the genus *Vampyroteuthis*.

Order Octopoda. There are eight uniform tentacles with suckers that are devoid of horny rims. The true internal shell is vestigial or absent, but a unique external shell is present in *Argonauta*. Other genera include

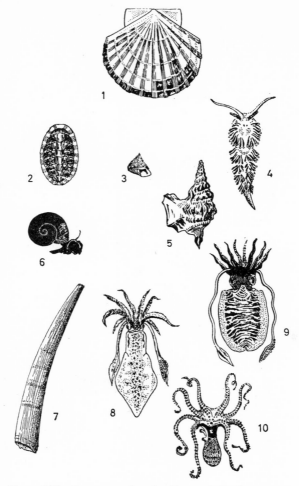

Figure 1.23. Some examples of molluscs: 1. 'Scallop' *Pecten maximus*; 2. A 'chiton', *Lepidochitona cinereus*—an amphineuran; 3. 'Top shell' *Calliostoma zizyphinum*—a prosobranch gastropod; 4. A 'nudibranch' *Facelina auriculata*—an opisthobranch gastropod; 5. 'Pelican's foot shell' *Aporrhais pes-pelicani*; 6. 'Ram's horn snail' *Planorbis corneus*—a freshwater pulmonate gastropod; 7. 'Elephant-tusk shell' *Dentalium*; 8. 'Common squid' *Loligo forbesi*—a decapod cephalopod; 9. 'Common cuttlefish' *Sepia officinalis*—a decapod cephalopod; 10. 'Common octopus' *Octopus vulgaris*—an octopod cephalopod. [1, 4, 8, 9 and 10 are after Barrett and Yonge, 1958]

PHYLUM MOLLUSCA

Octopus, 'octopus', *Eledone*, 'curled octopus', *Tremoctopus*, *Ocythoë*, and *Opisthoteuthis*.

CULTURAL METHODS FOR MOLLUSCS
(1) MARINE MOLLUSCS

Some of the large molluscs are difficult to maintain, but some small species will survive for reasonably long periods in large tanks of cool well-aerated sea-water.

(2) FRESHWATER MOLLUSCS

Pulmonates such as *Planorbis* can easily be maintained in balanced aquaria and require very little attention. Apart from their egg masses being somewhat unsightly in an aquarium containing fish, they do excellent work in keeping down algal growth.

Special feeding methods for these and other species are: (*i*) Feeding with small pieces of dried lettuce leaves. These are prepared by boiling lettuce leaves for a few seconds, then allowing the leaves to dry on clean sheets of glass. The dry leaves should then be stored in glass air-tight jars; (*ii*) Feeding with a gel of sodium alginate containing various nutritive substances. The recipe for this is [Standen, (1951)]:

'Bemax'	1 g
Dried milk	0·5 g
Powdered dried lettuce	1 g
Sodium alginate	1 g
Distilled water	100 ml.

The water which should be hot but not boiling is agitated in an enamel container by means of a mechanical stirrer. Add the ingredients slowly with the sodium alginate last. A viscous soupy liquid results. Whilst still hot it is poured into a flat china or enamel dish to form a thin layer. This layer is then flooded with 2 per cent calcium chloride solution. This forms a gel of calcium alginate which is insoluble. The gel can be lifted and cut into strips. It is washed once in cold water, then left to dry. When added to the aquarium water it will not go mouldy or foul the water.

(3) TERRESTRIAL PULMONATES

Terrestrial pulmonates such as *Helix*, should be kept in glass, or earthenware containers fitted with gauze lids, and fed on lettuce leaves and on whole oats which have been rolled in calcium carbonate powder. The container should be kept in a cool shady place. The bottom of the container should be covered with 2–3 in. of loamy soil, which should be kept damp, and with several layers of dead leaves on top of the soil, the uppermost layer remaining dry.

Slugs may be kept in a similar way, but the container should be kept in an even darker place. It is not necessary to roll the oats in calcium carbonate. The food for snails can be supplemented with bread, raw potatoes, turnips and most green vegetables.

KILLING AND PRESERVATION METHODS
Marine Forms

The majority of marine molluscs must be narcotized before any attempt to fix the animals is made, due to the fact that they are strongly retractile. Narcotization is, however, unnecessary with cephalopods as they soon die when removed from the sea. Narcotization is carried out after the animals have been placed into a large container of sea-water which has then been put into a cool place away from direct sunlight. After a time the animals will expand, and it is only then that the narcotization should be carried out. Disturbing the water as little as possible, the chosen narcotic is slowly added to the surface of the water, either in soluble crystal form or in liquid form.

Menthol is added in crystal form, and narcotization takes from 12–24 h; magnesium sulphate may be added in crystal form until a concentration of 1 per cent is obtained after $\frac{1}{2}$ h, though it may be necessary to increase this strength with some species. The time required will vary from 1–5 h. Alcohol may be added very slowly to the sea-water, taking care to avoid allowing the strong alcohol to come into contact with the animals. Formalin may be used in a similar way to alcohol, but it should be added a few drops at a time as a 1 per cent solution, repeating every 15 min until the animals are narcotized. This method works particularly well with some species of nudibranchs.

Some marine lamellibranch molluscs will relax if they are placed into a 0·5 per cent solution of propylene phenoxetol. Good results have been obtained with *Cardium edule*, *Nucula*, *Mytilus edulis*, *Arctica islandica*, *Spisula subtruncata*, various members of the Veneridae, and was partially successful with *Mya arenaria*.

When fully narcotized (too long a time in the narcotic will cause rapid decomposition of the animal), large molluscs, particularly opisthobranchs, should be injected with a quantity of the selected fixative before being plunged into the fixing solution. Small specimens do not require the injection. As molluscs are best dissected immediately, it is frequently unnecessary to preserve them.

Although formalin seems to be as good a general preservative for molluscs as any other fixative, a few notes are given below on some special methods which have been found to be satisfactory with respect to certain species:

Haliotis—Crofts (1929) used specimens which had been preserved in a mixture of equal parts of 90 per cent alcohol, 2·5 per cent formalin in sea-water, and glycerol. They were previously narcotized with menthol. It is also of interest to note that the following treatment is said to be helpful for dissection of the pedal nerve cords: maceration in 5 per cent potassium dichromate in sea-water, or in Béla Haller's fluid, for 1–7 days, until the nerves show up opaque against the translucent mass of pedal muscle. The dissection is further helped by immersing the macerated specimen in strong saline solution. Béla Haller's fluid is:

Glacial acetic acid	1 part
Glycerol	1 part
Water	2 parts

For histology, fixation of the tissues in Bouin's fluid or in Flemming's without acetic acid, was preferred.

Sepia—Tompsett (1939) states that formalin should be used for general dissection work; the eyes and brain should be injected with 10 per cent formalin, and after slitting open the mantle, the whole animal should be immersed in 4 per cent formalin.

Freshwater Molluscs

Lamellibranchs, such as *Anodonta* and *Unio*, will relax and die in a suitable state for dissection if placed into hot water for a few seconds, and as soon as the shell-valves gape a piece of wood or cork should be inserted, and the animal transferred to warm water until the foot extends and does not retract when pricked with a needle. When this state is reached the animal is suitable for dissection. If they are required for display purposes, they should be immersed in 4 per cent formalin, in which they may be stored provided that the formalin is neutralized, or after 24 h fixation they may be transferred to 70 per cent alcohol or to 1 per cent phenoxetol solution. For histological sections, specimens may be fixed in Bouin's fluid, Zenker's solution, Gilson's fluid, or Heidenhain's 'Susa'.

Freshwater gastropods may sometimes be successfully extended by gradually warming the water in which they are contained. Menthol sprinkled on to the surface of the water is usually successful but relaxation takes several hours. Air should be excluded from the jar. They may be dissected as soon as they no longer respond to a prick from a needle, or they may be preserved in a mixture of equal parts of 4 per cent formalin and glycerol. Fixation in Bouin's fluid,

Zenker's or Gilson's fluid is recommended if the animals are to be used for histological purposes.

Terrestrial Pulmonates

Although some workers have recommended the addition of a few drops of an alcoholic solution of phenoxetol to the water containing the pulmonates, the author has not found this method to be reliable enough to use when a large number of animals are to be killed for a given time.

A more reliable method which will result in 95 per cent of the animals being properly extended is to asphyxiate them. Tap-water is boiled for at least 30 min to get rid of any air. This is poured into a suitable glass container with a flat ground top. The container is covered and the water allowed to cool. Then the animals are introduced and the lid is again replaced, this time sealing the rim with Vaseline. It is important that the container be completely filled with the cool boiled water.

If this technique is properly carried out, the animals should be dead in about 12 h, but occasionally the time required will be 24 h. They may be dissected as soon as they appear to be dead. If they are to be preserved for display or dissection purposes, they should be immersed in 4 per cent formalin for several hours (injecting large specimens), then transferred to a mixture of 4 per cent formalin (neutral) and glycerol, or to 1 per cent phenoxetol solution.

Other variations of this killing method are: (*i*) to add some tobacco to the water; (*ii*) to use fizzy lemonade or soda-water instead of cool boiled water; (*iii*) to prepare a stock solution of alcohol (90 parts), and turpentine (10 parts), then use 10 per cent solution of this stock mixture in water.

PRESERVATION OF THE SHELLS OF MOLLUSCS

When the shell is small and delicate the animal should be killed in the usual way, then a hook inserted into its foot. By this means as much of the animal as possible should be removed. If any still remains, place it into warm water for a while. Dry in an incubator for a short time, then place into fine dry sand—this will cause the remaining soft parts to shrink and they will often drop out.

Larger shells should be washed in warm water and cleaned with a soft brush, and then allowed to dry. If it has an operculum, the inside of the shell may be packed with cotton wool and the operculum glued to this in position.

THE PREPARATION OF RADULAE

(*i*) Boil the whole head (or the whole body if the animal is small) in 10 per cent aqueous potassium hydroxide solution for a while, until all the soft tissues have disintegrated. The radula and the mandible (if the latter is present) will be easily seen in the solution.

(*ii*) Decant the fluid carefully, then wash the radula in several changes of distilled water. It may be necessary to brush large radulae with a soft brush to remove the last traces of tissue.

(*iii*) Arrange the radula along the length of a clean glass slide, and gently compress it with another slide. Bind the two slides together and immerse for at least 10 min in 70 per cent alcohol.

(*iv*) The top slide should then be removed, after which the composition of the radula is changed by first of all treating it with a solution of 5 per cent oxalic acid for 5 min, followed by a further 5 min in 1 per cent potassium permanganate solution. The radula should then be stained with a 1 per cent aqueous solution of dahlia violet. It may then be mounted in glycerol-jelly to form a temporary mount or it may be dehydrated rapidly, cleared in xylene and mounted in Canada balsam. An alternative staining method, which is less attractive but does away with the necessity of modifying the chitin with oxalic acid and permanganate, is to stain the prepared radula in a saturated solution of chlorazol black E in 70 per cent alcohol. Then the radula is differentiated in Milton or terpineol, before being dehydrated, cleared, and mounted in euparal or Canada balsam.

EXTRACTION AND MOUNTING OF THE LOVE-DART

In true members of the Helicidae, the love-dart, Liebespfeil, or *telum veneris*, is contained in the dart sac, which is attached as a sort of pocket to the vagina, near to its orifice. It consists of a straight, or curved, sometimes slightly twisted tubular shaft of calcium carbonate, tapering to a fine point above, and enlarging gradually, more often somewhat abruptly, to the base. The sides of the shaft are sometimes furnished with blades. In *Helix aspersa* the dart is about $\frac{5}{16}$ in. long, and $\frac{1}{8}$ in. wide at its base. The dart is almost confined to the family Helicidae, but not all of the members of this family possess a dart.

When present, it may be extracted together with the radula and jaw by macerating the animal in 10 per cent potassium hydroxide solution. When removed from the macerating fluid it should be washed in several changes of distilled water, then dried. It may be mounted in a dry cell, or mounted together with its respective shell on a piece of black card and contained in a glass-covered box.

PHYLUM ANNELIDA
The annelids are metamerically segmented worms, i.e., worms which have

a body consisting of a linear series of segments, each of which is of the same fundamental plan. There is a single pre-oral segment, the prostomium. The body wall, in the main, consists of an outer layer of circular muscle, and an inner layer of longitudinal muscle. There is an extensive coelom. A closed blood system is usually present. The nerve cord is ventral and double, with a pair of ganglia in each segment and a pair of pre-oral cerebral ganglia. The excretory system is nephridial. Some annelids have a trochosphere larval stage.

Annelids are modified for an active, sedentary, or parasitic life, in the sea, fresh water or on the land.

Class Archiannelida. A group of small marine worms, which have a ciliated epidermis, and show little or no segmentation. Chaetae are rarely present. This group is widely regarded as being a heterogeneous assortment of aberrant polychaetes. Examples are *Polygordius* and *Dinophilus*.

Class Polychaeta. Annelids with clear segmentation and with a spacious perivisceral coelom. With parapodia (muscular projections which are locomotory in swimming forms) bearing chaetae. With a distinct head usually bearing eyes, palps and tentacles. Sexes are usually separate, asexual division occurs in some species. All marine.

Subclass Errantia. Polychaetes with a generally wormlike body, made up of numerous similar segments; parapodia with acicula (modified setae which act as skeletal supports); swimming, crawling and burrowing forms. Examples are *Nereis, Aphrodite, Tomopteris, Glycera*.

Subclass Sedentaria. Polychaetes with the body usually divided into various distinct regions. Usually with simple parapodia, without acicula. Head is usually small or much reduced; typically tube-dwelling worms. Examples are *Arenicola, Chaetopterus, Cirratulus,* and *Sabella*.

Class Myzostomaria. Ectoparasitic on echinoderms, especially crinoids, these annelids are much flattened, and are sometimes considered to be aberrant Polychaetes. An example is *Myzostomum*.

Class Oligochaeta. Annelids with clear segmentation, but with no parapodia and with reduced chaetae. The prostomium is small with no appendages and usually no eyes. Hermaphrodite. A glandular clitellum is present for cocoon formation. Oligochaetes generally are found in fresh water and terrestrial habitats. They are generally classified on the relative positions of the testes, their duct apertures and the spermathecae. Some are parasitic. Examples are *Stylaria, Enchytraeus, Tubifex, Lumbricus, Allolobophora,* and *Digaster*.

Class Hirudinea, the 'leeches'. Annelids with only 33 body segments. There may appear to be more than this number due to the fact that the segments are subdivided externally by annuli. No parapodia or chaetae are present. Posterior and anterior suckers are usually present. The mouth is ventral and inside the anterior sucker, while the anus is dorsal and outside the posterior sucker. An ingrowth of botryoidal tissue greatly reduces the coelom. Hermaphrodite. Majority are freshwater dwellers, but some live in moist soil, while others are marine. They are either predators on such animals as worms or snails, or parasitic on vertebrates. Examples are *Hirudo, Haemopis, Pontobdella,* and *Helobdella*.

Class Echiurida. The only remaining group of gephyreans (Sipunculida, Priapulida, Echiurida) which is still generally regarded as an annelid. The

Echiurida are relatively large annelids with little or no trace of segmentation, and with a non-retractile proboscis. They are marine and are adapted for a sluggish life hidden in rock crevices or buried in sand. A pair of ventral chaetae is present. Examples are *Echiurus*, and *Bonellia*.

THE COLLECTION OF ENCHYTRAEID WORMS FROM SOILS

The following method (O'Connor, 1955, 1962) is a modification of one devised by Baermann (1917). It is said to give results which are comparable with those obtained with the Nielsen extractor (Nielsen, 1952–3) but is far simpler and is probably less influenced by variations in design.

Heat is applied to soil spread on a sieve resting in a funnel full of water (*Figure 1·24*). The worms move downwards through the sieve into the funnel from which they can be collected by releasing the spring clip. This method has proved suitable for a wide variety of woodland soils, peats, vegetable debris and agricultural land.

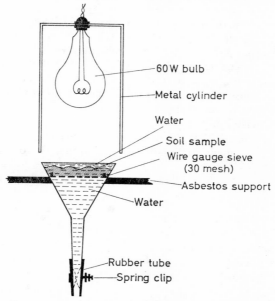

Figure 1.24. Modified Baermann funnel extractor unit in section (O'Connor, 1958)

The apparatus consists of a polythene funnel (*d* 11 cm, 60 degrees included angle) in which rests a wire-gauze sieve (*d* 9 cm, 30 mesh). The funnels are inserted in holes (*d* 9 cm) in an asbestos board, and have a rubber tube with spring clip attached to the outlet. An electric light bulb (60 W) is suspended above each funnel and is enclosed in a metal cylinder (*d* 11 cm, *h* 18 cm). The funnels are arranged in batteries of twelve supported on a light metal-alloy framework. The light bulbs and their cylinders are attached to a removable frame and are wired in parallel. Heating is controlled by a rheostat or, alternatively, by gradually lowering the frame from a height of about 10 cm. O'Connor (1957) recommends that the soil samples (*d* 6·3 cm and 6 cm deep) are obtained with a cylindrical sampler split longitudinally so that it can be opened and the exposed core subdivided into natural divisions of the profile before removal from the sampler; this procedure minimizes the risk of damage to organisms by compression. Each soil horizon is again subdivided into 2 cm layers, and each subcore (*V* 187 cm³) is placed surface downwards on the sieve plate in the funnel. The funnel is then filled with water so that the soil is completely submerged. The worms which collect in the funnel stem are withdrawn by releasing the spring clip. The heating of the funnel is gradually increased in steps (soil temperature in middle of sample increases from about 17–38°C over a period of 3 h). When the temperature at the surface of the soil sample has reached 45°C—after about 3 h—extraction is completed.

If the soil samples are dry, they should be moistened with a fine jet of water before immersion in the funnel. If the soil temperature is low they must be gradually equilibrated to room temperature over a 24 h period prior to extraction.

It is worth noting that the metal cylinders which enclose the light bulbs may conveniently be made from 'National Dried-milk' tins.

CULTURAL METHODS
Marine Annelids

These are not easily maintained for long periods of time, but some species of *Nereis* will survive for several weeks, in large, well-aerated marine aquaria. Several species have been reared to sexual maturity from the egg stage. They will feed on other small worms or small pieces of chopped crab or mussel.

Oligochaeta

Lumbricus terrestris—These are usually gathered at night during or following warm rain, when the ground has been thoroughly soaked. They are easily seen with a strong electric torch. The best collecting grounds are closely cut lawns where the soil is rich. After collection put the worms into a pail containing some freshly cut grass. In the morning, examine them and discard any injured or abnormal ones. Transfer the worms to large wooden boxes filled about 12 in. deep with approximately equal parts of old leaves and leaf loam gathered from woods. Never use heavy clay soil. It must be kept moist but never saturated. A thick layer of dead leaves on top of the mixture helps to prevent it from drying up. No other food is necessary as the worms eat the decaying leaves. If, however, light loamy soil is used, it is necessary to feed the worms every two or three weeks by spreading a paste of bread crumbs or corn meal on to the surface of the soil. Do not use too much food or it will rot, and foul the loam, killing the worms. The worms must not be over-crowded—about 25 worms per ft.^{3} is a suitable population. The box may be covered with a sheet of glass, and the whole box kept in a cool place—temperatures about 16°C usually prove fatal.

Allolobophora nocturna and A. longa—These are usually found in well-manured ground, and can be kept as *Lumbricus*, but a liberal quantity of rotted cow manure should be added to the leaf-loam mixture.

Eisenia foetida—These have been kept in partly rotted cow and horse manure.

Tubifex—These small aquatic oligochaets, which are used as food for fish and many other animals, are easily kept in aquaria fitted with slowly running water. The aquaria should have a layer of mud, sand and decaying leaves as a substrate.

Enchytraeus albidus—This semi-aquatic oligochaet is also used as food for small fish and amphibia. They may be cultured like earth-worms, and fed sparingly with small pieces of bread soaked in milk, or on mashed potatoes buried deep. A successful culture has been kept in a small wooden box, so constructed that the perforated sides were all removable. The box was filled with damp loam containing the worms, and a small quantity of boiled oat porridge was placed on the loam under each side. The box was kept in a room with a temperature about 18°C. The worms tended to congregate on any one particular side, and when required the sides were removed in turn, until largest number of worms was seen. The small white cocoons which are found in the soil may be removed and kept in Petri-dishes on damp filter paper. Being transparent, the development and hatching can be watched through a microscope.

Hirudo medicinalis—This has been cultured on a large scale, particularly in France. It will live for many years and will breed in aquaria, or in earthenware jars, which are kept half full with fresh water in a cool shady place. The leeches are given to wandering so the aquaria must have well-fitting lids, perforated with very small

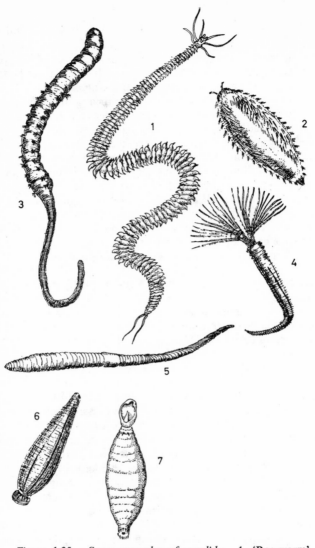

Figure 1.25. Some examples of annelids: 1. 'Rag-worm'
Nereis virens, an errant polychaete; 2. 'Sea mouse' *Aphrodite
aculeata,* an errant polychaete; 3. 'Lug-worm' *Arenicola
marina,* a sedentary polychaete; 4. *Sabella pavonina,* a
sedentary polychaete (after Barrett and Yonge, 1958); 5.
'Earthworm' *Lumbricus terrestris,* an oligochaete; 6.
'Medicinal leech' *Hirudo medicinalis,* a hirudinean; 7.
Echiurus, an echiurid [after a drawing in B.M.(N.H.) guide]

holes. They do not require feeding more often than once in six months, and they will suck the blood of any mammal. They will also feed on a frog which may be added to the aquarium.

Haemopis sanguisuga—This may be cultured like *Hirudo*, but will eat small earthworms, insect larvae and snails.

KILLING AND PRESERVATION METHODS

All annelids must be narcotized before being fixed to prevent them from contracting.

Polychaetes, Archiannelids, and Myzostomaria

The following method for killing *Arenicola marina* was devised by Professor G. P. Wells. It is suitable for all marine annelids, but the optimum time for narcotization will vary with different species. Two solutions are required:

Solution A
Magnesium chloride .. .. 70 g
Tap-water .. .. to 1 l.
Solution B
40 per cent formaldehyde solution .. .. 40 ml.
Solution A .. .. 960 ml.

The worms are immersed in Solution A until they are fully narcotized (about 3 h). If the worms are left for too long a time in this solution they become accommodated, and begin to recover. When properly narcotized the worms are carefully transferred to a long narrow container, or a dish with perspex partitions, containing Solution B. The reason for the special dish is that the worms should be kept straight during the fixation process. After 24 h in Solution B, the worms (*Arenicola* in particular) are ideal for dissection purposes. The worms may be stored in a fresh change of Solution B, or in 4 per cent formalin. After narcotization by the above method, it is usually easy to remove tubiculous polychaetes from their tubes.

Oligochaetes

Both terrestrial and aquatic forms will relax when placed into weak alcohol solution (less than 30 per cent). This is an excellent method for killing earthworms. Alternative methods are to add a few drops of chloroform to the water containing the worms, or by immersing the worms in 0·8 per cent nitric acid or 1 per cent chromic acid. Whichever method is used, the worm should be washed free from any attached debris before being fixed. Fixation is carried out with formol-alcohol. The worms may be stored in this solution with the addition of glycerol to 5 per cent.

If the worms are required for histological purposes, better fixation usually results from fixation in Zenker's fluid, or Heidenhain's 'Susa'. After a short period in the fixative, earthworms, or indeed any worms which contain soil or sand in the gut, should be cut into inch-long pieces. The gut contents are then washed out by inserting a pipette into one cut surface of each piece. When this has been carefully carried out, the worms are returned to the fixative for the recommended period of time. This method enables good sections to be cut and is far superior to the method whereby the gut is filled with wet filter-paper.

Hirudinea

Although the 7 per cent magnesium chloride solution which is used for relaxing polychaetes is isotonic to sea-water, this solution is also an efficient narcotizing agent for leeches. The leeches are allowed to swim in the solution, and will usually die in an extended condition after a few minutes. When dead they may be used for immediate dissection. If they are required for display or histological purposes they should be introduced into lengths of glass tubing of a suitable diameter before being placed in the chosen fixative. Alternatively they may be gently compressed between two glass slides. Recommended fixatives are formol-alcohol for display purposes, and Zenker's fluid, Heidenhain's 'Susa', or Bouin's fluid for histological material.

Echiurida

Echiurids should be narcotized in 7 per cent magnesium chloride in tap-water, making sure that the proboscis is fully extended and relaxed. Fix the animals in formol-alcohol. Store if required in a fresh change of fixative.

PHYLUM ONYCHOPHORA

Protoarthropods in which the exoskeleton is thin and soft, and with the body and limbs unjointed; the head is poorly defined and formed of three segments—the first preoral with preantennae, the second with jaws, and the third with oral papillae—the body consists of uniform segments each with two parapodia-like limbs ending in claws; the body-wall is well developed, with outer circular and inner longitudinal muscle layers; a tracheal respiratory system is present with spiracles scattered irregularly. The sexes are separate.

Until recently the Onychophora were regarded as a class of the Arthropoda, but most modern workers treat them as a separate phylum. Much of their structure is annelidan, and this group appears to be a link between the Annelida and Arthropoda.

PHYLUM TARDIGRADA

All the present-day forms are terrestrial, with a discontinuous distribution in tropical and sub-tropical forests, but the mid-Cambrian fossil *Aysheaia* from the Burgess Shales of Canada was marine.

There are two families of living Onychophora:

Family Peripatidae. Members have a larger number of segments, than members of the Peripatopsidae. They become bleached when preserved in alcoholic solutions. An example is *Peripatus*.

Family Peripatopsidae. Have fewer segments than members of the Peripatidae. Retain the characteristic blue and green colour when preserved in alcohol. An example is *Peripatopsis*.

Figure 1.26. Onychophora: Peripatus

CULTURAL METHODS

Species of Onychophora are easily maintained provided that warm humid conditions can be obtained. An aquarium 12 in. × 6 in. × 6 in. makes an ideal container. The bottom should be covered with a 1 in. layer of gravel and this in turn covered with a 2 in. layer of moist loamy soil. Stock with a moisture-loving plant such as *Tradescantia*, and provide shelter in the form of pieces of tree bark and irregular stones. Feed with wood-lice and occasionally give small pieces of meat, but remove any uneaten meat before it becomes foul. Cover the aquarium with a loose-fitting glass lid. It is essential that the atmosphere in the aquarium is of a very high humidity, and a check should be made daily to see that the soil is kept moist. A jam jar filled with water and containing an immersion heater and a thermostat may be placed in one corner. This will help to keep the atmosphere both warm and humid.

KILLING AND PRESERVATION METHODS

Onychophora should be killed in the vapour of ethyl acetate or chloroform. When dead an injection, using a hypodermic syringe, of a little formol-alcohol should be made into the ventral side of the animal. The animal should then be stored in formol-alcohol.

PHYLUM TARDIGRADA

Commonly known as 'water bears', or 'bear animalcules', the tardigrada are a small group of aquatic protoarthropods of uncertain affinity. The

77

size never exceeds 1 mm. There are four pairs of stumpy legs which resemble those of *Peripatus*. They live in damp places, and on moss; others live in fresh water, and some are marine.

Order Heterotardigrada. A pair of lateral cirri on each side of the 'head'. They are usually marine.

Order Eutardigrada. There are no cirri. Most species dwell in fresh water. An example is *Macrobiotus*.

There appear to be no published cultural techniques.

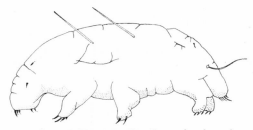

Figure 1.27. A tardigrad, much enlarged

KILLING AND PRESERVATION METHODS

Tardigrads are very small and it is therefore a problem to find a simple method for obtaining, killing and fixing these animals. Those species which live on moss are probably the kinds to obtain. Collect moss in a polythene bag to prevent it from drying. On arrival at the laboratory, take small pieces of moss and agitate them vigorously in a little water in a small Petri-dish. Unless a dissecting microscope giving a high magnification is available it will be necessary to examine the water and moss using a compound microscope with a × 50 magnification. The transmitted light must be carefully adjusted to make the tardigrads visible, and it is usually better to have the light on the dim side rather than have it too bright. After finding the tardigrads, transfer them to a slide on which has been placed a drop of polyvinyl lactophenol containing 0·01 per cent cotton blue. The tardigrads should be added to the polyvinyl lactophenol with as little water as possible. Cover the specimen with a coverslip, and allow to dry at room temperature.

PHYLUM PENTASTOMIDA

The Pentastomida or 'tongue-worms' are elongated wormlike parasites with secondary annulation; they have two pairs of claws at the side of the mouth. They infest the nasal passages and lungs of carnivorous mammals and snakes. The ripe eggs are sneezed on to the ground where they are picked up by the secondary host. An embryo develops which burrows into the liver, kidneys, or other organs of the new host, and if this host is then eaten by a suitable carnivorous host the parasites make their way to the nasal passages or lungs and become mature. Examples are *Linguatula*, and *Porocephalus*.

There appear to be no published cultural methods.

Figure 1.28. A typical pentastomid: Porocephalus armillatus, a parasite from the lung of a snake (from a photograph)

KILLING AND PRESERVATION METHODS

Pentastomids may be killed, fixed and stored in 3–5 per cent formalin or 70–90 per cent alcohol, or formol-alcohol.

PHYLUM ARTHROPODA

Arthropods are metamerically segmented, bilaterally symmetrical coelomate animals, which typically have a pair of jointed appendages on each segment, at least one of these pairs of appendages being modified as jaws. The head is well developed, and consists of a variable number of segments. The central nervous system consists of a double ventral nerve cord, with a pair of ganglia in each segment and a pair of preoral cerebral ganglia. The coelom is reduced, but the body cavity consists of a haemocoel. There is a well developed chitinous exoskeleton, and because of this, growth has to occur in jerks each time the animal moults and throws off its old exoskeleton and develops a new one. Growth occurs immediately after each moult. The process of moulting is known as ecdysis. The tough exoskeleton also complicates respiration, and in many aquatic forms, gills or branchiae are developed from vascular outgrowths of the integuments of the body wall. In terrestrial forms, however, a system of respiratory tubes or tracheae is developed. To provide attachments for muscles a kind of endoskeleton is formed by intrusions of the exoskeleton into the body cavity, and in some forms this may be so complicated as to form an endophragmal skeleton. The arthropoda comprise some 760,000 described species, 34,000 being recorded in the British Isles. It is the largest and most successful animal phylum, and its members have invaded every possible habitat, many even acquiring the power of flight. A full classification of this phylum is beyond the scope of this book, and the following is only a simplified version.
Class Trilobita, 'trilobites'. This class is entirely extinct.
Class Merostomata. Primitive aquatic forms which respire by gill books.
Order Eurypterida. An extinct order. Includes *Eurypterus*.
Order Xiphosura, 'king or horseshoe crabs'. Includes *Limulus*.
Class Arachnida. Terrestrial arthropods which respire by lung-books, and may be with or without tracheae, or may respire by tracheae alone.

Order Scorpiones, 'scorpions'.
Order Opiliones, 'harvestmen'.
Order Acari, 'mites and ticks'.
Order Aranei, 'spiders'.

Class Pycnogonida, 'sea spiders'. The Pycnogonids are aberrant marine arthropods which lack special respiratory structures. Appendages usually consist of a pair of chelicera, a pair of pedipalps, and five pairs of legs, the first pair being ovigerous (to which in males and occasionally in females the egg masses are cemented).

Class Crustacea. Typically aquatic arthropods which possess gills. The body is divisible into a head of six segments (the first disappearing, the second and third both preoral and with antennae, the fourth with mandibles, and the fifth and sixth with maxillae), a thorax (the region anterior to and including the segment with the genital opening), and an abdomen. The limbs are modified for swimming, walking, food capture, respiration and reproduction. The sexes are usually separate, and the development is usually via a nauplius stage. The majority are free-living and live in aquatic habitats, but a few are ecto- or endo-parasites.

Subclass Branchiopoda.
Order Anostraca, 'fairy shrimps'.
Order Notostraca, 'apus'.
Order Cladocera, 'water fleas'.
Order Ostracoda.
Subclass Copepoda, 'copepods'.
Subclass Cirripedia, 'barnacles'.
Subclass Malacostraca.
Division Leptostraca.
Order Nebaliacea.
Division Syncarida.
Order Anaspidacea, 'mountain shrimps'.
Division Peracarida.
Order Mysidacea, 'opossum shrimps'.
Order Isopoda, 'woodlice', etc.
Order Amphipoda, 'whale lice', etc.
Division Eucarida.
Order Euphausiacea, 'krill'.
Order Decapoda.
Suborder Macrura, 'prawns', 'shrimps', 'lobsters', 'crayfish'.
Suborder Anomura, 'squat-lobsters', 'hermit-crabs', 'cocoa-nut crabs'.
Suborder Brachyura, 'true crabs'.
Division Hoplocarida.
Order Stomatopoda, 'mantis shrimps'.

Class Myriapoda. The Myriapods are terrestrial arthropods with a tracheal system, and with pairs of segmentally arranged spiracles; the head is of six segments with the first three preoral the first disappearing, the second with antennae, the third limbless, the fourth with mandibles, and the fifth and sixth with or without maxillae; the body is usually elongated with numerous segments, most of which bear walking legs. The sexes are separate and the development direct.

Subclass Diplopoda, 'millipedes'.

Subclass Chilopoda, 'centipedes'.

Subclass Symphyla; e.g., *Scutigerella*.

Class Insecta. The insects are typically terrestrial Arthropoda with a tracheal system, and with pairs of segmentally arranged spiracles; the head is of six segments, with the first three preoral, the first disappearing, the second with antennae, the third limbless, the fourth with mandibles and the fifth and sixth with maxillae; the body is divisible into a thorax of three segments, each with a pair of walking legs, and an abdomen of not more than 12 segments, most of which are limbless; the sexes are separate, and the development is either direct or via a larval stage.

The number of insects, both of species and individuals, far exceed those of any other group of animals. To some extent they have invaded fresh water, but very few spend their whole lives in water. There are almost no marine representatives.

Subclass Apterygota. Primitive wingless insects which do not undergo metamorphosis.

 Order Collembola, 'springtails'.

 Order Thysanura, 'bristletails'.

Subclass Pterygota. Winged insects.

Infraclass Exopterygota. Insects which develop the wings externally. The development is via unspecialized larval stages, and therefore shows incomplete metamorphosis.

 Order Ephemeroptera, 'mayflies'.

 Order Odonata, 'dragonflies'.

 Order Plecoptera, 'stone flies'.

 Order Blattaria, 'cockroaches'.   ⎫

 Order Mantodea, 'praying mantids'. ⎬ = 'Orthoptera'

 Order Saltatoria, 'grasshoppers'.   ⎭

 Order Phasmida, 'stick insects'.

 Order Isoptera, 'termites'.

 Order Dermaptera, 'earwigs'.

 Order Psocoptera, 'book lice'.

 Order Mallophaga, 'biting lice'.

 Order Anoplura, 'sucking lice'.

 Order Thysanoptera, 'thrips'.

 Order Hemiptera, 'bugs'.

Infraclass Endopterygota. Insects which develop wings internally, and pass through specialized larval and pupal stages, thereby undergoing complete metamorphosis.

 Order Neuroptera, 'lacewings'.

 Order Megaloptera, 'alder flies'.

 Order Raphidiodea, 'snake flies'.

 Order Coleoptera, 'beetles'.

 Order Mecoptera, 'scorpion flies'.

 Order Trichoptera, 'caddis flies'.

 Order Lepidoptera, 'butterflies', 'moths'.

 Order Diptera, 'flies'.

 Order Siphonaptera, 'fleas'.

 Order Hymenoptera, 'ants', 'wasps', 'bees', etc.

For those who require a detailed classification of the Arthropoda, that given in *A Classification of Living Animals* by Lord Rothschild

(1961) is recommended. For a full classification of insects, the system found by Imms (1957), or the Martynov system found in Grassé (1951) are recommended. The Martynov system is used by Rothschild.

THE COLLECTION OF TERRESTRIAL ARACHNIDS, MYRIAPODS, AND INSECTS (Bayliss and Monro, 1941)

The general method of collecting these arthropods is to sweep vegetation with a strong net of unbleached calico or bolting-cloth, or beat bushes over an inverted umbrella or a light-coloured cloth. The majority of arachnids and myriapods hide themselves away from light, and these should be looked for in dark places, under stones, fallen branches, and in heaps of rotting vegetation. Some are found in the loose bark of trees and in crevices.

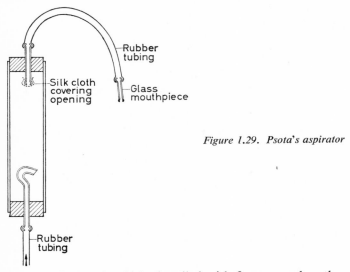

Figure 1.29. Psota's aspirator

Large specimens should be handled with forceps, unless they are delicate in which case they should be manoeuvred into a glass tube or other suitable container.

Small arthropods, particularly insects which live in crevices or settle on leaves, should be picked up by means of an aspirator or exhauster, or 'pooter'. Two forms of aspirator are shown: *Figure 1.29* is Psota's aspirator, which was devised for picking up small beetles. *Figure 1.30* is Beamer's aspirator.

When collecting in this manner the collector should have a large number of glass tubes fitted with efficient stoppers and three-quarters full of 70 per cent alcohol. Some empty tubes should be carried for the capture of living specimens, and still others containing fixatives which are suitable for mites and other special arthropods. A cartridge belt is a convenient method of carrying such tubes.

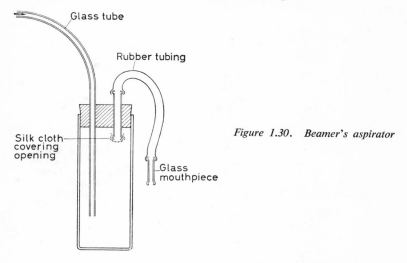

Figure 1.30. Beamer's aspirator

A potato-trap which can be used for catching woodlice, can also be used for catching some arachnids. This consists of a potato through which a long, narrow hole has been bored. The hole is plugged at one end with a piece of potato. This trap is left on the ground and lightly covered with leaves or litter. When taken up, and after removing the plug of potato, the contents are shaken out into a dish.

Two kinds of trap for myriapods are: (*i*) a shallow pit is dug in the ground, and this is lined with hay or grass to retain the moisture, and baited with bits of potato, beans, etc. A tile or board is laid over the bait, and the pit may, if desired, be filled in with soil. In dry weather the pit should be constantly watered; (*ii*) this trap consists of a piece of sacking laid on the ground or lightly buried, and kept moist. This is most easily done by allowing a corner of the sacking to dip into a container of water buried in the ground.

Small arthropods and other terrestrial animals can be collected in bulk by using a Berlese funnel (*Figure 1.31*). It consists essentially of a funnel supported on a stand. A sieve is placed over the mouth of the funnel, and litter is placed on the sieve. Heat is applied to the surface of the litter by means of an electric light bulb which is supported a few inches above the litter. A cylinder of metal encloses the bulb and the sieve and is provided with a perforated lid. The most complete result is to use a 25 W bulb, generating a temperature of 30–40°C, and allowing it to act for 25–30 h. The animals are driven through the sieve and fall into 70 per cent alcohol.

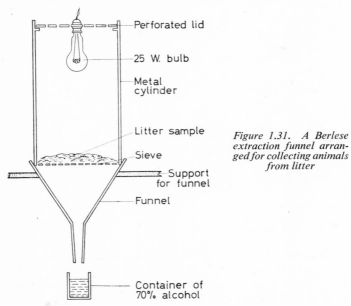

Figure 1.31. A Berlese extraction funnel arranged for collecting animals from litter

Water mites may be collected by sweeping water weeds with a hand-net, or by tow-netting. They can also be searched for by washing bunches of weeds and by examining submerged stones covered with moss. The lining material of nests and burrows may be treated with a Berlese extraction funnel, and will often reveal ticks and mites.

NOTE: Collembola which are easily collected from litter by using a Berlese funnel, can be made to sink in the 70 per cent alcohol by adding a few drops of ether to the alcohol.

SOME CULTURAL METHODS
The Culture of Artemia Salina

The 'brine shrimp' as well as being an easily obtained anostracan for class study, is also a useful supplementary food for carnivorous fish. Before being fed to freshwater fish they should be washed for several minutes in running tap-water in order to remove the salt.

The original supply of *Artemia* eggs are sprinkled on to the surface of an aquarium filled with sea-water and maintained at a temperature around 30°C. A simple method of feeding them is to add a small quantity of yeast to the water every few days. Just sufficient yeast to make the water slightly milky should be added, and no more should be given until the water has cleared. The first feed should be given when the nauplii appear, which is usually about 24–48 h after the eggs have been added. The culture should not be allowed to become overcrowded. When the brine shrimps reach maturity the sexes will pair off, and large quantities of eggs will float to the surface of the water. These should be collected and dried, as they will not develop unless they have been previously dried. As the water level drops, due to evaporation, it should be made up regularly with glass-distilled water. The sea-water must be well aerated, and the aquarium should be fitted with a loose-fitting cover.

The Culture of Daphnia

Before starting a culture of *Daphnia*, a rich culture of a green fresh-water, unicellular alga should be obtained. Such a culture often develops in an aquarium which is kept in a light window. Once a week, some of the soupy green water should be added to the tank containing the *Daphnia*. The best results are often produced in large porcelain sinks. Some *Elodea canadensis*, which will produce sufficient oxygen to aerate the water, should be grown in the sink. Alternatively a suspension of yeast can be added as food instead of the green algae, but care should be taken to avoid overfeeding with yeast as this will cause the water to become foul. Every few months, some of the *Daphnia* should be transferred to a fresh culture tank, and when they have settled down the old culture solution should be discarded after the *Daphnia* have all been removed.

The Culture of Cyclops

A method which is frequently successful is to mix an ounce of dried sheep manure in a gallon of water, and allow it to stand for several days until a rich culture of protozoans have developed. The cyclops can then be added. Occasionally add a few lettuce leaves or a small piece of meat and allow it to rot. Care should be taken to avoid the water becoming foul. Start a fresh culture every few months.

The Culture of Freshwater Gammarus and Asellus

Provided that the aquarium in which they are placed is well established and contains a quantity of mud and rotting leaves taken from the bottom of a pond, *Asellus* and *Gammarus* will live and breed readily.

The Culture of Woodlice

Oniscus can be maintained in boxes of soil rich in humus. The soil must be kept damp, and the temperature should be kept at about 20°C. Pieces of rotten wood or tree bark should be provided for the woodlice to congregate beneath. The humus in the soil will provide the main part of their diet, but this may be supplemented by adding a slice of raw potato from time to time.

The Culture of Crayfish (*Astacus fluviatilis*)

Crayfish are generally easy to maintain. But occasionally, if the water is unsuitable, they may only survive for a short time. In such a case it may be necessary to obtain a large supply of water from a suitable chalky river. They may prefer running water, in which case it is necessary to dechlorinate the water before admitting it to the aquarium. The aquarium should have a bottom layer of fine gravel and mud, and some chalk should be added at regular intervals. It should be provided with plant pots placed on their sides to provide shelter for the crayfish. They should be fed regularly with small pieces of raw meat or fish, but any uneaten food must be removed to prevent the water from becoming foul.

The Culture of Myriapods

Centipedes are easily kept in well-covered jars or aquaria partly filled with rich soil and decaying leaves. The soil should be kept very damp but not wet, and the atmosphere in the aquarium must be kept at maximum humidity. The animals should be kept away from direct light, and should be provided with flat stones or pieces of wood beneath which they can hide. Centipedes will feed on small earthworms, maggots, etc., but millipedes will feed on the decaying leaves.

The Culture of Blowflies and Bluebottles

These flies are very useful as food for all except the very large or very small frogs, toads, and many lizards. Many amphibians can live on an exclusive diet of flies. The maggots can also be used as a supplementary food for some birds, but if given in too great a quantity become indigestible.

Provided that a controlled temperature of about 16–18°C is available, these flies are easily bred. The only drawback being the unpleasant smell involved.

The original supply may be obtained from a dealer. The larvae (maggots or 'gentles') are purchased. Alternatively, in the summer a dead animal or a piece of raw stale meat should be left outside on a wire netting grid which is supported above a large bowl filled to a depth of 2–3 in. with bran. It is advisable to place the whole set-up inside a large animal cage to prevent birds from eating the bran and maggots. Fly eggs will be laid on the meat and will rapidly develop into maggots, which will drop off into the bran, where they will soon pupate. If the pupae are collected at regular intervals they may be kept in a refrigerator for about 1 month without coming to any harm. On removal from the refrigerator the flies will usually hatch out in 24 h provided that they are in a warm atmosphere.

Cages for flies are easily constructed from a wooden frame one foot cube, with a solid base covered with some strong material such as mosquito netting. One side of the cage should be fitted with a sleeve of material which can be closed when not in use. When the flies are required it is a simple matter to collect them in small glass tubes.

Flies should be fed on a mixture of equal proportions of milk and water, which should be placed in a dish filled with cellulose wadding. The top of the food bowl should be sprinkled with a small quantity of sugar and casein. The food should be changed daily. When there are some mature flies in the cage, a small piece of raw meat should be introduced on to which eggs will be deposited.

For further information see *UFAW Handbook* 'On the Care and Management of Laboratory Animals', 2nd Edn. 1957.

The Culture of House-flies (*Musca Domesticus*)
(after McFerran, 1957)

House-flies are useful as food for small frogs and some lizards. They are, however, more trouble to rear than blowflies and bluebottles, since a special medium is necessary for the larvae. The original flies should be caught and placed in cages similar to those described for culturing blowflies. They should be fed in the same way. The mature flies will deposit their eggs on the food bowl, when it has dried a little. For this purpose the previous day's food bowl should be left in the cage. Provided that they are kept moist the eggs may be kept in a refrigerator for about 1 week.

A satisfactory medium for the larvae is:

Bran	8 oz.
Fishmeal	6 oz.
Lukewarm water	1 pint
Molasses or malt extract	1 tablespoon
Baker's yeast	1 teaspoon

Make a suspension of the yeast and molasses in the water, and wait until the yeast forms a froth on the top. Mix in the bran and fishmeal thoroughly until it is of a loose moist consistency. It may be necessary to add more water or more bran and fishmeal to get the correct consistency. Put the medium into bowls to a depth of about 3 in., and place the eggs just below the surface of the medium. Then cover the bowls with gauze, and place the bowls in an even temperature of 24°C. The pupae should be present after about 7 days. It may be necessary to moisten the medium on the second day, but towards the end of the week the medium should be allowed to become dry and crumbly, as it is then that the larvae will pupate. When the flies start emerging the bowls can be placed into the cages, but if a controlled supply is required the pupae can be collected by emptying the medium into a large bowl of water, where the pupae will float on the surface and can be strained off and dried. When dry they may be kept in a refrigerator for about 2 weeks. The life-cycle will be completed in about 10 days at 24–26°C.

The Culture of Drosophila

Wild *Drosophila* flies may be captured by placing some ripe bananas in a large glass jar. The top of the jar should be covered with a funnel which will allow the flies to enter, but make it difficult for them to escape. If special strains are required these must be obtained from a research institute which breeds them in large numbers.

There are several cultural methods for *Drosophila*, but the one given below appears to be the most successful.

Tap-water	..	..	..	..	5 l.
Maize meal	..	..	..	..	840 g
Agar agar	..	..	..	..	45 g
Nipagin solution	..	..	..	120 ml.
Molasses ..	..	..	..	$1\frac{1}{2}$ dessertspoons
Dried dead yeast	..	..	..	..	25 g

The nipagin solution is prepared as follows: 1 g nipagin M powder dissolved in 10 ml. 95 per cent ethyl alcohol. The medium itself is prepared by boiling the dried dead yeast in the water for 15 min. Then add the other ingredients one at a time, stirring all the time while boiling and until dissolved. If the medium appears to be too thick, then dilute with a little extra water.

The medium is then poured into clean sterilized bottles to a depth of less than 1 cm for *Drosophila subobscura*, and to a depth of 1 in. for *D. melanogaster*. Strips of paper towelling should be cut and pushed into the bottles for the larvae to climb on to when they are about to pupate. Then inoculate the bottles with selected flies, and place the bottles in a 25°C constant-temperature room. Half-pint milk bottles make excellent culture jars.

When the larvae are required for chromosome preparations the yeast concentration should be increased for about 1 week before the preparations are required (see page 251).

The Culture of Cockroaches

The cockroach which is usually kept for dissection purposes is *Periplaneta americana*. There is a mistaken idea that cockroaches will not breed in captivity, but this is not the case provided that certain conditions are met.

Escape-proof cages, some means of heating, and a regular supply of certain foodstuffs are the main requirements. An efficient cage is described by Dinnes (1951). The approximate dimensions of the cage are 4 ft. × 1½ ft. × 2 ft., and it has two separate compartments (18 in. × 18 in. × 12 in.) for housing the insects, and a lower division (48 in. × 18 in. × 10 in.) for a heater. The cage is constructed from ¾ in. aluminium angle for the framework; ¼ in. asbestos for the floor, back, front and sides; glass inserts for the roof and front of the rearing compartments and fine copper-mesh ventilating gauze for their inner walls.

The temperature of the cages should be maintained at 75–80°F (28°C). The bottom of the rearing compartment should be covered with a thick layer of damp vermiculite or sawdust, into which the oothecae will be deposited. The damp vermiculite or sawdust also helps to keep the atmosphere in the cage reasonably humid.

The most suitable foodstuffs are crushed oats, fats, grated nuts, cabbage leaves, carrots, apples, and crushed feeding cubes or pellets of any of the proprietary brands. Water should be provided in a glass dish filled with absorbent cotton wool, so that the insects cannot drown. It is convenient to have a length of rubber tubing running down to the water dish from the roof of the cage, the upper end of the tubing being fitted with a small glass funnel. This allows the dish to be kept filled without the necessity of opening the cage. Some crumpled newspaper or brown paper should be provided for the cockroaches to hide themselves.

The author has successfully reared a sizeable colony of the Madagascan cockroach, *Gomphadorhina porteutosa*, by keeping them in cages of a similar size but without built-in heaters. The cages are kept in a constant-temperature, constant-humidity room. If such a room is available this is by far the simplest way of rearing large numbers of any species of cockroach, or indeed any insect.

Culture of Locusts (after P. Hunter-Jones, 1956)

The culture of the African migratory locust (Locusta migratoria migratorioides R and F)

This locust occurs throughout tropical Africa, and it is the easiest locust to rear under laboratory conditions.

Cages—As will be seen from the diagram (*Figure 1.32*) the cage is essentially a wooden box, fitted with a removable false floor of perforated zinc and with a glass panel in one side for observation

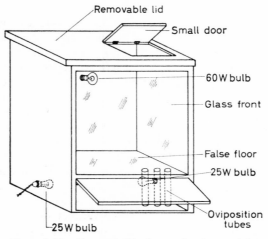

Figure 1.32. Cage suitable for rearing locusts (after P. Hunter-Jones)

purposes. The whole roof should be removable to facilitate cleaning operations. A small door in the roof or in the front or side of the cage, will enable food to be introduced without the locusts escaping. The perforated zinc floor allows the faeces to fall through, but the perforations must not exceed a diameter of 2 mm, as the hoppers (young locusts) will escape. The false floor is supported clear of the true floor of the cage by at least 4 in.; this is to enable oviposition tubes to be inserted below holes which are cut into the false floor. A convenient size for the cage is 15 in. × 15 in. × 20 in. tall. A cage with a capacity of about 2 ft.³ can produce between 100 and 300 adult locusts at the same time. The cage is heated by means of two electric light bulbs fitted between the false and main floors, and a third lamp at the top of the cage. If the cages are kept in a room with constant temperature–constant humidity the individual heating of the cages is not required.

Temperature—A day temperature of about 34°C (93°F) and a night temperature of 28°C (82°F) are recommended. The temperature readings should be taken about 4 in. above the false floor and well away from the walls of the cage. Two 25 W bulbs below the false floor and one 60 W bulb at the top of the cage will usually provide this sort of temperature. The 60 W bulb is switched off at night.

Feeding—Feed daily with a supply of fresh grass and dry wheat bran (middlings). The amount required is determined by experience, but as a guide some grass should still be left soon after feeding. Shallow dishes filled with moist soil may be kept and sown with wheat. When the wheat has grown to a few inches in height, the bowl may be put into the cage. When the wheat shoots have been eaten, the bowl is removed and placed to one side where it will usually grow a second crop of green shoots. This is a particularly useful method for obtaining fresh food in winter. A shallow dish of water must be provided for the adults, but this is unnecessary for the hopper stages.

Humidity—A relative humidity of 50–60 per cent at night and 30–50 per cent in the daytime is recommended. This humidity is generally provided by the fresh grass. High humidity should be avoided as it encourages disease. If the humidity is frequently too high, a ventilator of perforated zinc should be fitted in the roof and one side of the cage.

Perches—Numerous dry, branched twigs must be stood upright in all cages to serve as perches so that the hoppers can moult and sit near to the top heating bulb.

Egg-laying—As already stated, oviposition tubes are placed beneath holes in the false floor. Narrow tubes of glass or metal, plant pots or jam jars will serve as oviposition tubes. They must be at least 1¼ in. in diameter and 4 in. deep. The containers are full of tightly packed moist sand. A rather coarse, washed sand is best and should be mixed with 15 parts of water per 100 parts by volume of dry sand. Cages which contain only hoppers do not, of course, require oviposition tubes, and holes are not cut in the false floor in these cages.

Cleaning—Daily cleaning, by removing uneaten grass, and faeces, and any dead locusts and moults, must be regularly carried out. Every four to six weeks, the whole cage must be thoroughly cleaned and sterilized. First of all the contents are completely removed, the cage swept out, then scrubbed inside and out with hot water. The twigs are discarded. Boiling water is poured over the inside and outside of the cage and finally the cage is disinfected with a solution of 0·5 g of chlorocresol in 100 ml. of hot water.

The life cycle—Mature locusts copulate frequently and it is desirable to have an approximately equal number of males and females in each cage. At the temperatures recommended above, *Locusta* adults mature in about four weeks from fledging and then have an egg-laying life of 6-8 weeks. The eggs are laid in moist sand, in batches or 'pods'. The number of eggs in each pod varies from 30 to 100; the eggs are about the size of rice grains, and are laid in a regular order to form a tube about 4 in. long. The mature female lays a pod every five or six days. The average number of pods laid by a single female is six, but it may be as many as 17. The incubation period at 28°C is about 16 days, while at 32°C it is 11 days. If the sand becomes excessively dry during the incubation period, it may be remoistened by adding about 3 ml. of water to the surface. Periodically the oviposition tubes containing pods of eggs are transferred to hopper cages, so that the newly hatched hoppers will have room to move about. A sprinkling of bran should be placed on the floor of the cage so that food is readily available, as the hoppers start to feed shortly after hatching. It is possible to produce a complete generation in nine or ten weeks, and as many as five generations in one year.

The desert locust (*Schistocerca gregaria* Forsk)

This is more difficult to breed and is therefore less suitable for teaching purposes. The hopper stages require a higher humidity during the first instar than do hoppers of Locusta, but otherwise the requirements are the same. The humidity can be increased by standing a flask of water with a gauze wick inside the cage.

At the recommended temperature, the adult stage is usually reached in four or five weeks after hatching. An initial density of 1,000 hoppers in a cage of 2 ft.³ is recommended and this should yield between 100 and 200 adults.

Diseases—There are two diseases which are responsible for heavy mortalities in locust stocks. Both diseases are clinically similar, and can be referred to as 'gut rot'. The eyes become red, and the abdomen becomes so soft and flaccid that it may fall off; at this stage the locust is a mass of the bacterium causing the disease and is therefore highly infectious to other locusts. The food in the cage gets contaminated from the faeces of the infected locusts and if the faeces and corpses are left in the cages the other locusts will soon become infected and die. The only remedy is to clean the cage out regularly and sterilize it in the manner described above.

The Culture of Mealworms (after McFerran, 1957)

Mealworms are the larval stage of the beetles *Tenebrio molitor* or *T. obscurus*. They are excellent food for mammals which show insectivorous tendencies; insectivorous birds, insectivorous lizards, terrapins, frogs and toads. They should, however, always be supplemented with other foodstuffs. Mealworms are expensive to purchase from dealers and if a small constant supply is required it is well worth going to some trouble to breed them in the laboratory.

About six boxes are required. The boxes should be made of well-seasoned wood or perspex. If made from perspex the outside should be painted dull black. In either case the inside top edge should be fitted with a metal or plastic overhang, to prevent the mealworms from escaping. The boxes should be at least 1 ft. deep, the other dimensions depending on the size of the colony to be bred. A lid should be fitted with large ventilation holes.

Bran mixed with oatmeal should be placed on the floor of the first box, and some pupae or adult beetles introduced. This layer should be left undisturbed except when cleaning out the box to restart another colony when the life-cycle has been completed. As the bran-oatmeal mixture is used up, more is added. Newspaper, and soft cloths should be placed on top of the bran-oatmeal for the beetles to chew through and on which they will lay their eggs. Pieces of bread and small pieces of root vegetables should be placed on top of the newspaper. Leave the bread in the box even after it has become hard and dry, as the beetles will lay some of their eggs on it. When any small larvae are seen, a shallow tray filled with finely grated root vegetables and some bran should be placed on top of the newspaper. A little lettuce may be given. This supplementary food should be changed every few days to prevent the growth of moulds. As the larvae grow, gradually increase the quantity of root vegetables. The top of the box should be covered with a piece of damp sacking, which is placed under the lid. This and the vegetables help keep the humidity relatively high, which in turn prevents the mealworms from becoming cannibalistic. Care must also be taken, however, to ensure that the box does not become wet, or mite infestation will occur.

Generally, when the larvae become fully grown they will collect in the paper, and when they pupate they should be removed and placed into the second box which should have been prepared in a similar way. If the newly emerged beetles are left in the original culture box they frequently eat the remaining pupae.

Mealworms are very resistant to changes in temperature, but the temperature does have a great effect on the duration of the life-cycle, which can be as much as two years. The life-cycle may be reduced to 4 or 6 months by maintaining a temperature of 85°F (29–30°C) with a fairly high humidity. As the life-cycle takes such a long time it is obvious that a large breeding stock is required to provide even a small supply of mealworms.

THE PRESERVATION OF ARACHNIDS AND MYRIAPODS

Formalin is to be avoided for preservation of these arthropods. Killing and preservation may be carried out by immersing the animals in 70–90 per cent alcohol, which should be changed after 12–24 h. For the best results, certain groups require special treatment:

(*i*) Terrestrial ticks and mites should be killed and preserved in Oudeman's solution. A simplified formula is:

70 per cent alcohol	22 parts
Glycerol	1 part
Glacial acetic acid	2 parts

(*ii*) Aquatic mites should be killed and fixed in Viet's solution, which is:

Glacial acetic acid	3 parts
Glycerol	11 parts
Distilled water	6 parts

(*iii*) Mites are best displayed by mounting them on slides in Berlese's medium. An excess should always be used, as this medium contracts greatly on drying. Berlese's medium is:

Gum arabic (acacia)	15 g
Chloral hydrate	16 g
Glucose syrup	10 g
Glacial acetic acid	5 ml.
Water	20 ml.

The mites are placed into this medium while alive. After two or three weeks the coverslips should be ringed with gold-size. It is desirable to have the dorsal and ventral aspects of each sex displayed.

(*iv*) Spiders, opilionids, and pycnogonids may be killed in 70 per cent alcohol and stored in a fresh change of solution. A still better method is to kill and store the animals in the following modified Oudeman's solution (different from that used for terrestrial mites and ticks):

70 per cent alcohol	85 parts
Glycerol	5 parts
Glacial acetic acid	5 parts

This solution is particularly recommended for the storage of spiders.

KILLING AND PRESERVATION METHODS FOR CRUSTACEA

Branchiopoda and Ostracoda—Kill in 5 per cent formalin or better still in alcoholic Bouin's fluid. This consists of:

80 per cent alcohol	150 ml.
40 per cent formaldehyde solution	60 ml.
Glacial acetic acid	15 ml.
Picric acid	1 g

After fixation for 24 h in either solution, the specimens should be transferred to 70 per cent alcohol for storage.

Copepoda—Kill and fix in 5 per cent formalin or in alcoholic Bouin's fluid, or in Heidenhain's 'Susa'. Store in 5 per cent formalin except when 'Susa' is used, in which case the specimen should be transferred to 70 per cent alcohol containing some Lugol's iodine, and then after 24 h transferred to 5 per cent formalin.

Branchiura—Kill by any of the methods so far described for other crustacea, or they may be plunged into a 10 per cent aqueous solution of potassium hydroxide until dead, then transferred to 50 per cent alcohol for about 15 min. They should always be stored in 70 per cent alcohol.

Cirripedia—Allow the barnacles to become active, then add some crystals of menthol to the surface of the water. Do not disturb. After several hours they will become narcotized and may then be killed and fixed with hot saturated aqueous solution of mercuric chloride. After ½–1 h, transfer the specimens to several changes of iodized alcohol. Then, when the iodine ceases to become decolorized, transfer to 70 per cent alcohol in which the specimens should be stored.

Decapoda—Kill large forms, such as *Carcinus*, *Astacus* and *Homarus*, by injecting a quantity of chloroform into the body cavity through the soft tissue at the base of a limb. Very few of the limbs will be shed if killed in this fashion. A large *Carcinus* crab requires about 5 ml. of chloroform. Another method for marine forms is to transfer the specimens to a large container of fresh water and to add a quantity of chloroform to the water. This should be agitated vigorously as the chloroform forms a layer at the bottom of the container.

Small forms die rapidly if placed into 70 per cent alcohol, or alcoholic Bouin's fluid. To preserve decapods for any length of time in fluid, they should be kept in a mixture of 95 parts 70 per cent alcohol, and 5 parts glycerol.

There are two methods for preserving large crabs and lobsters in a dry state. The first method is to remove the carapace of the fresh animal or, better still in the case of a lobster, bisect the animal at the junction of the thorax and abdomen, and with a hook scoop out all of the soft parts. Pack the carapace with fine dry sand or cotton wool and allow to dry slowly in a warm atmosphere. When dry, glue the parts together with a transparent plastic adhesive. The second method which gives much better results is to kill the animal by injecting through the soft parts with formol-acetic-alcohol. Then pinning the animal out into a natural position allow it to dry thoroughly in a warm place. The drying process should be very gradual. A lobster may take about two weeks. When it is thoroughly dry, the animal should be painted with a thin solution of polyvinyl acetal alvar in a mixture of 1 part amyl acetate and 3 parts absolute alcohol (see page 351). This method has given some excellent results with crabs and lobsters. If carefully carried out most of the blue colour of *Homarus vulgaris* will be preserved.

KILLING AND PRESERVATION METHODS FOR INSECTS

(A) Killing Methods

Apterygota—These may be killed by immersing the insects in 70 per cent alcohol containing a few drops of glycerol. Alternatively, they may be killed, fixed, cleared and mounted in one simple operation, by putting one or two drops of polyvinyl lactophenol on to the centre of a clean glass slide, and then adding the insect. After a few seconds orientate the insect into a suitable position and add a coverslip. Some surplus medium should be left around the edge of the coverslip to compensate for the shrinkage which takes place as it dries.

Pterygota—The majority of insects which are to be used for general dissection may be satisfactorily killed in the following ways: terrestrial insects should be killed in the vapour of ethyl acetate; and aquatic insects should be placed into a small glass jar containing a mixture of chloroform and water to which one or two drops of a 'wetting agent' such as 'Teepol' has been added, and toluene. The mixture should have been allowed to stand for a few minutes before introducing the insects. In this time, the chloroform will have formed a layer underneath the water, and the toluene will be floating on top of the water. The depth of the water should be about 2 in. Insects die very rapidly when killed in this manner.

After killing, dissection work should commence immediately. When pterygote insects are required for display purposes, or for entomological collections, special killing methods should be employed. Briefly these may be listed as follows (after Wagstaffe and Fidler, 1957):

Ephemeroptera—Kill in a laurel bottle (see page 99), a cyanide bottle, or in the vapour of strong ammonia.

Odonata—Starve the insects for two days, then after strapping the wings back with a length of paper, kill in a laurel bottle or a cyanide bottle, or in the vapour of strong ammonia.

Plecoptera—Kill in ethyl acetate vapour or in a cyanide bottle.

Blattaria, Mantodea and Saltatoria—Starve for one day, then kill in the vapour of benzene.

Isoptera—Kill in the vapour of ethyl acetate. Queen termites shrink if allowed to dry, so they should be preserved in 70 per cent alcohol after the distended abdomen has been injected with formol-alcohol.

Phasmida—These should be starved for 24 h then killed in the vapour of benzene or ethyl acetate.

Dermaptera—Kill in the vapour of benzene, or in a laurel bottle.

Psocoptera—Kill by immersing in 70–80 per cent alcohol, or kill and mount in polyvinyl lactophenol as for Apterygota.

Phthiraptera—Kill by immersing in 70–80 per cent alcohol, or kill and mount in polyvinyl lactophenol as for Apterygota.

Thysanoptera—Kill in a 0·5 per cent solution of ethyl acetate in 50 per cent methyl alcohol. Then after a few hours, transfer to 80 per cent alcohol.

Hemiptera—Heteroptera should be killed in a laurel bottle or in the vapour of ethyl acetate or benzene. Homoptera should be killed in a laurel bottle, but Coccidae may be preserved *in situ* by allowing the leaf containing them to dry in a glass-topped container, whilst scales and alate males may be killed and stored in lacto-alcohol. Lacto-alcohol is prepared as follows:

Lactic acid (B.P. 87·5 per cent)	..	..	80 ml.
66 O.P. alcohol ..	.. .. ..	..	74 ml.
Water ..	.. ..	..	46 ml.

Neuroptera, Megaloptera and Raphidiodea—Kill in a laurel bottle or in the vapour of chloroform.

Coleoptera—Kill in a laurel bottle (in spite of this method being slow and uncertain in a few cases, it is an excellent method). Another method is to put the beetle into a small glass tube, then immerse the bottom of the tube into boiling water until the insect is dead. The vapour of ethyl acetate or carbon tetrachloride may be used. Larvae of coleoptera should be killed in Carnoy's fluid, then transferred to

70 per cent alcohol. Pupae should be killed in Pampl's fluid and then transferred to 70 per cent alcohol. Pampl's fluid is:

Glacial acetic acid	4 ml.
Distilled water	30 ml.
40 per cent formaldehyde solution	6 ml.
95 per cent alcohol	15 ml.

Strepsiptera—Kill in a 0·5 per cent solution of ethyl acetate in 50 per cent methyl alcohol. Then after a few hours transfer to 80 per cent alcohol.

Mecoptera—Kill in a laurel bottle or in the vapour of chloroform.

Trichoptera—Kill in a laurel bottle or in a cyanide bottle.

Lepidoptera—Imago: Killing in a laurel bottle causes excess stiffening and green colours to fade. The vapour of ethyl acetate may be used. Use the vapour of strong ammonia to kill Micro-lepidoptera. *Larvae:* If these are to be 'blown' and dried, then kill in the vapour of ethyl acetate or chloroform. If to be preserved wet, kill in Carnoy's fluid, then transfer to 70 per cent alcohol. *Pupae:* Inject with a fixative such as Carnoy's fluid.

Diptera—Imago: Kill in vapour of ethyl acetate or in a laurel bottle. *Larvae:* Kill and store in 70 per cent alcohol containing a few drops of glycerol, or better still in Peterson's KAAD. Leave in this solution for a few hours, then transfer to 95 per cent alcohol. Peterson's KAAD is:

Paraffin (kerosene)	10 ml.
66 O.P. alcohol	70–90 ml.
Glacial acetic acid	10 ml.
Dioxan	10 ml.

N.B. Dioxan is a very toxic vapour, and any inhalation of its vapour must be avoided.

Pupae and puparia: Kill and store in 80 per cent alcohol.

Siphonaptera—Kill and store in 70 per cent alcohol containing a few drops of glycerol.

Hymenoptera—Symphyta: Kill in ethyl acetate vapour or in a laurel or cyanide bottle; kill larvae in Carnoy's fluid then transfer to 70 per cent alcohol.

Apocrita—Parasitica: Kill in a cyanide bottle followed by relaxation in a laurel bottle, or kill in ethyl acetate vapour. *Larvae:* As for Symphyta larvae. *Formicoidea:* Kill in a cyanide or laurel bottle, or in ethyl acetate vapour. Wingless varieties may be killed and stored in a relaxed condition in Donisthorpe's fluid, which consists of:

Glacial acetic acid	5 ml.
66 O.P. alcohol	37 ml.
Distilled water	58 ml.
Mercuric chloride	0·12 g

Vespoidea and Aphoidea: Kill in a laurel bottle or in vapour of ethyl acetate. Ethyl acetate should be used for specimens with yellow coloration. *Larvae:* Kill in Carnoy's fluid, then transfer to 70 per cent alcohol.

The Preparation of a Laurel Killing Bottle (after Wagstaffe and Fidler, 1957)

Chop up a number of leaves of laurel (*Prunus Lauro-cerasus*)*, and pound in a mortar until well bruised. Fill a wide-mouthed bottle of a suitable size with these bruised leaves to a depth of 1 in. Cover them with a layer of cotton wool and this in turn with a disc of filter paper. The sides of the jar should be lined with blotting paper, to absorb condensation. The jar should be left stoppered for 2–3 days before it is ready for use. It should last for one season if properly stoppered.

The Preparation of a Cyanide Killing Bottle (after Wagstaffe and Fidler, 1957)

Use a wide-mouthed bottle about 3 in. in diameter and 4–5 in. deep fitted with a top-quality cork bung. The type of cork which has

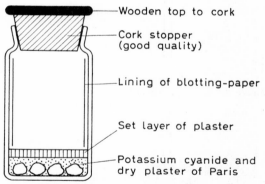

Figure 1.33. A cyanide killing bottle

a wooden top is preferable. In a good fume cupboard, break up $1\frac{1}{2}$–2 oz. of potassium cyanide. (N.B. The fumes of potassium cyanide are extremely toxic.) Fill the bottom of the bottle with this cyanide and with dry plaster of paris to a depth of $\frac{1}{2}$ in. Cover this with a $\frac{1}{2}$ in. layer of plaster which has been mixed with sufficient water to make it the consistency of thin cream. Set aside, in the fume cupboard, together with a warning notice, until the plaster has set and dried out. If any bubbles arise as it is drying they should be pricked

* The variegated variety of laurel is practically useless.

and wet plaster pushed down into the holes. The cork should be left off until the plaster has dried. The jar should never be left in strong sunlight, and it may be preferable to line it with blotting paper so that any moisture which condenses on the sides will not damage the specimens. The stopper should be firmly in position at all times. Such a prepared jar should last for one or two seasons. See *Figure 1.33*.

When exhausted the jar should be buried in a very deep hole where children and animals cannot reach it.

Preparation of a Bottle for Administering Other Killing Vapours

A convenient and easily made killing jar, as shown in *Figure 1.34*, can be made by using a wide-mouthed bottle, fitted with a deep

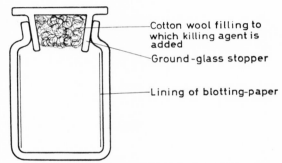

Figure 1.34. *A killing bottle for liquid killing agents*

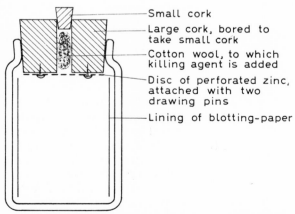

Figure 1.35. *Another type of bottle for liquid killing agents*

ground-glass stopper, the inside of which is hollow and into which cotton wool is packed. After lining the sides of the jar with blotting paper, all that is left to do is to apply a few drops of the chosen killing agent, ethyl acetate, benzene, carbon tetrachloride, chloroform, or ammonia, to the cotton wool, introduce the insect and replace the stopper.

Another type of jar which has the advantage of it being easy to remove one killing agent should it prove unsuccessful, and replace it with another without having to remove the stopper, is shown in *Figure 1.35.*

(B) Preservation Methods for Insects

(1) Preservation in a wet state

Larvae, and insects which are to be examined internally at a later date, or those which are required for future mouthpart preparations, should be preserved in one of the following fluids: (a) 70 per cent alcohol containing 5 per cent glycerol. This is particularly recommended for the preservation of adult insects, and the addition of glycerol keeps the limbs flexible; (b) Pampl's fluid:

Glacial acetic acid	4 ml.
Distilled water	30 ml.
40 per cent formaldehyde solution	6 ml.
95 per cent alcohol	15 ml.

This fluid is recommended by many workers for the preservation of insects which are to be used for future dissections. The author would only recommend preservation for this reason should it be impossible to arrange for the insects to be dissected immediately after they have been killed. Prolonged preservation in this fluid is to be avoided; (c) 2–3 per cent formalin, recommended for storage of Ephemeroptera and Plecoptera, after passing the insects through 70 per cent alcohol for several hours.

(2) Preservation in a dry state

When the insects are to be used for display purposes, drying is, in most cases, the best way to preserve them. The insects are generally killed and set in a suitable position so that the greater part of the insect is displayed. If the setting process is carried out immediately after death the insect will be in a relaxed condition. If, however, the insect has been kept for any length of time after death before it is set, the joints will have become stiff and the insect will have to be relaxed. Relaxing may be carried out by placing the insect on a filter paper inside a small desiccator. The bottom of the desiccator is covered with a small quantity of a warm solution of 50 per cent glycerol in water. The humid atmosphere in the desiccator is responsible for the relaxation which may take several hours. The insect should be set as soon as it is removed from the relaxing chamber.

(1) *Setting Boards*

There are a variety of setting boards intended for the very many forms of insects. Basically they consist of a strip of wood, usually 1 ft. in length and covered with a layer of good-quality cork. Running lengthwise down the middle of the cork is a groove. In selecting a particular setting board, the width of the board should be slightly greater than the maximum wing span of the insect, and the groove should be large enough to accommodate the body and the legs. Setting boards of the flat English pattern are usually obtainable in the following widths, in inches: $\frac{1}{2}$, $\frac{3}{4}$, 1, $1\frac{1}{4}$, $1\frac{1}{2}$, $1\frac{3}{4}$, 2, $2\frac{1}{4}$, $2\frac{1}{2}$, 3, $3\frac{1}{2}$, 4, $4\frac{1}{2}$ and 5.

(2) *Drying Boxes*

While the insects are drying on the setting boards they must be in a position where there is a free circulation of air, and where they are safe from attack by insect pests. The best answer to this problem is to place the boards into a drying box. This box is so constructed as to accommodate several setting boards arranged side by side, and has a large hole at each end which is covered with fine wire gauze. Drying boxes containing insects should always be stored on their sides, as there is then less chance of the insects being attacked by mites.

(3) *Pins*

Only proper entomological pins should be used for pinning insects. They are available in a wide range of lengths and thicknesses, and may be obtained coated with black enamel which makes them less liable to corrode than the plated type. A detailed discussion of the very many methods for the pinning and setting of insects is beyond the scope of this book, but the enthusiast is referred to *The Preservation of Natural History Specimens*, Vol. 1, Wagstaffe and Fidler, Witherby, 1957. This contains setting methods for most groups of insects, and other useful information.

(4) *Materials for Staging Insects*

A common method with some types of small insects is to gum them to card. The ideal card is best white Bristol board, which is available in several thicknesses. '4 sheet' (0·015 in.) and '6 sheet' (0·022 in.) are of useful thickness, but large heavy specimens may require a thicker board.

Another useful material is clear celluloid. The chief advantage of this method is that, being clear, it is possible to view the underside of the insect. It has one disadvantage in that it tends to turn brown on exposure to some chemicals such as *p*-dichlorobenzene. Moore (*Ent. Mon. Mag.*, 1949, 85, 102) recommends the use of xylonite, grade No. F.9665, 0·020 in. thick, ivory white and semi-matt surface.

Materials to Which Insects May be Pinned

(*i*) *Polyporus*

This is an ideal material for a base to which an insect may be pinned. It is the prepared flesh of a large bracket fungus, *Polyporus betulinus* (Bull.). It is possible to prepare the polyporus for oneself, but it is seldom as satisfactory as that obtained from a dealer. It is generally purchased in strips 1½–3 mm square and 15 cm long.

(*ii*) *Elder Pith*

In the late autumn, select branches about 1 in. in diameter of young wood of elder (*Sambucus nigra* L.). Cut them into 6 in. lengths, and allow them to dry. When dry, remove the outside woody layer, leaving a strip of pith.

SPECIAL PREPARATIONS OF ARTHROPODS

Potash Preparations

By this method, beautiful preparations of many insects and arachnids are easily produced. The insect or arachnid (fresh or preserved) is placed into a boiling tube containing about 5–10 ml. of 10 per cent aqueous potassium hydroxide solution. The tube is then stood in a beaker of boiling water. Boiling continues until the soft parts of the animal are macerated and the solution has become dark. This may take from a few minutes to several hours. Then the fluid is decanted, and the specimen washed with distilled water. Remove the specimen and arrange it on a clean glass slide with its dorsal side uppermost. Place a second slide on top of the specimen, and apply firm but even pressure until the specimen is completely flattened. It should be noted that the legs and other appendages should have been so arranged before pressing that they will arrange themselves in a suitable position for examination. After pressing, the two slides are bound together, and the whole is then placed on edge into a trough of 1 per cent acetic acid where it should remain for about 5 min. Then transfer to distilled water, and gradually dehydrate the specimen by taking it through the graded alcohols. After reaching 90 per cent alcohol, the slides should be unbound and the top slide removed. Place the other slide and the specimen on a staining rack and thoroughly dehydrate the specimen with several washes of absolute alcohol. The slide, together with the specimen, should then be immersed in xylene, and any air which is trapped in the specimen should be carefully removed with a needle or by finger pressure. Then, after removing from the xylene, cover the specimen with Canada balsam and add a clean coverslip. With a large specimen it is sometimes advisable to add a weight to the coverslip while the balsam is drying.

It should be noted that the wings of many insects when treated in this manner will become very distorted. In such a case, it is better to repeat the technique with a second insect and remove the wings before commencing. The untreated wings may then be dehydrated, cleared and mounted on the finished slide. Very dark insects may require bleaching. This may be carried out before or after macerating in potassium hydroxide. The specimen should be placed into a 1 per cent aqueous solution of potassium permanganate for about 30 min, then transferred to a 5 per cent aqueous solution of oxalic acid. Alternatively, Mayer's chlorine bleach may be used (see page 196). N.B. Be careful to avoid spilling the potash solution or getting any on to the hands or clothes, as it is extremely caustic.

Preparation of the Mouthparts of an Insect

The preparation of the mouthparts of cockroach is described as follows; the mouthparts of other types of insects may be prepared in a similar manner.

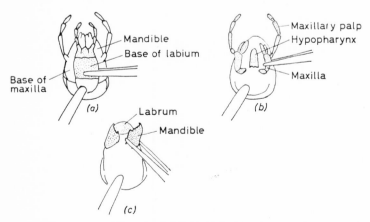

Figure 1.36. Illustrating the order of removing cockroach mouthparts: shaded areas indicate the mouthparts which are removed

(*i*) Remove the entire head of the insect, unless the insect is very small, in which case leave it entire.

(*ii*) Macerate in 10 per cent aqueous potassium hydroxide solution until the muscle tissue of the head is macerated (see previous method).

(*iii*) When sufficiently macerated (this point can usually be determined by the fact that the specimen will sink quickly and remain on the bottom of the tube when the tube is removed from the heat source), decant the fluid, and wash in distilled water.

(*iv*) Place the head, ventral side uppermost, on to a clean glass plate. Hold it securely with a mounted needle, and with a fine pair of forceps carefully remove the labium [*Figure 1.36(a)*] and place it into a small Petri-dish or solid watch glass, in distilled water.

(*v*) Slip the forceps under each part in turn, carefully remove both of the maxillae, followed by the hypopharynx, again placing them into the dish of distilled water [*Figure 1.36(b)*].
NOTE: The hypopharynx will have come into view after the labium was removed.

(*vi*) Finally, remove the mandibles and then cut off the labrum together with a small piece of the clypeus. Place these in the distilled water [*Figure 1.36(c)*].

(*vii*) Dehydrate the mouthparts by transferring them through 90 per cent alcohol to absolute alcohol, then clear in xylene.

(*viii*) Place the mouthparts on to a clean glass slide arranged in a suitable position. Then make a ring of Canada balsam so that it surrounds the mouthparts, but is smaller than the diameter of the circular coverslip which will be used. Add a drop of balsam to the centre of the coverslip, and apply this carefully to the mouthparts, taking great care to see that no air is trapped and that the mouthparts do not become disarranged.

CLEARING AND MOUNTING SMALL DELICATE INSECTS

The potash method is unsuitable for some small and delicate insects. The following method gives good results with the majority of small insects:

Transfer the insect to a mixture of equal parts by weight of chloral hydrate crystals and liquid phenol for about two weeks at 25°C. After this time the insect should be perfectly cleared. If the insect in question is coarser in structure it may be placed in the same solution at a temperature of about 42°C, when it will be cleared in about 48 h. After removing the insect from the solution, transfer it to absolute alcohol for a few minutes before mounting it in

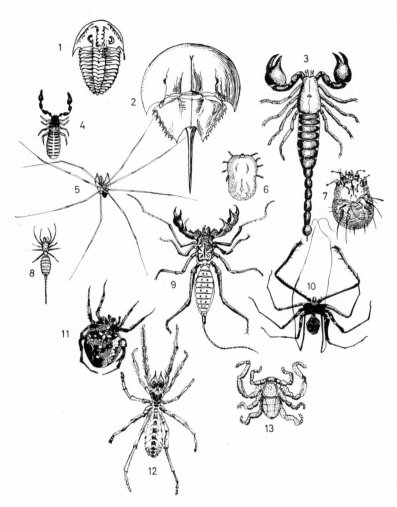

Figure 1.37. *Arachnids, trilobites and xiphosurans:* 1. *Callavia,* Lower Cambrian trilobite; 2. *Limulus,* a xiphosuran ('king crab'); 3. *Centrurus,* a scorpionid ('scorpion'); 4. *Chelifer,* a pseudoscorpion; 5. *Phalangium,* an opilionid ('harvest man'); 6. *Margaropus,* an acarine ('cattle tick'); 7. *Sarcoptes scabiei,* an acarine ('itch mite'); 8. *Koenenia mirabilis,* a palpigrad; 9. *Thelyphonus,* a uropygid ('whip scorpion'); 10. *Damon,* an amblypygid; 11. *Epeira,* an araneid ('garden spider'); 12. *Galeodes,* a solifuge ('false-spider'); 13. *Cryptostemma,* a ricinulid. [1, 2, 4, 6–10, 12 and 13 are from B.M.(N.H.) works, by courtesy of the Trustees of the British Museum (Natural History); 3 is after Bullough, 1950; 5 and 11 are from photographs]

Berlese's fluid. Apply a coverslip with gentle pressure and ring with gold-size. Berlese's fluid is:

Chloral hydrate crystals	..	..	up to 160 g
Gum arabic (gum acacia)	..	..	..	15 g
Glucose syrup ..	..	..	..	..	10 ml.
Glacial acetic acid	..	..	..	..	5 ml.
Distilled water ..	..	..	..	..	20 ml.

Dissolve the gum arabic in the distilled water, using heat if necessary.

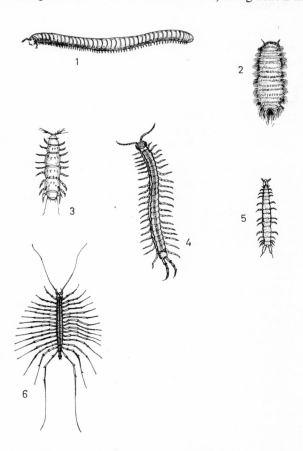

Figure 1.38. Diplopods, pauropods, chilopods, and Symphyla: 1. *Julus,* a diplopod ('Millipede'); 2. *Polyxenus,* a diplopod ('Millipede'); 3. *Pauropus,* a pauropod; 4. *Scolopendra,* a chilopod ('Centipede'); 5. *Scutigerella,* a symphylan; 6. *Scutigera forceps*—a North American centipede [1–6 are from **B.M. (N.H.)** works, by courtesy of the Trustees of the British Museum (Natural History)].

Add the glucose syrup, then the chloral hydrate to saturation. Finally add the acetic acid.

The Preparation of the Endophragmal Skeleton of Crustacea

The endophragmal skeleton consists of a system of calcified plates in the thorax which serves chiefly as an attachment for muscles, but is also a framework for the viscera.

The preparation of the endophragmal skeleton of *Eupagurus* is described, and will serve as a guide to the preparation of these structures in other crabs, lobsters and crayfish.

Remove all of the carapace behind the cervical groove, separating it from the underlying epimera. Cut off the abdomen at the peduncle, and each limb a few joints from the proximal end. Carefully clean out the gut and stomach, after cutting a window in the cephalic shield, and such portions of the underlying muscle, etc., as can be scraped away without damaging the skeleton, then boil gently in 10 per cent aqueous potassium hydroxide solution for a short time until the skeleton is clean. Wash and transfer to 70 per cent alcohol.

The Preparation of Histological Sections of Spiders

Choose a spider which has just moulted, kill it in chloroform vapour, and fix it for 24 h in Petrunkevitch's solution, or Dubosq–Brasil.

Petrunkevitch's solution is:

60 per cent alcohol	..	..	..	.. 100 ml.
Nitric acid (s.g. 1·42)	..	..	..	.. 3 ml.
Ether	.. ..	..	..	.. 5 ml.
Cupric nitrate	..	..	..	.. 2 g
p-nitrophenol	..	..	..	.. 5 g

Dubosq–Brasil (alcoholic Bouin) fixative is:

80 per cent alcohol	..	..	..	.. 150 ml.
40 per cent formaldehyde solution	..		..	60 ml.
Glacial acetic acid	..	..	..	.. 15 ml.
Picric acid	..	..	..	.. 1 g

After fixation, transfer to 70 per cent alcohol and give at least three changes in order that the fixative be completely removed from the specimen. Take the spider up through the usual grades of alcohol to absolute alcohol, then transfer to either (*a*) equal parts of absolute alcohol and ether for 24 h, then transfer to 8 per cent celloidin in absolute alcohol-ether mixture, transfer to 2 changes of toluene, then embed in wax, or (*b*) transfer to 1 per cent celloidin in methyl benzoate for 24 h, then embed in paraffin wax, after washing in benzene.

It should be possible to obtain reasonably good sections of spiders by using the above technique.

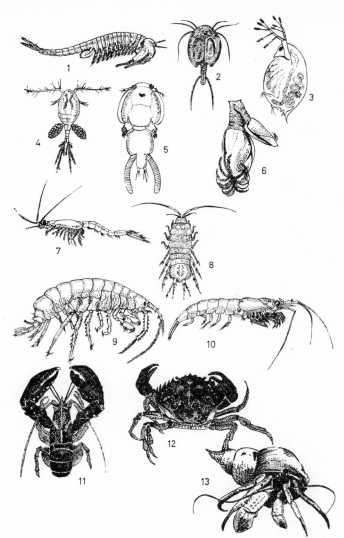

Figure 1.39. Crustaceans: 1. *Chirocephalus*, an anostracan ('fairy shrimp'); 2. *Lepidurus*, a notostracan ('tadpole shrimp'); 3. *Daphnia*, a cladoceran ('water flea'); 4. *Cyclops*, a copepod; 5. *Caligus rapax*, a parasitic copepod from a marine fish; 6. *Lepas anatifera*, a cirripede ('goose barnacle'); 7. *Mysis*, an 'opossum shrimp'; 8. *Asellus*, a freshwater isopod; 9. *Gammarus*, an amphipod; 10. *Meganycitiphanes norvegica*, a euphausid, which form the chief food of the baleen whales—krill; 11. *Homarus vulgaris*, a macruran ('lobster'); 12. *Carcinus maenas*, a brachyuran ('shore crab'); 13. *Eupagurus bernhardus*, an anomuran ('hermit crab'). [6 is from a photograph; 11, 12 and 13 are after Barrett and Yonge (1958).]

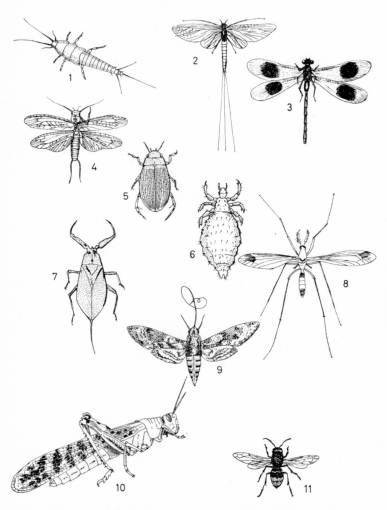

Figure 1.40. Insects: 1. *Lepisma*, a thysanuran ('silver-fish'); 2. *Ephemera*, an ephemeropteran ('mayfly'); 3. *Agrion*, a zygopteran ('damsel fly';) 4. *Perla*, a plecopteran ('stonefly'); 5. *Dytiscus*, a coleopteran ('great diving beetle'); 6. *Pediculus*, an anopluran ('human body louse'); 7. *Nepa*, a hemipteran ('water scorpion'); 8. *Ctenophora*, a dipteran ('crane-fly'); 9. *Herse*, a lepidopteran ('convulvulus hawk moth'); 10. *Locusta*, saltatorian ('locust'); 11. *Vespa*, a hymenopteran ('hornet')

Methods for the collection of spiders are given in some detail in *The World of Spiders*, Collins, New Naturalist Series.

Culture of Spiders

Members of the family Thomisidae are reputed to be easily maintained under simple laboratory conditions.

The Preparation of Histological Sections of Insects

Unfortunately, sections of insects are very difficult to prepare. The hard chitinous exoskeleton is a serious obstacle to the successful cutting of sections, and the use of a chitin softener such as diaphanol is only a partial answer to the problem, since the staining of tissue which has been treated with diaphanol is very difficult. The formula for diaphanol is:

Diaphanol	20 ml.
Distilled water	13 ml.
25 per cent nitric acid	1–1·5 ml.

By far the best method is to use insects which have just moulted. Immediately after the final moult, kill the insect with chloroform vapour and then fix it in Dubosq–Brasil (picric acid, 1 g; glacial acetic acid, 15 ml.; 40 per cent formaldehyde solution, 60 ml.; 80 per cent alcohol, 150 ml.). With large insects, it is recommended that some of the fixative is injected into the mouth and anus, and a small ventral slit should be made into one side of the abdomen. Fix for 24–48 h, then transfer to 90 per cent alcohol, changing the solution several times during 24 h. Transfer to absolute alcohol (2 changes of 12 h in each) and then to 1 per cent celloidin in methyl benzoate for several weeks. The insect is then embedded according to the method of Petrefi (see page 217).

By following this method it should be possible to prepare reasonably good sections of most insects at thicknesses of 10–15 microns. Recommended staining techniques are Weigert's haematoxylin with Van Gieson's stain, or Weigert's haematoxylin followed by the Masson's trichrome technique (see page 244).

PHYLUM ECHINODERMATA

The echinoderms are coelomate animals built on a pentaradiate plan. (This plan, however, is derived from a bilateral symmetry which is exhibited by the larval stages.) Echinoderms have no definite head or brain. There is a calcareous endoskeleton (which at first glance may appear to be an exoskeleton) and this is composed of separate pieces or plates, which frequently bear spines and other structures. One unique feature of echinoderms is the presence of a water-vascular system, derived from the coelom, which consists of numerous podia or 'tube-feet' and a vascular

PHYLUM TECHNOLOGY

system which connects with the outside sea by a pore or cluster of pores (madreporite). Although this water-vascular system may be absent in some adult forms it is always present in juvenile stages. Echinoderms are exclusively marine. All radiate animals have a body which is differentiated into oral and aboral surfaces, and the echinoderms are no excepttion, but in the holothurians, 'sea cucumbers', they are orally-aborally elongated and lie upon one side which is sometimes flattened.

Subphylum Pelmatozoa. The major part of this subphylum consists of extinct forms. Members are attached throughout life or at least in early life by the aboral surface. The attachment is usually by means of a stalk made up of calcareous plates, but occasionally it may be direct. The upward directed oral surface bears both mouth and anus. The primary function of the podia is to catch food. The viscera is enclosed in a calcareous test, the theca.

Class Heterostelea. Extinct forms, from the Cambrian to Lower Silurian.

Class Cystidea. Extinct forms from Middle Ordovician to Middle Devonian time, which reached their height in Silurian times.

Class Blastoidea. Extinct forms, from Ordovician to Permian times.

Class Crinoidea. There are still many living forms from this class, and although many extinct forms were attached by a stalk, the majority of living forms are free moving. The oral surface is directed upwards, and the anus is also on the oral surface and is frequently mounted on a tube. The theca is differentiated in an aboral cup (the calyx), and an oral roof (the tegmen) which is frequently membranous. There are movable arms, usually branched, which arise from the junction of the calyx and tegmen. This class has existed since Ordovician times. An example is *Antedon*.

Class Edrioasteroidea. Extinct forms of discoidal shape which had no arms or stalk. Existed from the Lower Cambrian to the Carboniferous.

Subphylum Eleutherozoa. Echinoderms without a stalk, and which move with the oral surface downwards or lying on one side. In the majority of cases they are highly pentamerous, and generally the water-vascular system is used for locomotion and not for the gathering of food. When an anus is present it is generally situated on the aboral surface.

Class Holothuroidea, 'sea cucumbers'. Members of this class lie on one side, and this side may be modified. They are elongated in the oral-aboral axis and exhibit secondary bilateral symmetry. The mouth is surrounded by a number of tentacles which are connected with the water-vascular system. The endoskeleton is present only as microscopic calcareous plates which are embedded in the body wall. These plates or ossicles may be entirely absent. The distribution of the podia (tube-feet) varies, and may be absent altogether. Examples are *Holothuria* and *Synapta*.

Class Echinoidea, 'sea urchins, sand-dollars, etc.' Globular or discoidal in shape, the echinoids are free-living echinoderms, with no arms, and are covered with large numbers of movable spines and pedicellariae. The anus and the madreporite are situated on the aboral side. The endoskeleton is in the form of a continuous test, and consists of closely fitting calcareous plates. The test, composed of alternating columns of ambulacral and interambulacral areas, is pierced by pores for the podia to extrude, the pores being confined to the ambulacral areas. The mouth is on the functionally lower surface and is surrounded by a membraneous area, the

peristome. The mouth usually contains a complex masticatory apparatus, the 'lantern of Aristotle'.

Subclass Endocyclica (Regularia). Echinoids of globular or occasionally oval shape. The mouth and anus are at opposite poles. Lantern is well developed in all species. The common British sea urchin, *Echinus esculentus*, is a member of this subclass.

Subclass Exocyclica (Irregularia). Echinoids which have a somewhat flattened, oval or circular or occasionally heart-shaped test which has become bilaterally symmetrical. The anus and surrounding periproct has moved posteriorly to a posterior aboral or oral position. The podia are generally not concerned with locomotion. A lantern is present in some forms, except in the order Spatangoida, which contains the common 'heart urchins', *Echinocardium* and *Spatangus*.

Class Asteroidea, 'starfish'. Usually flattened, and mostly of a pentagonal shape, having five (but sometimes more) rays or arms which radiate from a central disc. Sometimes the arms may be very reduced and in other cases lengthened. The oral surface downwards towards the substratum. The podia, which are locomotory in function, are situated in deep ambulacral grooves. The endoskeleton is flexible or may be composed of separate ossicles. The anus and madreporite are situated on the aboral surface. Pedicellariae are present. Examples are *Astropecten*, *Luidia*, *Solaster* and *Asterias*.

Class Ophiuroidea, 'brittle-stars or serpent-stars'. Of a flattened pentamerous shape, but easily distinguished from asteroids by the presence of long slender movable arms which are sharply set off from the central disc. There are no ambulacral grooves, and no anus and intestine. The madreporite is situated on the oral surface. There are no pedicellariae. Ophiuroids are able to move quickly by walking motion of the arms and not by the action of tube-feet. The commonest order, Ophiurae, are represented by forms which have unbranched arms that are capable of moving only in a horizontal plane. Examples are *Ophiura*, *Ophiothrix* and *Ophiocomina*. The remaining order, Euryalae, contains forms with arms which often branch and which can move in a vertical plane. An example is *Gorgonocephalus*.

Class Ophiocistioidea. Extinct Palaeozoic forms.

CULTURAL METHODS

Many types of starfish may be maintained for a considerable time, in well-aerated marine aquaria. The temperature should ideally be below 10°C, and should never be allowed to exceed 15°C. *Asterias* prefers live food, particularly *Mytilus edulis*, but will often accept chopped mussel when hungry.

Small specimens of *Echinus esculentus*, *Psammechinus miliaris*, and many other endocyclic echinoids will survive for long periods of time in properly maintained marine aquaria, and will feed on finely chopped raw fish, shellfish and lean beef.

Ophioderma and other brittle-stars may survive if fed on finely chopped raw fish or shellfish.

Crinoids, clypeastrids and spatangids, as well as all holothurians,

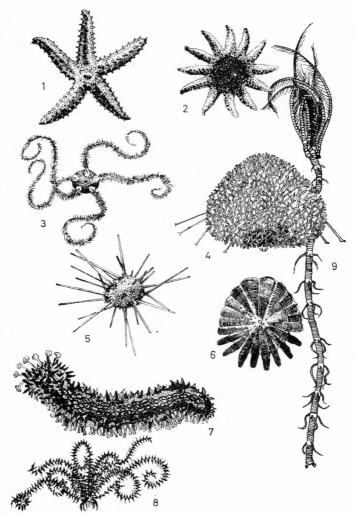

Figure 1.41. Some examples of echinoderms: 1. *Asterias glacialis*, an asteroid ('starfish'); 2. *Solaster*, an asteroid ('sun star'); 3. *Ophiothrix*, an ophiuroid ('brittle star'); 4. *Echinus*, an echinoid ('sea urchin'); 5. *Cidaris*, a regular echinoid; 6. *Rotula*, an irregular echinoid; 7. *Holothuria*, a typical holothurian ('sea cucumber'); 8. *Antedon*, a free-living crinoid ('feather star'); 9. *Metacrinus*, a stalked crinoid ('sea lily') [7 is after Barrett and Yonge (1958); 5 and 6 are from photographs]

are difficult to rear in the aquarium, since they all feed on specialized microscopic food. They may survive without food for a few days or even weeks.

KILLING METHODS
Crinoidea

Sedentary forms should be placed head downwards in a narrow container, e.g. a measuring cylinder, of suitable dimensions. The tentacles should be carefully arranged before adding 90 per cent alcohol. Change the alcohol the following day and store in 90 per cent alcohol.

Free-living crinoids should be placed in fresh water until they are completely narcotized, then preserved in 70 per cent alcohol which should be changed after 24 h.

Holothuroidea

These must be narcotized before fixation, and this may be carried out by using one of the following methods: the use of fresh water, or by adding menthol crystals to the surface of the sea-water containing the specimens, or by the gradual addition of magnesium chloride or magnesium sulphate crystals. Then grip the animal with blunt forceps just behind the tentacles, to prevent any possible retraction while the tentacles are plunged for a few minutes in 5 per cent sea-water formalin. With a hypodermic syringe inject 70 per cent alcohol into the cloacal opening and also through the body wall into the perivisceral coelom. Then preserve the entire animal in 70 per cent alcohol. Alternatively the animal may be injected with and preserved in 5 per cent formalin, but the formalin solution must be neutralized to prevent the ossicles and calcareous ring from dissolving.

Echinoidea

If the tube feet are required in a fully extended condition it is necessary to narcotize the animal before it is killed. This should be carried out with menthol, magnesium chloride or magnesium sulphate. However, when the animals are required for dissection purposes it is unnecessary to narcotize them, and they may be killed directly by immersing them in 70 per cent alcohol or 5 per cent neutral formalin, after cutting a small hole in one side of the test, and making a slit in the peristomial membrane. 70 per cent alcohol is recommended for general preservation, but 5 per cent formalin is sometimes better when the specimens are required for dissection purposes. Alternatively, dissect living specimens.

Asteroidea

Here again, if the tube feet are required in an extended condition it is necessary to narcotize the animals before they are killed. To do this the animals should be placed mouth uppermost in a dish of sea-water and menthol, or magnesium chloride, or magnesium sulphate added until the animals are completely narcotized. Then inject the disc and the arms with 5 per cent neutral formalin and immerse the animal in 70 per cent alcohol. Dissection may be facilitated by preserving the animals in 5 per cent formalin which has not been neutralized. Some workers prefer to dissect fresh narcotized specimens.

Ophiuroidea

These should be narcotized by the gradual addition of alcohol to the sea-water, or alternatively by placing the animals in fresh water. They should then be preserved in 70 per cent alcohol.

DRY PRESERVATION METHODS

Many echinoderms preserve well in a dry condition. The drying process is carried out in the following way: place the animal on a piece of cork of suitable dimensions, and push pins into the cork at points surrounding the specimen. Tie the animal down by passing thread from one pin to another. Then place the specimen in an incubator at 37°C until it is completely dry. The specimen is then removed from the cork, attached to a perspex backing plate and mounted in a perspex museum jar. The colour usually fades when the drying process is carried out and the specimens may be carefully painted with oil colours. Probably the best method of all for preserving echinoderms and many other specimens is freeze drying (see page 321).

THE KILLING AND PRESERVATION OF ECHINODERM LARVAE

The ideal way to kill echinoderm larvae is first of all to narcotize them in sea-water to which a 5 per cent aqueous solution of chloral hydrate or 1 per cent aqueous solution of stovaine (amyl chlorohydrin) is gradually added. When fully narcotized, draw off as much of the water as possible and flood with Bouin's fixative. Leave to fix for at least 2 h, then transfer to 30 per cent alcohol. At 15 min intervals take the larvae through 50 per cent and 70 per cent alcohol, in which they may be stored. Alternatively, fix and store in 5 per cent formalin.

SPECIAL PREPARATIONS OF ECHINODERM MATERIAL
(after Wagstaffe and Fidler, 1957)
(1) THE PREPARATION OF ECHINOID TESTS

After killing, cut the peristomal membrane which surrounds the mouth, and carefully withdraw the 'Aristotle's lantern'. Place the lantern in 5 per cent neutral formalin or 70 per cent alcohol for 24 h. Using a stiff nylon toothbrush, rub off all of the spines, podia and pedicellariae, and then, using a pair of curved forceps, carefully remove all of the soft tissue from the inside of the test. Wash out the inside with a strong jet of hot water taking care not to damage the periproct. When the test has been completely cleaned, place it on a filter paper, and allow it to dry. The fixed lantern should be dried slowly and then tied to a length of thread, the other end of the thread being tied to a strip of white xylonite (grade No. F.9665—0·020 in. thick), on which the data have been written. The piece of xylonite is then bent and pushed into the mouth of the test. As the xylonite strip springs back inside, it firmly secures the lantern.

A second preparation should be made of each specimen, should this be possible, and in this case the spines and pedicellariae should be left in place. It may also be necessary to leave the Aristotle's lantern in position, and in this case it is necessary to cut a small hole in one side of the test through which the soft tissues are extracted.

Tests which have had the spines removed may be stored in cotton wool in boxes, but this is unsatisfactory for those with spines remaining, as the cotton wool becomes entangled on the spines. In this case the specimen should be tied down to a piece of stiff card using nylon monofilament, and this secured in a storage box or mounted in a perspex display case.

(2) THE PREPARATION OF A DISARTICULATED ARISTOTLE'S LANTERN

Cut the peristomal membrane and carefully withdraw the lantern. The lantern may be disarticulated by either leaving it in hot water until the soft parts have disintegrated, or by using the papaine or trypsin maceration method (see page 343). The cleaned parts of the lantern may then be attached to a square of clear perspex of suitable dimensions using a transparent cement. The structure of the skeletal part of the lantern is of great importance in the systematics of regular echinoids. If an intact lantern is required, it should be dried slowly after removing it from the test.

(3) THE PREPARATION OF PEDICELLARIAE

Carefully remove some of the pedicellariae from the echinoderm, and put them in distilled water in a watch glass.

For stained mounts

Replace the water with 10 per cent potassium hydroxide solution to which has been added a few drops of alizarine red S (saturated alcoholic solution). Leave to stain for 15 min, then dehydrate gradually through ascending grades of alcohol, clear in xylene and mount in Canada balsam.

For dry mounts

Transfer the specimens to a test tube and half fill the tube with 10 per cent potassium hydroxide solution. Heat the tube in a water bath for 10–20 min, then pour away the caustic solution and replace with distilled water. Agitate the tube and pour away the water, then replace it with fresh distilled water. The whole process should then be repeated if the pedicellariae are not completely clean. Finally, rinse in acetone and then allow to dry, before mounting them in a dry cell using gum tragacanth to attach the pedicellariae. If the pedicellariae disarticulate, reduce the time of potash treatment.

(4) THE PREPARATION OF HOLOTHURIAN OSSICLES

Isolated ossicles are prepared by boiling a small piece of skin of an holothurian in 10 per cent potassium hydroxide solution for several minutes until the skin has disintegrated and the ossicles have become detached. Allow the ossicles to settle, then pour away the fluid. Rinse in several changes of distilled water until they are clean, and then treat with three changes of absolute alcohol. Pour away the alcohol, and replace with xylene. The ossicles may then be picked up in a pipette with a minimum of xylene and transferred to the centre of a clean slide in a drop of neutral Canada balsam. Cover with a coverslip and leave to dry.

Ossicles in situ may be demonstrated by removing a small rectangle of skin from the holothurian and fixing it for several hours in 70 per cent alcohol, or any non-acid fixative. The skin may then be stained with anthracene blue (see page 247) or in a very dilute solution of Ehrlich's haematoxylin in distilled water. When the nuclei are sufficiently stained the cytoplasm may be lightly stained with eosin or light green. Dehydrate gradually through the ascending grades of alcohol, clear in xylene and mount in neutral Canada balsam. The ossicles of *Synapta* make very beautiful preparations.

The calcareous ring, a ring of calcareous plates which encircles the pharynx of holothurians, and probably homologous, at least in part, with the Aristotle's lantern of echinoids may be prepared in a similar way to that for the preparation of isolated ossicles.

(5) SECTIONS OF SPINES

Sometimes it is necessary to examine the internal structure of a spine, and a section may be prepared in the following way: embed a short length of spine in hot, pure Canada balsam on a clean microscope slide, and allow the balsam to harden. Then rub the spine down with carborundum powder in water on a glass plate, washing the spine frequently with water. When the spine has been rubbed down to the required thickness, wash the section thoroughly with water, then allow it to dry. Add some thin Canada balsam and a coverslip.

PHYLUM CHAETOGNATHA

Commonly known as 'arrow worms' the chaetognatha are small bilaterally symmetrycal marine coelomates. They have no circulatory or excretory systems. The general shape of the body is torpedo like, and with a few exceptions they are all of planktonic habit. The body of chaetognaths is transparent, and is provided with one or two pairs of lateral fins, and a horizontal tail fin. The rounded head is armed at each side of the mouth with a set of grasping spines. These animals are capable of covering their head by drawing over it a fold of the body. The head bears a pair of eyes. They are hermaphroditic, and the eggs which are shed into the sea develop into a non-swimming form which resembles the adult. The chaetognaths are among the most common marine animals.

CULTURE METHODS

There appear to be no published methods for culturing chaetognaths. They appear to be very difficult to maintain for long periods of time. Regeneration was studied by Kulmatycki (1918) in *Spadella cephaloptera*, probably the only chaetognath that can be kept in good condition in the laboratory long enough to follow the course of regeneration.

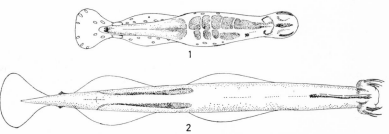

Figure 1.42. Two examples of Chaetognatha: 1. *Spadella;* 2 *Sagitta*

Except *Spadella*, which is benthonic, chaetognaths lead a planktonic existence. They are highly predaceous, carnivorous animals, eating almost any type of small animal with which they may come into contact.

KILLING AND PRESERVATION METHODS

Better preparations of chaetognaths are made from specimens which have been previously narcotized. The mouthparts in particular

119

will be much better displayed. Narcotization should be carried out by the addition of menthol crystals to the water, or alternatively by the gradual addition of chloral hydrate to the water.

When narcotized, the chaetognaths should be fixed in one of the following solutions, taking care that the animals are as straight as possible before adding the fixative: Bouin's fluid, Gilson's fluid, or 5 per cent formalin. If Bouin's fluid is used, the fixation time should be about 12 h; if Gilson's fluid is used the time should be about 1–3 h depending on the size, and the specimens should then be treated with iodine solution, followed by several changes in 50 per cent alcohol, then store in 5 per cent formalin. Specimens should never be stored in 70 per cent alcohol, but always kept in 5 per cent formalin. It is interesting to note that the important plankton indicators, *Sagitta setosa*, and *S. elegans* show a marked difference in appearance when preserved in 5 per cent formalin. The former species remains transparent, but *S. elegans* quickly becomes opaque.

PHYLUM POGONOPHORA

Pogonophora are solitary, tube-dwelling, worm-like marine animals, living mainly in the abyssal depths of the oceans. The body is regionated

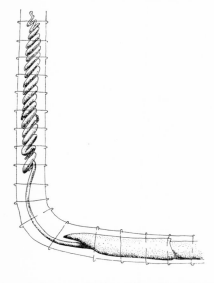

Figure 1.43. Pogonophora. Siboglinum, anterior portion in its tube (after Caullery, 1944, by courtesy of McGraw-Hill Book Co., Inc.)

in a similar way to that of hemichordates, and bears one to many tentacles on the protosome. There are no gill slits and no digestive tract. Pogonophores are extremely slender and long worms and secrete their own tube in which they dwell. The sexes are separate. First discovered in 1899, there are now at least 22 known species.

Little has been written about the techniques required to kill and preserve pogonophores, but the author would suggest that they would no doubt respond to prefixation narcotization in 7 per cent magnesium chloride solution. Suggested fixatives are 5 per cent formalin (made up in sea-water), Bouin's fluid, or Zenker's fixative.

PHYLUM HEMICHORDATA

Hemichordates comprise marine animals which at first glance will appear to be completely unrelated. They include both solitary and colonial forms, the majority being of worm-like appearance. They are coelomates, and the body is made up of three regions of unequal length and of different structure. There is a preoral gut diverticulum known as the stomochord, a structure regarded until recent years as being a simple notochord, and for this reason the hemichordates were arranged in the phylum Chordata as a separate subphylum. There is a simple circulatory system and a nervous system in the epidermis. There may be tentaculated arms on the second body region. The sexes are separate and in the Enteropneusta, a characteristic free-swimming larva is produced, the tornaria. They are a small group of animals, there being less than 100 known species.

Class Enteropneusta, 'acorn worms'. Worm-like solitary forms, with no tentacular arms but with a straight intestine and numerous gill slits. Includes such genera as *Balanoglossus*, *Saccoglossus* and *Ptychodera*.

Class Pterobranchia. These hemichordates occur as aggregates or colonies, and are of small size. They are enclosed in some form of secreted encasement, and may be with or without gill slits. The digestive tract is U-shaped. Tentacular arms are always present.

Order Rhabdopleurida. True colonies of pterobranchs, each member being continuous with its neighbour and at the same time enclosed in its own secreted tube. There are no gill slits and two tentaculated arms. Includes the genus *Rhabdopleura*.

Order Cephalodiscida. Aggregations of pterobranchs living in a common encasement, and with individual members being entirely separated from one another. One pair of gill slits and four to nine pairs of tentaculated arms are present. Includes the genus *Cephalodiscus*.

Class Planctosphaeroidea. Only the larval stage is known, and this is transparent, spherical in shape, and pelagic, with its surface covered in branched ciliated bands.

CULTURAL METHODS FOR HEMICHORDATA

Some of the smaller species of enteropneusts, such as *Saccoglossus*, will survive for a few days or weeks in aerated sea-water kept at 10°C and supplied with a mixture of mud and sand, taken preferably from where the animals were obtained.

KILLING AND PRESERVATION OF HEMICHORDATA

Before fixation is carried out, the hemichordates should be thoroughly narcotized. This is best carried out by the gradual addition of

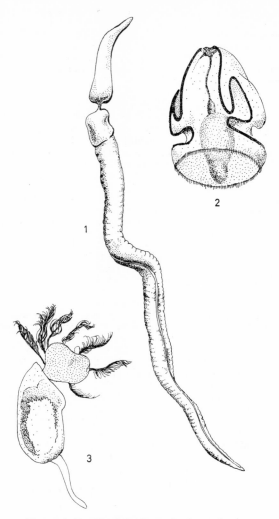

Figure 1.44 Hemichordata: 1. *Saccoglossus;*
2. *Tornaria larva;* 3. *Cephalodiscus kempi*

95 per cent alcohol to the sea-water containing the animals until a concentration of 1 part alcohol to 9 parts sea-water is obtained. Enteropneusts may be relaxed by immersing them in 7 per cent aqueous magnesium chloride solution.

Fixation should be carried out by transferring the animals to 5 per cent sea-water formaldehyde solution (this is the best fixative to use for display specimens), or sea-water Bouin's fluid (this is the best method when histological work is to be carried out). After fixation for 24 h, formalin-fixed specimens should be transferred to a fresh change of sea-water formaldehyde, and Bouin-fixed material should be transferred to 70 per cent alcohol, in which they may be stored.

Hemichordates offer no particular difficulties when histological sections are required. Excellent sections of enteropneusts are easily prepared from Bouin-fixed material embedded by the Petrefi method (see page 217).

PHYLUM CHORDATA

The body of a chordate is bilaterally symmetrical, and in higher forms is divided into head, trunk and post-anal tail regions. At least in some stage of development a notochord is present. (A notochord is a skeletal rod lying ventral to the central nervous system.) In higher forms (subphylum Vertebrata) the notochord is replaced during development to a greater or lesser degree by the vertebral column. The pharynx possesses lateral openings or pouches (pharyngeal or visceral clefts) which may be transitory, appearing only during development. An endostyle or its homologue (the thyroid) is also present. The central nerve chord is dorsal and tubular. There is a well-developed blood vascular system, typically possessing a heart, ventral to the gut, through which the blood flows forward. Typically the sexes are separate, and a perivisceral coelom is present.

Subphylum Urochorda—Chordates in which the body is not regionally divided and the coelom is absent; there is a notochord in the tail of the larva but this is usually lost in the adult; the larva also possesses a post-anal tail; an atrium is present in the adults into which the pharyngeal clefts open; the central nervous system is separated from the epidermis and, in the adult, is reduced to a single, solid, elongated ganglion, although in the larva the central nervous system is more prominent and hollow; there is, typically, a well-developed blood system with a ventral heart through which the direction of flow of the blood is reversed from time to time; the body of the adult is enclosed in a test composed of tunicin, a substance related to cellulose; most of the members of this subphylum are hermaphrodite.

Class LARVACEA. Urochordata in which the adult retains the form of the larva and possesses a tail; the test is temporary and barrel shaped, and is gelatinous and not composed of tunicin; there are two pharyngeal clefts and no atrium; budding does not occur; the nervous system is relatively well developed; members are free swimming and pelagic. Examples are *Oikopleura*, *Appendicularia*.

Class ASCIDIACEA, 'sea-squirts'. Urochordata in which the adult has lost the larval tail and is variable in form; the test is permanent and thick; there are several pharyngeal clefts usually subdivided by longitudinal and transverse bars; an atrium is present which opens dorsally; budding usually occurs; the nervous system is reduced to a single ganglion; the adult is always sedentary.   Examples are *Clavelina, Ciona, Ascidea, Phallusia, Botryllus.*

Class **THALIACEA**, 'salps'.   Urochordata in which the adult lacks a tail; the test is permanent;   there are either two large or numerous small pharyngeal clefts which are not subdivided by longitudinal bars; an atrium is present which opens posteriorly;   there is a complex stolon from which budding occurs;   the nervous system is degenerate;   the members are pelagic. Examples are *Pyrosoma, Salpa, Doliolum.*

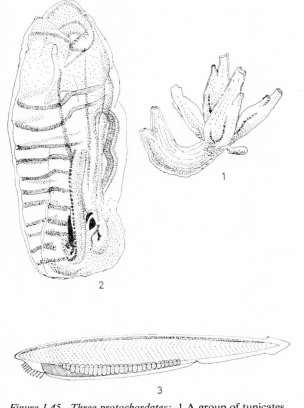

Figure 1.45. Three protochordates: 1 A group of tunicates, *Ciona intestinalis;* 2. A large salp, *Salpa maxima;* 3. A cephalochordate, *Amphioxus lanceolatus*

Subphylum Cephalochordata (= *Acrania*), 'Lancelets'—Chordata in which the body is divided into two regions, a trunk and a post-anal tail; there is a well-developed notochord extending the entire length of the body both in the larva and the adult; the post-anal tail is present in both the larva and the adult; in the adult a large atrium is present into which the numerous pharyngeal clefts open; there is a well-developed hollow, dorsal nerve cord lying above the notochord; there is a well-developed blood system in which the blood flows forward along the contractile ventral vessel, but no heart is present; there is no test; sexes are separate; members are marine and the larva is planktonic and bears a strong resemblance to the adult which is an active animal usually found burrowing in the sand and shell-gravel. Examples are *Branchiostoma* (= *Amphioxus*), *Asymmetron*.

The aforementioned three subphyla are often loosely termed 'the protochordates', and complete the list of invertebrates. The remaining subphylum is:

Subphylum Vertebrata—The vertebrates are chordates which show a marked advance in complexity of structure and activity on the Cephalo-chordata; there is a high degree of cephalization so that a definite head can be recognized; special sense organs are well developed and there is a definite brain enclosed in a cranium; during development the notochord is replaced to a greater or lesser degree by a vertebral column; an endo-skeleton of cartilage or cartilage and bone, of which the vertebral column is part, is well developed and this is associated with a large and complex musculature; the organs of nitrogenous excretion are kidneys; a true muscular heart is present as part of the ventral blood vessel; visceral clefts are restricted in number and are primarily associated with respiration and not with feeding; although an endostyle may be present in the larvae of certain more primitive vertebrates, it becomes replaced in the adult by a thyroid gland; a system of endocrine glands is present and there is one or more portal systems of veins. A simplified classification of the vertebrates is given below:

Class AGNATHA (= MARSIPOBRANCHII), (jawless vertebrates). The mouth is round and not bounded by jaws; the vertebral column is but feebly developed, for there are no centra and the notochord persists throughout life; the larva of living members of this class has an endostyle and other ciliated tracts in the pharynx.

Order Osteostraci. An extinct order; e.g., *Cephalaspis* (Silurian, Devonian).

Order Anaspida. An extinct order; e.g., *Birkenia* (Devonian).

Order Hetrostraci. An extinct order; e.g., *Thelodus* (Silurian).

Order Cyclostomata. The modern lampreys and hagfish; all traces of paired fins and girdles are absent; e.g., *Petromyzon*, 'lamprey', *Myxine*, 'hagfish'.

Class PLACODERMI ('archaic jawed fish'). Extinct.

Order Arthrodira; e.g., *Dinichthys* (Devonian).

Order Acanthodii ('spiny sharks'); e.g., *Climatius* (Devonian).

Class CHONDRICHTHYES (= SELACHII), (shark-like fish). Fish with an endoskeleton which is composed entirely of cartilage usually impregnated with calcium salts. Exoskeleton of placoid scales; upper jaw (palato-quadrate) and the lower jaw (Meckel's cartilage) are each single cartilages; except in the Holocephali the gills are not covered by an operculum; tail is heterocercal; spiral valve in intestine; a swim-bladder is lacking; fertilization is internal and male has an intromittent organ (claspers); eggs are usually large yolked and enclosed in horny capsules.

Order Cladoselachii (primitive sharks). Extinct; e.g., *Cladoselache* (Devonian).

Order Elasmobranchii, 'sharks', 'skates', 'rays'. Chondrichthyes with numerous teeth developed in continuous succession; pectoral fins have three basal pieces (pro-, meso-, and meta-pterygium), from which a

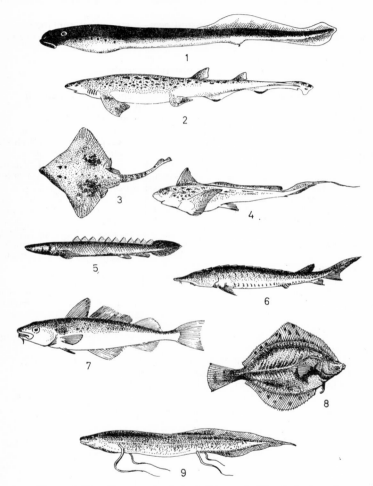

Figure 1.46. Some examples of fishes: 1. 'Brook lamprey' *Lampetra planeri*, male; 2. 'Spiny dogfish' *Squalus* (= *Acanthias*) *vulgaris*), an elasmobranch; 3. 'Skate' *Raia batis*, an elasmobranch; 4. 'Rabbit fish' *Chimaera monstrosa*, a holocephalan; 5. 'Nile bichir' *Polypterus bichir*, a chondrostean; 6. 'Sturgeon' *Acipenser sturio*, a chondrostean; 7. 'Cod' *Gadus morrhua*, a teleost; 8. 'Flounder' *Pleuronectes flesus*, a teleost; 9. 'African lung-fish' *Protopterus annectans*, a dipnoan

number of pre-axial radials spread out. Examples are *Scylliorhinus, Raia, Torpedo*.

Order Holocephali, 'chimaeras'. Jaw is attached to the skull, but with a complete hyoid arch which is free from the cranium (holostylic); there are numerous calcified rings around the unconstricted notochord; an operculum is present; in living members the skin is naked except for the claspers where a few placoid scales are found. Examples are *Chimaera, Callorhynchus, Harriotta*.

Class OSTEICHTHYES (higher bony fish). By the time the adult stage is reached the major part of the cartilaginous endoskeleton has been replaced by bone; and membrane bones have also been added; bony scales as exoskeleton; mouth is terminal; swim-bladder is present (except in rare cases when it is secondarily absent); jaw suspension of a variable type; in most primitive members of this group the tail is heterocercal but in the highest teleosts it has become homocercal.

Subclass Actinopterygii (ray-finned fish).

Order Chondrostei. Members have a skeleton which is largely cartilaginous; with ganoid scales; with a heterocercal tail. Examples are *Cheirolepis* (Devonian Palaeoniscid); *Acipenser*, 'sturgeon'; *Polyodon*, 'spoonbill sturgeon'; *Polypterus*.

Order Holostei. Skeleton of bone and cartilage (a greater proportion of bone than in Chondrostei); ganoid scales; with swim-bladder, conus arteriousus and spiral valve (bulbus arteriosus also present in *Amia*). Examples are *Lepidosteus*, 'gar pike'; *Amia*, 'bowfin'.

Order Teleostei. Spiral valve absent; conus arteriosus absent; proximal end of ventral aorta is dilated to form a bulbus arteriosus, a structure which differs from a conus in being part of the aorta and not of the heart (its walls do not contain striped muscle, and are not rhythmically contractile); optic nerves do not form a chiasma but simply cross one another; scales are cycloid or ctenoid; a swim-bladder is present which in the more primitive forms (Isospondyli) preserves in the adult its opening to the pharynx, but in the higher forms becomes completely separated. Examples are *Clupea*, 'herring'; *Scomber*, 'mackerel'; *Anguilla*, 'eel'; *Hippocampus*, 'sea horse'; *Solea*, 'sole'; *Cyprinus*, 'carp'; *Salmo*, 'salmon' and 'trout'; *Remora*, 'shark sucker'; *Periophthalmus*, 'mud-skipper'.

Subclass Sarcopterygii (fish with internal nostrils).

Superorder Crossopterygii (lobe-finned fish). A line runs transversely across the skull between the frontal and parietal bones which divides it into two portions.

Order Rhipidistia. (All extinct.) Examples, *Osteolepis, Eusthenopteron*.

Order Actinistia (Coelacanths); e.g., *Coelacanthus, Undina, Latimeria*, 'coelacanth'.

Superorder Dipnoi (true lungfish). Not only do the lungfish breathe by means of gills, like ordinary fish, but they have a lung; gills covered by an operculum; primary cranium persists with little ossification, but has added to it a number of investing bones. Pectoral and pelvic arches are cartilaginous; exoskeleton of overlapping cycloid scales; intestine contains a spiral valve; conus arteriosus present; optic nerves form a chiasma.

Order Monopneumona (with single lung); e.g., *Epiceratodus*, 'Australian lungfish'.

Order Dipneumona (with two lungs); e.g., *Protopterus*, 'African lungfish'; *Lepidosiren*, 'South American lungfish'.

Class AMPHIBIA. Vertebrates which during their development have only partially succeeded in overcoming the difficulties attending life on land. The adults haunt damp environments, or else have become secondarily adapted to a complete aquatic life. Except for a few salamanders

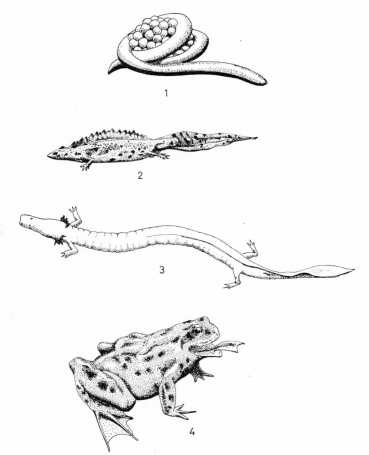

Figure 1.47. Four examples of amphibians: 1. *Ichthyophis glutinosa*—guarding eggs—an apodan (from a photograph); 2. 'Crested newt' *Triturus cristatus*—a urodele (from a photograph); 3. 'Olm' *Proteus anguinus*—a urodele; 4. 'Common frog' *Rana temporaria*—an anuran [after a drawing in B.M. (N.H.) Guide, 1898]

which are viviparous, amphibians are compelled to breed in fresh water; the earliest amphibians appear to have evolved from the crossopterygian stock; the major differences being that they had pentadactyl limbs, and a middle ear apparatus. Modern amphibia are characterized by having a smooth, moist skin rich in gland cells, which acts as a respiratory surface; scales are absent (except in the Apoda); gills are present in the larvae and may persist into adult life; lungs which open into the bucco-pharyngeal cavity via a glottis are present in adults; there are two auricles and a single ventricle in the heart; a urinary bladder is present as a large diverticulum of the cloaca; except in the Seymouriamorpha there are two occipital condyles; lateral line organs are present in larvae and in aquatic adults.

Order Labyrinthodontia. The skull is completely roofed with deeply sculptured membrane bones; they have a labyrinthodont tooth structure as in Crossopterygii; all extinct.

Order Seymouriamorpha. Combine both amphibian and reptilian characteristics; single occipital condyle; all extinct. (Regarded as reptiles by majority of palaeontologists.)

Order Phyllospondyli. Extinct order.

Order Lepospondyli. Extinct order.

Order Gymnophiona (= Apoda). Vermiform limbless amphibians, without tail; eyes reduced; centra of vertebrae are amphicoelous; skin contains scales. Examples are *Ichthyophis, Siphonops*.

Order Caudata (= Urodela). Tailed amphibians; limbs feebly developed or absent; vertebrae usually opisthocoelous; ossification of skull is much reduced; both external and internal gills may persist in the adult and if they do, then the lungs tend to atrophy. Examples are *Cryptobranchus, Amblystoma, Salamandra, Triturus, Proteus, Necturus, Siren* ('salamanders', 'axolotls', 'newts', etc.).

Order Salientia (= Anura). Tail absent in adult; gill slits close in adult; vertebral column remarkably short (may be as few as five vertebrae); ribs only rarely present; the limbs are adapted for both swimming and jumping, fore limbs being short and hind limbs long with a web between the digits. This order which contains the frogs and toads is subdivided into five suborders according to the type of vertebral centra. Examples are *Liopelma, Pipa, Xenopus, Bufo, Hyla, Rana*.

Class REPTILIA. Vertebrates which are completely adapted to life on dry land, both as adults and in their embryonic development; eggs are large yolked and enclosed in a shell; embryo enclosed in embryonic membranes (amnion); skin is dry and bears horny epidermal scales (bony plates may also be present); the division of the heart into right and left halves is complete or nearly so; visceral clefts never develop gills; skull articulates with the vertebral column by means of a single condyle; in most reptiles the outer casing of dermal bones over the cranium is incomplete owing to the presence of one or more windows (temporal vacuities) which develop to allow a greater space for the housing of the jaw muscles— the number of temporal vacuities and their relations to the dermal bones of the skull provide a basis for the classification of the group; the lower law consists of several bones.

Subclass Anapsida. Reptiles with no temporal vacuities, although the bones may be emarginated from the hinder end of the skull.

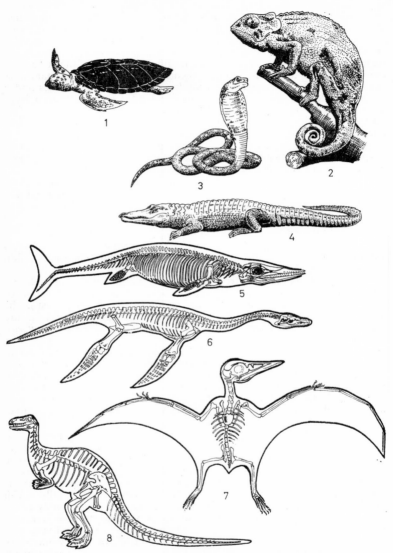

Figure 1.48. Some examples of reptiles: 1 'Green turtle' *Chelonia mydas*; 2. 'Chameleon' *Chameleo*; 3. 'Cobra' *Naia*; 4. 'Mississippi alligator' *Alligator mississippiensis* (by courtesy of Odhams Press Ltd.); 5. *Ichthyosaurus*, an extinct aquatic reptile; 6. *Plesiosaurus*, an extinct aquatic reptile; 7. *Pterodactylus*, an extinct flying reptile; 8. *Megalosaurus*, an extinct dinosaur

Order Cotylosauria (stem reptiles)—*Seymouria* is often placed in this group instead of in the Amphibia. All extinct. An example is *Diadectes*.

Order Chelonia ('turtles', 'tortoises' and 'terrapins'). The trunk is relatively short and protected by a dorsal shield (carapace) and a ventral shield (plastron)—typically each shield is composed of bony plates covered with large horny epidermal plates (tortoise shell); teeth are lacking, but are replaced by a horny beak; a short bony secondary palate is present; limbs of aquatic forms are adapted as paddles. Examples are *Testudo*, 'tortoise'; *Chelonia*, 'green turtle'.

Subclass Ichthyopterygia.

Order Ichthyosauria (the ichthyosaurs). Those reptiles most adapted to an aquatic life; body streamlined; jaws with numerous teeth; limbs paddle shaped; a large vertical tail fin present; skull has a single temporal vacuity. All extinct. An example is, *Ichthyosaurus* (Jurassic).

Subclass Synaptosauria.

Order Sauropterygia ('plesiosaurs', 'nothosaurs' and 'placodonts'). Adapted to a marine or estuarine life; small head borne on a very long flexible neck; fore limbs form large paddles, hind limbs usually smaller; tail short and bears no fin; skull has a single temporal vacuity. All extinct. Examples are, *Plesiosaurus* (Jurassic), *Nothosaurus* (Triassic), *Placodus* (Triassic).

Subclass Lepidosauria. Diapsid or modified diapsid skull (having two temporal vacuities); no antorbital fenestra; teeth usually acrodont or pleurodont.

Order Eosuchia. Extinct forms from Permian to Eocene.

Order Rhynchocephalia. From Triassic to Recent; have unmodified diapsid skull with acrodont dentition. An example is *Sphenodon*, 'tuatara', New Zealand.

Order Squamata. From Triassic to Recent. With a modified diapsid skull; teeth acrodont or pleurodont; vertebrae amphicoelous, or procoelous; all recent forms have hemipenes, and an egg-tooth.

Suborder Lacertilia (= Sauria), 'lizards'. Although there are some limbless lizards, there are always traces of girdles present; rami of lower jaw are united by suture so that the gape of the mouth is not excessively large. Examples are *Iguana*, 'iguana'; *Draco*, 'flying lizard'; *Chamaeleo*, 'chamaeleon'; *Gekko*; *Scincus*, 'skink'; *Lacerta*; *Anguis*, 'slow worm'; *Heloderma*, 'gila monster'; *Varanus*, 'monitor'.

Suborder Ophidia (= Serpentes), 'snakes'. Limbs and (with the exception of a rudiment of a pelvic girdle in some, e.g. 'pythons') limb girdles are absent; rami of lower jaw never united by suture; no urinary bladder. Examples are *Python*, 'python'; *Boa*, 'boa'; *Eunectes*, 'anaconda'; *Natrix*, 'grass snake'; *Naia*, 'cobra'; *Dendroaspis*, 'mamba'; *Hydrophis*, 'sea snake'; *Vipera*, 'adder'; *Crotalus*, 'rattle snake'.

Subclass Archosauria (ruling reptiles). Diapsid type of skull; many tend towards a bipedal gait, while some others having once acquired a bipedal gait have slumped back to a four-footed pose. Triassic to Recent.

Order Thecodontia (ancestral forms). All extinct. Examples are *Ornithosuchus, Euparkeria*.

Order Crocodilia. Have lost their bipedal gait, but have developed a false palate (nostrils remain at tip of snout). Examples are *Alligator*, 'alligator'; *Crocodylus*, 'crocodile'; *Gavialis*, 'gharial'.

131

Figure 1.49. Some examples of birds: 1. 'Ostrich' *Struthio camelus*, a ratite; 2. 'Emperor penguin' *Aptenodytes forsteri*; 3. 'Black vulture' *Catharistes urubu*, a falconiform; 4. 'Flamingo' *Phoenicopterus roseus*, an anseriform; 5. 'Black swan' *Chenopis atrata*, an anseriform; 6. 'Macaw' *Ara*, a psittacid; 7. 'Tawny owl' *Strix aluco*, a strigiform (from a drawing by R. Peterson); 8. 'Blackbird' *Turdus merula*, a passeriform (from a drawing by R. Peterson)

Order Pterosauria (flying reptiles). All extinct. Jurassic–Cretaceous.

Order Saurischia (reptile-like dinosaurs). Have the triradiate pelvic structure developed in many thecodonts. Usually carnivorous, except for the Sauropoda. All extinct.

Suborder Theropoda. Bipedal with long hind limbs and short fore limbs; carnivorous. Examples are *Compsognathus, Tyrannosaurus.*

Suborder Sauropoda. Quadrupeds, and include the largest four-footed animals of all time; massively built, with powerful limbs, a long tail, and a long neck terminating in a small head; many almost certainly lived an amphibious existence. Examples are *Brontosaurus, Diplodocus, Brachiosaurus* (Jurassic).

Order Ornithischia (bird-like dinosaurs). Have a tetraradiate pelvic structure, with the main portion of the pubis rotated downwards and backwards so that it is parallel to and close beside the ischium, while a broad new process had developed forward and outward along the margin of the belly. Herbivorous. All extinct.

Suborder Ornithopoda (bipeds); e.g., *Camptosaurus.*

Suborder Stegosauria. Quadrupeds with a double row of protective plates down the back and tail: e.g., *Stegosaurus.*

Suborder Ankylosauria. Heavily armoured rather turtle-like quadrupeds; e.g., *Ankylosaurus* (Cretaceous).

Suborder Ceratopsia. Horned dinosaurs; e.g., *Triceratops* (Cretaceous).

Subclass Synapsida (forms leading towards mammals). Strange as it may seem the Synapsida were among the first of the reptile groups to appear; central stock of the group was carnivorous; trend was to improvement in quadrupedal locomotion; a single lateral opening in the temporal region.

Order Pelycosauria (Permian and carboniferous beds of North America and Europe); e.g., *Dimetrodon, Edaphosaurus.*

Order Therapsida. Mammal-like reptiles from the Karroo Beds of South Africa. Middle Permian to Middle Triassic.

Class AVES, 'birds'. Apart from the power of flight, and features associated with it, birds are essentially similar to reptiles, particularly archosaurs; feathers are almost the only distinguishing feature of the class, and even these are comparable with scales; warm blooded; fore limbs modified to form wings; only three digits to fore limb; hind limbs large and strong, and with considerable fusion of bones; cervical vertebrae are heterocoelous making the neck very flexible; many of the post-cervical vertebrae fuse; jaws are devoid of teeth; skull is really of diapsid type, but the lower border of the upper temporal vacuity has vanished, so that the two vacuities have become confluent; sternum is well developed and in flying forms it has a keel (carina); bones are usually very light but strong, and many contain air spaces into which project air sacs (thin-walled extensions from the lungs); there is only one carotico-systemic arch—the right-hand one; optic lobes are large resulting in a keen sense of sight.

Division 1. Archaeornithes. Extinct birds from the Upper Jurassic; primitive features include teeth on the jaws, the presence of claws on the wing digits, and a tail which had many separate vertebrae; the metacarpals were not fused together. Examples are *Archaeopteryx, Archaeornis.*

Division 2. Neornithes. This group as well as containing the extinct toothed cretaceous birds, including all remaining known birds. They all have a short tail whose component vertebrae are ankylosed together to form a pygostyle; the three metacarpals do not all remain distinct; the bones of the pelvis are ankylosed together and to a large though variable number of vertebrae. The living birds may be classified as follows:

Subclass Ratitae. Palate is palaeognathous; sternum is keel-less, though considerable traces of a keel remains in the embryo ostrich, showing that the loss of the keel is secondary. Flightless birds; fore limbs very small; hind limbs frequently well developed. The tinamous are sometimes included in the Ratitae, but the sternum does have a keel. Examples are *Struthio*, 'ostrich'; *Rhea*, 'rhea'; *Dromiceius*, 'emu'; *Casuarius*, 'cassowary'; *Apteryx*, 'kiwi'. The kiwis differ from all other birds in having the nostril at the tip of a long slender beak.

Subclass Impennes. This sub-class contains a single order: Sphenisciforms ('penguins'). Although primitive in many respects, they are in many ways among the most highly specialized of birds. The wings are incapable of functioning in flight, but are powerful flippers for swimming; metatarsal bones are but partially fused, in contrast to their intimate union in typical modern birds. Restricted to Southern Hemisphere. Examples are *Aptenodytes*; *Spheniscus*.

Subclass Carinatae ('true flying birds'). There is always a pygostyle; wings usually adapted for flight; tarsus has one or more canals for the passage of tendons. Usually a well-developed keel on the sternum. Some of the more important orders are listed below:

Order Colymbiformes, 'grebes', 'divers'.
Order Alciformes, 'razorbills', guillemots', 'puffins'.
Order Procellariiformes, 'albatross', 'petrels'. Tubular nostrils.
Order Pelecaniformes, 'cormorants', 'gannets', 'pelicans'. All four toes in webbed foot.
Order Ciconiformes, 'spoonbills', 'herons', 'storks'.
Order Anseriformes, 'flamingoes', 'ducks', 'geese', 'swans'.
Order Anhimiformes, 'screamers'.
Order Lariformes, 'terns', 'gulls', 'skuas'.
Order Charadriiformes, 'oystercatcher', 'avocet', 'curlew', 'jacanas'.
Order Ralliformes (= Gruiformes), 'rails', 'sun-bittern'.
Order Tinamiformes, 'tinamous'. Palaeognathous palate.
Order Galliformes, game birds, 'hoatzin'.
Order Columbiformes, 'pigeons', 'doves'.
Order Falconiformes, 'vultures', 'secretary-bird', 'hawks', 'eagles'.
Order Strigiformes, 'owls'.
Order Psittaciformes, 'parrots'. Zygodactylous foot (first and fourth toe turned backward).
Order Cuculiformes, 'cuckoos', 'plantain eaters'. Zygodactylous foot.
Order Piciformes, 'woodpeckers', 'barbets', 'toucans'. Woodpeckers have zygodactylous feet.
Order Trogoniformes, 'trogons'. First and second toe turned backwards.
Order Caprimulgiformes, 'nightjars', 'oilbirds', 'goatsuckers'.
Order Apodiformes, 'martinets'.
Order Coliiformes.

PHYLUM CHORDATA

Order Coraciadiformes, 'bee-eaters', 'hornbills', 'hoopoes'.

Order Passeriformes (perching birds). Have a very large first toe directed back and opposed to the other three. This order comprises about half the present bird population.

Class MAMMALIA Vertebrates which have most successfully adapted themselves to a completely terrestrial life; a few have reconquered the sea and fresh water and have become modified accordingly; mammals suckle their young (nourish the young with milk secreted by mammary glands); typically the skin is covered with hair; brain has large cerebral hemispheres and a large cerebellum; lower jaw consists of one bone the dentary; turbinal bones are found in the nasal cavity; an extensive secondary palate; dentition is heterodont and diphyodont; heart is completely divided into two halves; only one caротicо-systemic arch—the left; a muscular diaphragm completely separates the thoracic and abdominal cavities, and the ribs assist in respiratory movements; the cloacal region of the embryo becomes (except in the Monotremata) divided into two chambers by a partition, the perineum, so that the anus is separated from the urinogenital aperture.

The surviving members of the class are numerous and are the dominant land craniates of today. Simpson (1945) classifies them as follows, though in more detail:

Subclass Eotheria.

Order Docodonta. Primitive Mesozoic mammals from which the Monotremes may have evolved.

Subclass Prototheria. Primitive mammals in which the molar teeth are not trituberculo-sectorial or cannot be regarded as being derived from such teeth. There is a distinct coracoid and precoracoid in the pectoral girdle. Mandibular branch of fifth nerve penetrates the petrosal.

Order Monotremata. Edentulous when adult, the mono-tremes are confined to the Australian region; they are oviparous and have mammary glands without teats; a cloaca is present; bones of skull are very thin and fuse up to an early age, obliterating the sutures; there are no vertebral epiphyses, and the ribs are single headed; marsupial bones (epipubic bones) are present; no angle to the lower jaw. Pleistocene–Recent. Examples are *Tachyglossus* (= Echidna), 'spiny ant-eater'; *Zaglossus* (= Proechidna), 'New Guinea spiny ant-eater'; *Ornithorhynchus*, 'duck-bill'.

Subclass Allotheria. All members extinct.

Subclass Theria. This subclass includes the vast majority of mammals. The molar teeth are either trituberculo-sectorial or can be derived from such teeth. The scapula bears a spine and the coracoid is greatly reduced and fused with the scapula; there is no interclavicle; they have fully developed teats; cloaca is absent; never oviparous. Mandibular branch of the fifth nerve passes through the alisphenoid by the foramen ovale.

Infraclass Pantotheria. Basal therian stock, this little known group existed in Jurassic times.

Infraclass Metatheria.

Order Marsupialia. Confined to Australian region and to North and South America. Young are born in a very immature state, and develop in a pouch which is usually present. Allantoic placenta is absent (except in *Perameles*). There is a single sphincter around the vulva and anus; in the male the scrotum is anterior to the penis; marsupials

135

have a full dental formula $\frac{5.1.3.4.}{4.1.3.4.}$, only third premolar being replaced. There is an inflected angle to the lower jaw (except in *Tarsipes*); marsupial bones (epipubic bones) are present in the pelvis (except in *Thylacinus*); palatal vacuities are often present. Upper Cretaceous–Recent. Simpson divides the living marsupials into five superfamilies.

Superfamily Didelphoidea (opossum-like mammals of New World).

Superfamily Dasyuroidea, 'pouched mice', 'native cats', 'Tasmanian devils', 'Tasmanian wolf', 'marsupial mole'.

Superfamily Perameloidea, 'bandicoots'.

Superfamily Caenolestoidea, 'opossum-rats'.

Superfamily Phalangeroidea, Australian 'opossums', 'koala', 'wombats', 'kangeroos', and 'wallabies'.

Infraclass Eutheria (= Placentalia). This group includes all the remaining orders of mammals. An allantoic placenta is always present; vagina is never completely divided into two; scrotum is behind or beside penis; pouch, and epipubic bones absent; dental formula primitively $\frac{3.1.4.3.}{3.1.4.3.}$. Lower Cretaceous–Recent.

Cohort Unguiculata.

Order Insectivora. The basal group of placental mammals; small mammals in which fur is sometimes modified as spines; diet is either carnivorous or insectivorous; extremity of muzzle tends to project beyond the end of the lower jaw; testes retained within body cavity. There are five superfamilies of living insectivores.

Superfamily Tenrecoidea, *Solenodon*; 'tenrecs'; *Potamogale*.

Superfamily Chrysochloroidea, 'golden moles'.

Superfamily Erinaceoidea, 'hedgehogs'.

Superfamily Macrosceloidea, 'elephant-shrews'.

Superfamily Soricoidea, 'shrews', 'moles'.

Order Dermoptera, 'flying lemurs'. One living genus *Cynocephalus* (= *Galeopithecus*); parachute-like flying membrane stretched between fore and hind limbs. Dental formula $\frac{2.1.2.3.}{3.1.2.3.}$ Palaeocene–Recent.

Order Chiroptera, 'bats'. All are capable of flight. Wing membrane supported by fore limb, all digits taking part in its support.

Suborder Megachiroptera, 'fruit bats'. Crowns of molars are smooth with a longitudinal furrow; bony secondary palate continued behind last molar; second finger with claw. Oligocene–Recent.

Suborder Microchiroptera, 'insectivorous bats', 'vampire bats'. Crowns of molars acutely tubercular, marked by transverse furrows; palate not continued behind last molar; second finger not terminated by a claw. Eocene–Recent. Dental formula never exceeds $\frac{2.1.3.3.}{3.1.3.3.}$.

Order Primates. A large order of rather generalized Eutheria, showing specializations for an arboreal habitat and a bipedal gait. Plantigrade and usually pentadactyl animals with normally opposable pollex and hallux if present; a post-orbital bar is present; clavicles always present. Palaeocene–Recent.

Suborder Prosimii.

Infraorder Lemuriformes (lemurs of Madagascar and their fossil allies, and includes tree shrews).

Infraorder Lorisiformes (rather similar primates outside Madagascar).

Infraorder Tarsiiformes (living tarsier and its Eocene relatives).

Suborder Anthropoidea (monkeys, apes and Man). Incisors never exceed $\frac{2}{2}$, premolars and molars are bunodont; two thoracic mammae. Orbit completely separated from temporal fossa by a bony wall. Lower Oligocene–Recent.

Superfamily Ceboidea (= Platyrrhina). New-world monkeys.

Superfamily Cercopithecoidea (with Hominoidea = Catarrhina). Old World monkeys.

Superfamily Hominoidea (apes and Man).

Order Tillodontia. An extinct order of mammals.

Order Taeniodonta. An extinct order of mammals.

Order Edentata. Accessory articulations between the posterior dorsal and lumbar vertebrae are present; ischium unites with sacrum; dentition is reduced and teeth lack enamel.

Suborder Palaeodonta. Primitive basal stock found in North America. All other edentates are confined to South America or have emigrated into North America since the Pliocene. Palaeocene–Oligocene.

Suborder Xenarthra.

Infraorder Pilosa, 'sloths', and 'anteaters'. Covered with hair, the Pilosa are without a bony carapace; zygomatic arch is always incomplete; never with more than four or five simple cheek teeth; expanded acromium of scapula unites with the coracoid forming an arch. Oligocene–Recent.

Infraorder Cingulata, 'armadillos', and 'glyptodonts'. Body covered with bony scutes to form a carapace. This is flexible in armadillos, but was rigid in glyptodonts; the zygomatic arch is usually complete; always at least seven cheek teeth are present. Palaeocene–Recent.

Order Pholidota, 'pangolins'. Contains the sole genus *Manis*. Edentulous; covered with large overlapping scales and hair; skull is smooth, with no distinction between the temporal fossa and orbit; jugal absent, and zygoma is incomplete; manus is functionally tridactyl with large claws. Confined to Old World. Oligocene–Recent.

Cohort Glires.

Order Lagomorpha, 'rabbits' and 'hares'. Superficially similar to rodents, but with two pairs of upper incisors growing from persistent pulps; no canines; upper cheek teeth bite outside the lower ones, not inside as in rodents; dental formula is $\frac{2.0.3.3.}{1.0.2.3.}$ There is no alisphenoid canal; fibula ankylosed to tibia and articulating with calcaneum; wall of snout often fenestrated.

Order Rodentia. The largest order of mammals (more than half of the species of living mammals are rodents); one pair of upper and one pair of lower incisors grow from persistent pulps, and have enamel only on their outer faces; canines are absent, and a diastema is always present; upper cheek teeth bite inside the lower ones; lower jaw sometimes with an inflected angle; fibula does not articulate with the calcaneum; testes only descend in breeding season. Palaeocene–Recent.

Suborder Sciuromorpha, 'squirrels', 'beavers', 'marmots'. Slender zygomatic arch chiefly formed from jugal, which is not supported by a long maxillary process extending backwards beneath it; infraorbital opening generally small; well-developed clavicles; fibula not fused to tibia. Palaeocene–Recent.

Suborder Myomorpha, 'rats', 'mice', 'voles', 'hamsters', 'jerboas'. Slender zygomatic arch, in which the jugal does not extend far forwards, and which is supported underneath by a zygomatic process of the maxilla; premolars usually absent and first pair of molars much the largest; well-developed clavicles; tibia and fibula fused; the largest suborder of rodents. Oligocene–Recent.

Suborder Hystricomorpha, 'porcupine', 'guinea-pigs', 'capybara', 'coypu, 'Cape jumping-hare'. Stout zygomatic arch not supported by zygomatic process of maxilla; large infraorbital vacuity; only one premolar; fibula not fused to tibia; clavicles may be absent; mainly a South American group. Upper Eocene–Recent.

Cohort Mutica.

Order Cetacea, 'whales', 'dolphins', 'porpoises'. Mammals which are completely specialized for a marine life; a horizontally expanded caudal fin is present and often a fleshy dorsal fin as well; hair is almost entirely absent; fore limbs are converted into flippers (often with hyperphalangy); hind limbs are vestigial; external nares are in top of head and premaxillas have moved back to cover the frontals; supraoccipital has moved forward to meet the frontals; jugal is small. Middle Eocene–Recent.

Suborder Archaeoceti. Extinct. Middle Eocene–Miocene. Upward movement of nostril only just starting, and no telescoping of the skull; cheek teeth with cusps.

Suborder Odontoceti (toothed whales). Teeth are all simple pegs; telescoping of skull carried to the limit; only one nostril, and the skull is often asymmetric; manus always pentadactyl. Upper Eocene–Recent.

Suborder Mysticeti (whale-bone whales). Toothless but plates of baleen; paired nostrils; skull symmetrical; manus tetradactyl except in *Balaena*. Upper Eocene–Recent.

Cohort Ferungulata.

Superorder Ferae.

Order Carnivora. Difficult group to characterize, the only constant feature being the fusion of the scaphoid, lunar, and centrale in the carpus; other characteristic features are the retention of the full number of incisors, and the well-developed canines; post-canine dentition is always reduced; digits of feet usually five, and never reduced to less than four; toes are armed with claws which are frequently retractile. Palaeocene–Recent.

Suborder Creodonta. Primitive extinct carnivores forming one of the basal groups of placental mammals; usually with an unreduced dentition of $\frac{3.1.4.3.}{3.1.4.3.}$ No ossified auditory bulla; scaphoid and lunar not fused; no specially differentiated carnassials. Palaeocene–Pliocene.

Suborder Fissipeda. Modern land carnivores. Last upper premolar and first lower molar form the carnassials; upper molars, and second and third lower molars tubercular, sometimes disappearing; except in the Miacidae the auditory bulla is ossified; scaphoid, centrale and lunar fused; Palaeocene–Recent.

Superfamily Miacoidea. Basal stock of fissipedes; all rather small; extinct. Palaeocene–Eocene.

Superfamily Canoidea (= Arctoidea), 'dogs', 'bears', racoons', 'badgers', 'otters'. Tympanic bulla not divided into two chambers internally. Oligocene–Recent.

Superfamily Feloidea (= Aeluroidea), 'civits', 'mongooses', 'hyaenas', 'cats'. Auditory bulla is dilated and divided internally by a septum into two chambers; in this group the flesh-eating modifications reach their highest development. Oligocene–Recent.

Suborder Pinnipedia (aquatic carnivores). Modified for an aquatic life; both pairs of limbs are present and are modified as paddles; always covered with fur; no lachrymal bone or duct; incisors always less than $\frac{3}{3}$. Projecting canine teeth. Miocene–Recent. There are three families:

Otariidae (eared seals or seal-lions). Hind limbs turned forwards beneath body; skull has large post-orbital process and an alisphenoid canal; inflected angle to lower jaw.

Odobenidae, 'walrus'. Sole living genus is *Odobenus*. No incisors; large upper canines modified as stabbing tusks; cheek teeth modified for crushing. Miocene–Recent.

Phocidae (true seals). No external ears; hind limbs directed backwards; no post-orbital process or alisphenoid canal; angle of lower jaw not inflected. Miocene–Recent.

Superorder Protoungulata.
Order Condylarthra. An extinct order.
Order Litopterna. An extinct order.
Order Notoungulata. An extinct order.
Order Astrapotheria. An extinct order.
Order Tubulidentata, 'aard-vark'. Sole living genus is *Orycteropus*; confined to Africa; lives on termites; jaws somewhat reduced; dentition reduced to an indefinite number of peg-like cheek teeth (four or five); teeth lack enamel but are covered by cement and contain parallel tubular prolongations of central pulp cavity; clavicles are present; humerus has an entepicondylar foramen; pollex is lost; bifid terminal phalanges. Eocene–Recent.

Superorder Paenungulata.
Order Pantodonta. An extinct order.
Order Dinocerata. An extinct order.
Order Pyrotheria. An extinct order.
Order Proboscidea ('elephants'). Large to very large mammals with a very long proboscis which is used as a prehensile organ; second pair of incisors form tusks (only those of upper jaw in living elephants, but in lower jaw as well, or instead, in many extinct forms); skull bones much inflated with air sinuses; limbs straight and not bent at the elbow and knee; animal walks on tips of toes but the weight is carried by a pad under the posterior surface of the digits; testes never descend; pair of thoracic mammae. Upper Eocene–Recent.

Two living genera: *Elephas* (S. Asia) and *Loxodonta* (Africa). Dental formula of both is $\frac{1.0.3.3.}{0.0.3.3.}$, the cheek teeth succeed one another by

Figure 1.50. Some examples of mammals: 1. 'Duck-billed platypus' *Ornithorhynchus*, a monotreme; 2. 'Common hedgehog' *Erinaceus europaeus*, an insectivore; 3. 'Red kangaroo' *Macropus rufus*, a marsupial; 4. 'Bat', a chiropteran; 5. 'Chimpanzee' *Pan satyrus*, an anthropoid primate; 6. 'House mouse' *Mus musculus*, a rodent; 7. 'African elephant' *Loxodonta africanus*, a proboscidean; 8. 'Giant anteater' *Myrmecophaga*, an edentate; 9. 'Brown bear' *Ursus*, a carnivore (from a drawing by C. F. Tunnicliffe, by courtesy of Odhams Press Ltd.); 10. 'Sperm whale' *Physeter macrocephalus*, a cetacean; 11. 'Pangolin *Manis*', a pholidote; 12. 'Reedbuck' *Redunca redunca*, an artiodactyl

longitudinal motion along the jaw, only one being functional at any one time.

Elephas. Single lobe at end of trunk, rather small ears, manus with five nails, pes with four; ridges on cheek teeth are parallel, 4, 8, 12, 12, 16 and 24 on successive teeth.

Loxodonta. A pair of lobes at the end of the trunk; much larger ears; manus with four nails, pes with three ridges on cheek teeth are lozenge shaped, 3, 6, 7, 7, 8 and 10 on successive teeth.

Order Embrithopoda. An extinct order.

Order Hyracoidea. Rodent-like, small, plantigrade mammals, with a tetradactyl manus, and a tridactyl pes; digits have nails except digit of pes which has a claw and a cleft terminal phalanx. Dental formula is $\frac{1.0.4.3.}{2.0.4.3.}$ Upper incisors have persistent pulps, but enamel is only on the anterior face; they differ from rodent incisors in that they are pointed; large post-orbital process and an alisphenoid canal. Lower Oligocene–Recent.

Order Sirenia, 'sea cows'. Aquatic herbivorous mammals with separate anteriorly directed external nostrils, fin-like fore limbs without hyperphalangy, and no hind limbs; with a horizontal caudal fin; two pectoral mammae; bone is very dense. Eocene–Recent. Two surviving genera are

Dugong, 'dugong'.
Trichechus, 'manatee'.

Superorder Mesaxonia.

Order Perissodactyla (odd-toed ungulates). Inguligrade, large herbivores, in which the axis of the limb passes through the middle of digit three (mesaxonic); odd number of toes (never more than three) in hind foot; premolars are molarized; alisphenoid canal present; number of dorso-lumbar vertebrae always exceeds 22 in recent forms; scapula generally without acromion; femur with third trochanter; fibula does not articulate with the calcaneum; simple stomach.

Suborder Hippomorpha. Very little tooth reduction. Includes horses, titanotheres, and chalicotheres. L. Eocene–Recent.

Superfamily Equoidea, 'horses', 'palaeotheres'.
Superfamily Brontotherioidea, 'titanotheres'.
Superfamily Chalicotherioidea, 'chalicotheres'.

Suborder Ceratomorpha, 'tapirs' and 'rhinoceroses'. Orbit not closed by post-orbital bar; dentition (incisors and canines) often reduced; number of toes never reduced below three. L. Eocene–Recent.

Superfamily Tapiroidea, 'tapirs'.
Superfamily Rhinocerotoidea, 'rhinoceroses'.

Superorder Paraxonia.

Order Artiodactla (even-toed ungulates). A very large order, forming the dominant group of the ungulates; foot is paraxonic, with the axis passing between the third and fourth toes; pollex and hallux are usually absent; third and fourth metapodials often fuse to form the 'cannon bone'; no third trochanter on femur; fibula articulates with the calcaneum; incisors often reduced and premolars do not become molariform; always a post-orbital process and often a complete post-orbital bar; in lumbar region, the prezygapophyses wrap round cylindrical postzygapophyses; scapula usually lacks acromion. Eocene–Recent.

Suborder Suiformes (non-ruminants).

Infraorder Palaeodonta. Extinct; basal stock of artio-dactyls showing relationships to insectivores.

Infraorder Suina. Molars bunodont, canines enlarged, single stomach; do not chew cud. Eocene–Recent. Includes the 'pigs' and 'peccaries'.

Infraorder Ancodonta. Includes *Hippopotamus*, the 'hippopotamus'.

Suborder Tylopoda, 'camels' and 'llamas'. Stomach is three chambered; erythrocytes are elliptical; carpals and tarsals never fuse; only two toes on each foot. Eocene–Recent.

Suborder Ruminantia. Complex stomach of three or four chambers; chew cud; total loss of upper incisors; upper canines usually absent; feet always have a 'cannon bone'; horns, of which there are several types, are frequently present.

Infraorder Tragulina, 'chevrotains'. Possess much-enlarged upper canines; feet are less highly evolved in that they retain the lateral toes of both feet, though these are slender; stomach has three compartments; usually no horns.

Infraorder Pecora, 'deer', 'giraffes', 'prongbucks', 'ante-lopes', 'oxen', 'sheep' and 'goats'.

Superfamily Cervoidea, 'deer'. Characterized by their deciduous horns (antlers) confined with one exception—the reindeer—to the males; antlers are absent in only *Moschus* and *Hydropotes*; lateral toes always present but never complete.

Superfamily Giraffoidea, 'giraffes', 'okapi'. Non-deciduous horns which are always covered with hair, and are unbranched in living members; upper canines and lateral digits are absent.

Superfamily Bovoidea, 'prongbucks', 'antelopes', 'oxen', 'sheep' and 'goats'. No upper canines or incisors; only one orifice to lachrymal duct; lateral toes are completely absent except for small horny hoofs in which there may be a nodule of bone; horns are universally present in both sexes and, with the partial exception of the prongbuck, are never shed; the horns are never branched, but are of many shapes.

CULTURE METHODS FOR UROCHORDATES

Only certain members of the Ascidiacea are easily maintained in well-aerated sea-water kept at a temperature about 10°C. *Ciona intestinalis* will often survive for long periods of time if the aquarium conditions are suitable; *Ciona* appears to have no special breeding season. Ascidiacea must be supplied with microscopic food, and it may be necessary to maintain a culture of diatoms such as *Nitzschia*. The pH should be maintained at 7·5–8·0, particularly if the development of larvae is being studied. For purposes of rearing and developmental studies in general, the ascidians are divided into two groups according to whether they are viviparous or oviparous. As a general guide, except in a few instances, oviparous ascidians are comparatively large and produce a great many small eggs, viviparous ascidians being small and producing a small number of comparatively large eggs. Therefore, for rearing, one must start with the unsegmented eggs in the case of oviparous species, and with the active 'tadpole' larvae in the case of viviparous species.

Examples of oviparous species are: *Ciona intestinalis*; the species of *Ascidia*, and *Styela*. Examples of viviparous species are: species of *Botryllus*; *Clavelina*, and *Distaplia*.

Methods for artificial fertilization are given in '*Culture Methods for Invertebrate Animals*', Needham, Dover Publications.

KILLING AND PRESERVATION FOR UROCHORDATA
Ascidiacea

Narcotize by the addition of menthol crystals to sea-water containing the specimens after allowing the animals to extend. Alternatively, chloral hydrate may be added. Some ascidians may not require narcotization if hot preservative is poured directly on to them. The best fixatives are sea-water Bouin's fluid, and 5 per cent sea-water formaldehyde. Simple ascidians should also be injected with some of the fixative.

Thaliacea and Larvacea

It is not usually necessary to narcotize these animals before fixation is carried out. Fix as for ascidians.

CULTURAL METHOD FOR CEPHALOCHORDATES

Amphioxus will survive for several weeks or months if kept in a properly maintained marine aquarium. The bottom of the aquarium should be covered with a deep layer of shell gravel in which the animals can bury themselves. The temperature should be maintained around 10°C, and the sea-water should be aerated vigorously.

Amphioxus feeds by straining the water taken in through the mouth. The food which is in suspension in the water consists mainly of vegetable matter, which is usually in the form of diatoms, desmids, and vegetable debris.

In temperate seas, breeding takes place in early summer. The timing of the breeding season is so precise that the ova and spermatazoa of any particular group of animals are shed into the sea within a period of 24 h, and usually in the evening. When the eggs are fertilized, they develop into free-living larvae. The larvae develop for about three months before becoming sand dwelling like the adults.

KILLING AND PRESERVATION OF CEPHALOCHORDATES

It is unnecessary to narcotize cephalochordates before they are killed, and the killing is easily carried out by taking the animals from

143

sea-water and plunging them into a suitable fixative. To ensure the animals die in a straight position, they may be placed between glass microscope slides which are supported in a staining dish with grooved sides, though this procedure is not usually necessary. For general work, such as dissection, Bouin's fluid is recommended, but when histological work is to be carried out on the material Zenker's fixative is particularly recommended. Store in 70 per cent alcohol.

MACERATION OF AMPHIOXUS

Dissection is occasionally made difficult when the connective tissue which binds the myotomes is particularly tough. If this is the case, the preserved animals should be soaked in 20 per cent nitric acid for 24–48 h, then transferred to 70 per cent alcohol, after being thoroughly washed in several changes of 70 per cent alcohol.

For culture methods for fish, amphibians, and reptiles see Chapter 2. The *U.F.A.W. Handbook* is recommended for culture methods for several mammals.

KILLING AND PRESERVATION METHODS FOR AGNATHA

Lampreys and hagfish should be narcotized and killed in 5 per cent urethane (ethyl carbamate) solution in tap-water. Avoid touching urethane solution as it is believed to be highly carcinogenic. When respiration has apparently ceased and the animals are thought to be dead, transfer them to a suitable fixative. For general dissection work 5 per cent formalin is suitable, but for histological work Bouin's fluid or Zenker's fixative are recommended.

Ammocoete larvae ('prides') may be narcotized before killing. Killing is done by transferring them to Smith's formol–dichromate solution. Smith's fixative is:

Solution A
1 per cent aqueous solution of potassium dichromate
Solution B

40 per cent formaldehyde solution	200 ml.
Glacial acetic acid	50 ml.
Distilled water	1 l.

Mix equal quantities of Solutions A and B just before use.

N.B. Because of the carcinogenic properties of urethane, it is best avoided. A better substitute is MS-222 sandoz. MS-222 sandoz, also known as MS-222, TS-222, TS-222 sandoz, tricaine-sandoz, tricaine methanesulphonate, metacaine, and metacaine methane-sulphonate. MS-222 sandoz is a fine white crystalline powder and is the methanesulphonate of meta-aminobenzoic acid ethylester. Its molecular weight is 261·3, and it is soluble to 11 per cent in water to form a clear, colourless, acid solution. It is usually applied in a bath, i.e., immersion of the fish or small animals into a solution of MS-222 sandoz. For larger fish it may be sprayed on to the gills, or injected. It will dissolve readily in sea-water, spring water, or ordinary tap-water. It can be used in concentrations varying from 1:1,000 up to 1:20,000 or more, but is most effective in 1:2,000– 1:3,000 solutions. All fish are affected by MS-222, and depending on the size of the fish and the concentration of the solution the effect is manifest within 15 sec. Dr. Frank J. Bové reports in his descriptive leaflet on MS-222 sandoz that 'even 400 lb. sharks are anaesthetized within 1 min with a 1:1,000 sea-water solution. It has no effect on ciliary action, but its effect on muscular activity is rapid. MS-222 sandoz has no effect on the motility or fertilizing power of frog spermatozoa.' The recovery time from MS-222 sandoz is usually brief and complete. Prolonged exposure to weak solutions is not harmful, so that it is of great value in transporting live fish. Solutions stored at room temperature gradually lose potency, so fresh solutions should be prepared when required.

KILLING AND PRESERVATION METHODS FOR OTHER FISH

When possible, fish should be narcotized before they are killed, but the general practice with fish taken from the sea is to allow them to suffocate by keeping them out of water. MS-222 sandoz used at a suitable concentration is recommended when narcotization is to be carried out in the laboratory. For a guide as to the concentrations to be tried, Strzyzowski found that solutions of 1:10,000 anaesthetized all fish within 5–10 min. A 1:1,000 solution required only 60–90 sec but prolonging anaesthesia to 6 h at this concentration was dangerous, and prolonging to 12–24 h resulted in a 100 per cent mortality.

An alternative narcotic is 10 per cent urethane solution, but as has already been emphasized, this substance is carcinogenic and great care should be taken to avoid contact with the skin.

When narcotized, or when the fish is ready to be preserved, slit the belly of the fish a little to one side of the middle line. Place a stiff-paper label under the gill cover or, in the case of an elasmo-branch, into the mouth. Tie another plastic or parchment label to the tail end. Place in 2 per cent formalin and leave to fix for 2–12 h. Rinse the formalin away in running water, and transfer the fish to 50 per cent alcohol. In tropical climates it may be necessary to commence with a stronger alcoholic solution. After a day or two, transfer to 60 or 65 per cent alcohol, and then after a similar interval of time transfer to 70 per cent alcohol. After about a week test this alcohol and fortify it or change it if necessary. Wrap each specimen and pack it into its storage tank. This method (*B. M. Handbook*) has been found successful in climates when the temperature is around 29°C. In still hotter climates some fish will require stronger formalin injected into throat and belly as soon as they are caught, and a closer watch must be kept on them through the alcohol baths.

Because alcohol is expensive, post-fixation in 1 per cent phenoxetol, after initial fixation in 5 per cent formalin, is now becoming more popular. For example, the best way of preserving large numbers of 'dogfish' such as *Scyliorhinus* and *Squalus* is possibly the following method: unless the tail is required, cut it off about 1 in. behind the cloaca. Inject 5 per cent formalin into the severed ends of the caudal vein and caudal artery until one would expect it to have travelled around the entire circulatory system. Cut a small square hole in the roof of the skull, so that the brain is exposed. Immerse the fish in 5 per cent formalin for 24–48 h, then transfer to 1 per cent phenoxetol solution. Specimens will preserve well for years in this solution, and will be much more pleasant to dissect. If the circulatory system cannot be injected the fish should be fixed for a longer period of time, with their abdomens slit open, before being placed in phenoxetol.

Mention should be made of the fact that many deep-sea fish (bathypelagic) are very fragile, and when being preserved and stored they should be individually wrapped in linen, and preserved in separate containers. For the preservation of larval fish, fish eggs, and fragile oceanic fish, preservation in 4 per cent formalin gives better results than alcohol.

KILLING AND PRESERVATION METHODS FOR AMPHIBIA

Although amphibia may be killed in the vapour of chloroform or benzene, this method of killing usually results in the animals dying in a rigored condition, which is unsatisfactory when the animals are required for dissection. They may be killed in a relaxed condition by swimming them in a 10 per cent aqueous solution of urethane, keeping the animals submerged until they are dead. However, the carcinogenic properties of urethane are a disadvantage, and a safer method (though, of course, more expensive) is to kill the animals by swimming them in a solution of MS-222 sandoz.

Immersion of frogs (*Rana temporaria*) in 1:1,000 solutions of MS-222 sandoz produces anaesthesia within 5–6 min, and lasts for about 45 min; immersion for 20 min will given an anaesthesia which will last about $2\frac{1}{2}$ h; 4 h immersion gives an anaesthesia lasting about 10 h; immersion for longer periods sometimes causes death. MS-222 has to be used in high concentrations (about 6 per cent) before it is fatal to half the animals. If amphibia are properly anaesthetized in dilute solutions of MS-222 (say 1:3,000) they can then be killed humanely by transferring them to a dish of chloroform–water, which should be kept agitated. This method makes it unnecessary to employ strong solutions of MS-222.

For embryological work, when operations are to be carried out on amphibian larvae, dilutions of MS-222 in the order of 1:3,000 should be tried.

For general dissection work, freshly killed animals are preferable to preserved specimens, but this does not mean that amphibians should not be preserved and used for dissection. When dead, the peritoneal cavity should be injected with a small quantity of 5 per cent formalin. Then transfer to 3 per cent formalin in which the specimens may be stored; alternatively they may be transferred to 60 per cent alcohol for storage, but if alcohol is used a careful check must be kept to see that the alcoholic content does not drop below 60 per cent.

KILLING AND PRESERVATION METHODS FOR REPTILES
Chelonians

Chelonians are difficult animals to kill, and every effort should be made to ensure that the killing procedure is carried out in a humane way. The animal should be injected with a quantity of urethane solution (about 10 ml. of a fresh 10 per cent solution in normal saline, for a specimen of *Testudo graeca* of average size), making the injection into the peritoneal cavity via the soft tissue in the armpit. A long, strong hypodermic needle is necessary as the skin is often remarkably tough. Wait until the animal is completely anaesthetized (about 30 min) then inject 5 ml. of chloroform in a similar fashion. The animal can generally be regarded as being dead 5 min after this second injection. The procedure from this point depends on the purpose for which the animal is to be used. If it is to be used for dissection purposes, the dead animal should be held in a vice, and using a hack-saw the narrow isthmus of bone between the carapace and plastron cut through on each side of the body. The sawing should be carried out very carefully to ensure that the blood vessels which lie just below the bone are not severed. The ends of this isthmus of bone are very thick and they should not be sawn completely through, but split apart carefully using a small cold-chisel. The plastron should be left in place for the dissector to remove.

If the whole specimen is to be preserved for display purposes, the peritoneum should be injected with a quantity of 5 per cent formalin, then the entire animal preserved in 5 per cent formalin. Seventy per cent alcohol, or 1 per cent phenoxetol, solutions are alternative storage media, the latter only being used after a complete preliminary fixation in formalin.

Crocodilia

It is unlikely that the laboratory technician will be called upon to deal with large living specimens of crocodiles, but sometimes small specimens have to be killed and preserved. With one person holding the animal, a second person should inject sufficient nembutal intra-peritoneally or into the soft tissue at the back of the mouth. A strong hypodermic syringe should always be used. If a lethal dose can be given so much the better, but if not the crocodile should be finally killed in chloroform vapour after anaesthetization is complete. To preserve small specimens they should be injected intraperitoneally with a quantity of 5 per cent formalin, then transferred to 5 per cent formalin for at least a week, finally storing them in a fresh change of 5 per cent formalin, or in 70 per cent alcohol, or 1 per cent phenoxetol solution. With large specimens it is necessary to make a long incision in the abdomen, making the cut to one side and close to the pelvic girdle, so that the abdominal ribs are not damaged. Inject the gut with some 5 per cent formalin, then immerse the animal in a large bath of 5 per cent formalin for a few weeks. The specimen may be stored in formalin or in 1 per cent phenoxetol solution.

Lacertilia

Lizards should be narcotized and killed humanely by injecting them intraperitoneally with a lethal dose of nembutal; alternatively, chloroform vapour can be used. If the lizards are to be dissected, this should be carried out on freshly killed specimens. To preserve lizards, an incision should be made in the abdomen, and if the animal is of moderate size the gut should be injected with 5 per cent formalin. The entire animal should then be immersed in 5 per cent formalin for several days or weeks according to size. Store in fresh 5 per cent formalin or in 1 per cent phenoxetol solution.

Ophidia

Snakes do not always succumb to injections of nembutal, and killing in chloroform appears to be the most satisfactory way at present. Unfortunately, although snakes soon become anaesthetized in chloroform vapour, they take a long time to die, so care should be taken to leave them in the killing chamber for a sufficient time (about

1 h for *Natrix natrix*). Although the snakes will appear to have died in a rigored state, they are easily straightened out by pulling them through one's hand. Dissection is most easily carried out on freshly killed snakes. To preserve small snakes, the peritoneal cavity should be filled by injection with 5 per cent formalin then immersed in 5 per cent formalin for a few days. Large snakes should have an incision made in the body wall and care taken to ensure that the gut is injected with 5 per cent formalin and that the formalin solution, in which the snake is then immersed, fills the body cavity. Store in fresh 5 per cent formalin, 70 per cent alcohol or 1 per cent phenoxetol.

KILLING AND PRESERVATION METHODS FOR BIRDS
All birds readily succumb to coal-gas or chloroform vapour. Care should be taken to ensure that the birds are left in the killing chamber until they are dead. Dissection is best carried out on freshly killed birds after the feathers on the ventral side of the body have been completely plucked. If preservation is to be carried out, the entire skin should be carefully removed, and if the head and tarsi are not required on the preserved specimen, these should be removed with the skin and a cabinet-skin preparation made. The skinned carcase should have an incision made into the abdomen and the gut injected with 5 per cent formalin. It is then immersed in 5 per cent formalin in which it may be stored, or after a few days transferred to 70 per cent alcohol or 1 per cent phenoxetol solution.

KILLING AND PRESERVATION METHODS FOR SMALL LABORATORY MAMMALS
If the animals are required for dissection, killing with coal-gas is a good method because the formation of carboxyhaemoglobin makes the entire blood vascular system very conspicuous. A properly designed lethal chamber should be used, and for the first few minutes air should be allowed to enter the chamber along with the coal-gas (this results in the animals dying in a more peaceful way). If mice or hamsters are being killed, several can be dealt with at any one time, but larger animals such as rabbits should be killed individually. Alternative killing methods are chloroform vapour or injection of a suitable narcotic. A method for killing rabbits, which is recommended by U.F.A.W. and which the author has found to be excellent, is to inject a saturated aqueous solution of magnesium sulphate intravenously—about 5 ml. is usually sufficient, the rabbit becoming unconscious after about 2 ml. has been injected. The injection should be made into the vein, of either ear, which runs down the outside edge, making the injection towards the head. Only a properly trained technician should carry out injections.

Freshly killed mammals are preferable for dissection purposes. When preserving mammals it may be advantageous to remove the skin before proceeding. Although preservation in formalin is still common practice for mammals, embalming fluid is preferable (see page 286). The gut should be injected with the chosen preservative, and a large incision made in the abdominal wall; some preservative should be injected through the diaphragm into the thoracic cavity and some more injected subcutaneously in the neck region. A small hole should be trephined in the roof of the skull and the brain exposed. The mammal is then completely submerged in 5 per cent formalin or better still in embalming fluid. Although dry embalming works satisfactorily with human cadavers, it is not usually successful with other mammalian material.

REFERENCES

Introduction
Simpson, G. G. (1945). 'The principles of classification and a classification of mammals.' *Bull. Amer. Mus. nat. Hist.*, **85**

Phylum Protozoa
Corliss, J. O. (1953). 'Silver impregnation of ciliated protozoa by the Chatton–Lwoff technique.' *Stain Tech.*, **28**, 97

Couch, J. N. (1941). 'The structure and action of the cilia in some aquatic physomycetes.' *Amer. J. Bot.*, **28**, 704

Delamater, E. D. (1948). 'Basic fuchsin as a nuclear stain.' *Stain Tech.*, **23**, 161

Göhre, E. (1943). 'Untersuchungen über der plasmatischen Fienbau der Gregarinen mit besonderer Berücksichtigung der Sexualitätsverhaltnisse.' *Arch. Protistenk.*, **96**, 295

Huebschmann, C. (1952). 'A method of varying the average number of nuclei in the conidia of *Neurospora crassa*.' *Mycologia*, **44**, 599

Johnson, J. C. (1935). *Microscopic Objects: How To Mount Them.* London; English Univ. Press

Mackinnon, D. L. and Hawes, R. S. J. (1961). *An Introduction to the Study of Protozoa.* Oxford; Claredon Press

Wichterman, R. (1953). *The Biology of Paramecium.* New York; McGraw-Hill

Phylum Mesozoa
Whitman, C. O. (1882). 'Embryology, life-history, and classification of the dicyemids.' *Mitt. Zool. Stat. Neapel.* 4

Phylum Cnidaria
Barrett, J. and Yonge, C. M. (1958). *Pocket Guide to the Seashore.* London; Collins

REFERENCES

Bullough, W. S. (1950). *Practical Invertebrate Anatomy.* London; Macmillan

Wagstaffe, R. and Fidler, J. H. (1957). *The Preservation of Natural History Specimens*, Vol. 1. London; Witherby

Phylum Ctenophora

Wagstaffe, R. and Fidler, J. H. (1957). *The Preservation of Natural History Specimens*, Vol. 1. London; Witherby

Phylum Platyhelminthes

Barrett, J. and Yonge, C. M. (1958). *Pocket Guide to the Seashore.* London; Collins

Bullough, W. S. (1950). *Practical Invertebrate Anatomy.* London; Macmillan

Hamburger, V. (1942). *A Manual of Experimental Embryology.* Chicago; Univ. Chicago Press

Ristroph, C. A. (1934). *Turtox News.* Chicago

Phylum Aschelminthes

Brandwein, P. (1959). *Culture Methods for Invertebrate Animals.* New York; Dover Publications

Bullough, W. S. (1950). *Practical Invertebrate Anatomy.* London; Macmillan

Courtney, W. D., Polley, D. and Miller, V. L. (1955). 'TAF, an improved fixative in nematode technique.' *Plant Dis. Reptr*, **39**, 570–71

Franklin, M. T. and Goodey, J. B. (1949). 'A cotton blue lactophenol technique for mounting plant-parasitic nematodes.' *J. Helm.*, **23**, 175–78

Goodey, J. B. (1963). 'Laboratory methods for work with plant and soil nematodes.' *Min. of Agric., Fish. & Food. Technical Bull. No.* 2. London; H.M.S.O.

Hanley, J. (1949). 'The narcotization and mounting of Rotifera.' *The Microscope*, **VII**, No. 6, 154–59

Lang, K. (1948). 'Contribution to the ecology of Priapulus.' *Ark. Zool.*, **41A**, art. No. 5

Langeloh, H. (1936). 'Sinnesphysiologische Untersuchungen an Priapuliden.' *Biol. Centralbl*, **56**

Packard, C. E. (1959). *Culture Methods for Invertebrate Animals.* New York; Dover Publications

Seinhorst, J. W. (1959). 'A rapid method for the transfer of nematodes from fixative to anhydrous glycerin.' *Nematologica* **4**, 67–69

— (1962). 'On the killing, fixation, and transferring to glycerin of nematodes.' *Nematologica* **8**, 29–32

Wagstaffe, R. and Fidler, J. H. (1957). *The Preservation of Natural History Specimens*, Vol. 1. London; Witherby

Phylum Acanthocephala

Gettier, D. (1942). 'Saline requirements of *Neoechinorhynchus emydis.*' *Proc. Helm. Soc. Wash.*, **9**

Van Cleave, H. J. and Ross, E. (1944). 'Physiological responses of *Neoechinorhynchus emydis* to various solutions.' *J. Parasit.*, **30**

Phylum Phoronida

MacGinitie, G. E. (1959). *Culture Methods for Invertebrate Animals.* New York; Dover Publications

Phylum Ectoprocta

Brandwein, P. (1938). 'Culture of Pectinatella.' *Amer. Nat.*, **72**
Bullough, W. S. (1950). *Practical Invertebrate Anatomy.* London; Macmillan
Grave, B. H. (1959). *Culture Methods for Invertebrate Animals.* New York; Dover Publications
Wagstaffe, R. and Fidler, J. H. (1957). *The Preservation of Natural History Specimens*, Vol. 1. London; Witherby

Phylum Brachiopoda

Cloud, P. (1948). 'Notes on recent brachiopods.' *Amer. J. Sci.*, **246**
Elliott, G. P. (1955). In *The Preservation of Natural History Specimens*, Vol. 1 by Wagstaffe, R. and Fidler, J. H. London; Witherby
Joubin, L. (1886). 'Anatomie des brachiopodes inarticulés.' *Arch. Zool. Exp. Gén.*, ser. 2, **4**
Lacaze-Duthiers, H. de (1861). 'Historie de la thécidie.' *Ann. Sci. Nat. Zool.*, ser. 4, **15**
Morse, E. (1902). 'Observations on living Brachiopoda.' *Mem. Boston. Soc. Nat. Hist.* **5**

Phylum Mollusca

Barrett, J. and Yonge, C. M. (1958). *Pocket Guide to the Seashore.* London; Collins
Crofts, D. R. (1929). *L.M.B.C. Memoirs*, **XXIX**
Standen, O. D. (1951). 'Some observations upon the maintenance of *Australorbis glabratus* in the laboratory.' *Ann. Trop. Med. Parasit.*, **45**, No. 1
Tompsett, D. H. (1939). *L.M.B.C. Memoirs*, **XXXII**

Phylum Sipunculida

Hérubel, M. (1907). 'Recherches sur les sipunculides.' *Mém. Soc. zool. Fr.*, **20**

Phylum Annelida

Baermann, G. (1917). 'Eine einfache Methode zur Auffindung von Ankylostomum (Nematoden)—Larven in Erdproben.' *Meded. geneesk. Lab. Welteur.*, 41–47
Barrett, J. and Yonge, C. M. (1958). *Pocket Guide to the Seashore.* London; Collins
Nielsen, C. Overgaard (1952–3). 'Studies on Enchytraeidae. 1. A technique for extracting Enchytraeidae from soil samples.' *Oikos*, **4**, 187–96
O'Connor, F. B. (1955). 'Extraction of enchytraeid worms from a coniferous forest soil.' *Nature, Lond.*, **175**, 815–16

REFERENCES

O'Connor, F.B. (1962). 'The extraction of Enchytraeidae from soil.' In *Progress in Soil Zoology*, pp. 279–85. London; Butterworths

Phylum Arthropoda

Barrett, J. and Yonge, C. M. (1958). *Pocket Guide to the Seashore.* London; Collins

Bayliss, H. A. and Monro, C. C. A. (1941). 'Instructions for collectors.' *Brit. Mus. (Nat. Hist.)*, No. 9A

Bullough, W. S. (1950). *Practical Invertebrate Anatomy.* London; Macmillan

Dinnes, A. G. (1951). 'Rearing cage.' *Bull. Ass. sci. Tech.*, **2**, 731

Grassé, P. P. (1951). *Traite de Zoologie*, Tome X. Paris; Masson

Hunter-Jones, P. (1956). *Instructions for Rearing and Breeding Locusts in the Laboratory.* London; Anti-Locust Research

Imms, A. D. (1957). *A General Textbook of Entomology.* London; Methuen

McFerran, F. (1957). *U.F.A.W. Handbook on the Care and Management of Laboratory Animals*, 2nd Ed. 870–72

Rothschild, Lord (1961). *A Classification of Living Animals.* London; Longmans Green

Wagstaffe, R. and Fidler, J. H. (1957). *The Preservation of Natural History Specimens*, Vol. 1. London; Witherby

Phylum Echinodermata

Barrett, J. and Yonge, C. M. (1958). *Pocket Guide to the Seashore.* London; Collins

Wagstaffe, R. and Fidler, J. H. (1957). *The Preservation of Natural History Specimens*, Vol. 1. London; Witherby

Phylum Chaetognatha

Kulmatycki, W. (1918). 'Regenerationsfähigkeit der Spadella.' *Zool. Ang.*, **49**

Phylum Pogonophora

Caullery, M. (1944). *Siboglinum. Siboga Exped. Monogr.* 25 bis, livr. 138

Phylum Chordata

Bové, F. J. *MS-222 Sandoz, The Anaesthetic of Choice for Fish and Other Cold-blooded Organisms.* Basle, Switzerland; Sandoz, Ltd

Peterson, R., Mountford, G. and Hollom, P. A. D. (1954). *A Field Guide to the Birds of Britain and Europe.* London; Collins

Simpson, G. G. (1945). 'The principles of classification and a classification of mammals.' *Bull. Amer. Mus. nat. Hist.*, **85**

AQUARIUM AND VIVARIUM MANAGEMENT

AQUARIUM MANAGEMENT

Ideally the aquarium should be entirely separated from the rest of the department, and subdivided into tropical freshwater, cold freshwater, and marine sections. Each of these sections should, preferably, be in separate rooms which should be kept at a known controlled temperature, a regular daily check being made with a maximum–minimum thermometer which should be hung in the centre of each room. The rooms should be free from direct sunlight.

The actual aquaria should be so placed that they are all within easy access; if there is a shortage of space they may be arranged in tiers, but one must bear in mind that the upper tanks will always be more difficult to attend to. They should all be fitted with loose-fitting glass covers which permit a flow of air over the surface of the water.

TYPES OF AQUARIA

(a) All-glass Aquaria

These are best suited for cultures of small freshwater organisms. They should always be of a rectangular shape which gives the maximum surface area of water which will be in contact with the surrounding air. The well-known glass 'goldfish bowl' is unsuitable and should on no account be used. One disadvantage of all glass aquaria is that once cracked they cannot be repaired and are therefore useless.

(b) Angle-iron and Glass Aquaria

These are easily the most suitable type of aquaria for freshwater creatures. They are obtainable in a variety of sizes and have the advantage over all-glass aquaria in that they may be reglazed should they become cracked. The best size for most purposes is 24 in. long, 12 in. wide and 15 in. deep. When buying a new aquarium look for the following points:

(*i*) The frame corners should be square and the welded joints finished off smoothly.

(*ii*) The aquarium should not rock when placed on a flat surface.

(*iii*) The glass used should be perfect and free from any optical defects, and should be of adequate thickness for the tank's dimensions (see *Table 2.1*).

(*iv*) If possible the base should be made of slate, but if glass is used it should be at least $\frac{1}{4}$ in. plate and preferably wire reinforced.

(*v*) Glazing cement should be soft to the touch where visible outside the aquarium. Cements that dry out are liable to crack and this will cause leaks.

(*vi*) A new aquarium will sometimes leak; if this is severe the aquarium should be returned to the manufacturer. If, however, the leak is very slight it may sometimes be remedied by filling the aquarium with water containing a quantity of garden soil. If left for a few days, such small leaks will usually seal themselves. If this fails, the putty visible from outside, along the length which is leaking, should be scraped out and replaced with a length of 'Bostik' sealing strip. The joint should be perfectly dry before applying the sealing strip.

Table 2.1. The Thickness of Glass Required for Aquaria of Different Dimensions (after Evans, 1952)

Depth (in.)	*Sizes of Glass for Glazing Aquaria*								
	10	12	18	24	30	36	48	60	72
10	15 oz.	21 oz.	26 oz.						
12	15 oz.	26 oz.	32 oz.	32 oz.	32 oz.				
15	—	26 oz.	42 oz.	42 oz.	$\frac{1}{4}$	$\frac{1}{4}$	$\frac{1}{4}$	$\frac{3}{8}$	
18	—	32 oz.	$\frac{1}{4}$	$\frac{1}{4}$	$\frac{1}{4}$	$\frac{3}{8}$	$\frac{3}{8}$	$\frac{3}{8}$	$\frac{1}{2}$
24	—	—	$\frac{1}{4}$	$\frac{1}{4}$	$\frac{3}{8}$	$\frac{3}{8}$	$\frac{3}{8}$	$\frac{3}{8}$	
30	—	—	—	$\frac{3}{8}$	$\frac{3}{8}$	$\frac{3}{8}$	$\frac{1}{2}$	$\frac{1}{2}$	$\frac{1}{2}$t
36	—	—	—	$\frac{3}{8}$	$\frac{3}{8}$	$\frac{1}{2}$	$\frac{1}{2}$	$\frac{1}{2}$t	$\frac{1}{2}$t

Fractions indicate plate glass; $\frac{1}{2}$t $= \frac{1}{2}$ in. *toughened plate*

Types of glass: Drawn clear sheet: 15 oz.–32 oz. ($\frac{3}{32}$ in.–$\frac{5}{32}$ in. thick)
Heavy drawn: 42 oz.–3$\frac{1}{2}$ lb. (plate substitute, $\frac{3}{16}$ in.–$\frac{1}{4}$ in. thick)
Polished plate: $\frac{1}{8}$ in.–$\frac{3}{4}$ in.
Toughened plate: $\frac{1}{4}$ in.–$\frac{3}{4}$ in. (five times stronger than plate)
Wired polished or figured plate: $\frac{1}{4}$ in.–$\frac{3}{4}$ in. (for aquarium base)

Aquaria of this type must be kept well painted or they will rust. The preparation of the aquarium, prior to painting, is important. It should be freed from rust by rubbing with a hard wire brush, followed by a rub with emery cloth. Two coats of aluminium paint should then be applied to the surfaces of the angle iron, and this should be followed by a flat undercoat. When this undercoat has dried thoroughly it should be followed by at least two coats of good quality enamel of the required colour. Pay particular attention to the top bars of the aquarium. When glazing, fit the base into position first, then the front and back, followed by the two sides.

The aquarium putty or cement must adhere well to the glass and the aquarium frame, and must not set hard. It must also be non-toxic to the aquarium's inhabitants. A tank of the dimensions recommended will take about 2½ lb. of putty. There are several ready-mixed proprietary putties on the market which will meet these requirements.

(c) Plastic Aquaria

These are easily made from sheet perspex, and are suitable for aquaria up to 18 in. in length. For details of construction see page 314. The main disadvantage of perspex aquaria is that they are easily scratched when cleaning.

(d) Porcelain Sinks

These make excellent marine aquaria. They have a large surface area, and keep the sea-water cool. A system of marine aquaria should consist of a number of porcelain sinks of varying dimensions, enabling a wide variety of marine animals to be kept. They are strong and are easily cleaned, their only disadvantage is that they are very heavy.

COVERS FOR AQUARIA

Ideally these should be made of glass. Unless the aquarium is supplied with adequate mechanical aeration the cover should be supported above it, leaving an air gap about ½ in. around the edge. A simple way of doing this with angle-iron aquaria is to attach a ½ in. thick cork to the top of each corner of the frame with 'Bostik' adhesive.

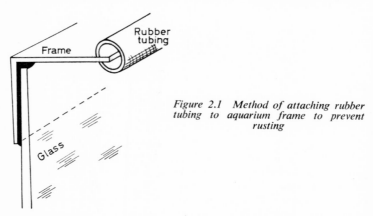

Figure 2.1 Method of attaching rubber tubing to aquarium frame to prevent rusting

Provided that the aquarium is supplied with mechanical aeration, pieces of split rubber tubing may be attached to the inside edge of the top lengths of angle iron. If these fit close together at the corners of the tank, they prevent condensed water from forming on the metal frame, which in turn prevents the formation of rust (see *Figure 2.1*).

Lighting

Light is essential for the healthy growth of water plants. The light source must be above the aquarium, as strong side-lighting is detrimental to fish. Daylight is by far the best lighting for aquaria, but its intensity cannot be controlled, and in Great Britain it is usually insufficient for aquarium lighting. Ordinary electric lamps give a satisfactory light and may be mounted in special shades which also act as aquarium covers. Fluorescent light units are available for aquarium use, and if these are employed the 'warm tint' fluorescent tubes should be used. Remember that all artificial light sources give heat, which may be beneficial in the case of tropical aquaria but must not be allowed to affect the temperature of cold-water aquaria. A 24 in. aquarium receiving no daylight will require two 40 W lamps burning for 8 h each day for plants to receive sufficient light.

HEATING FOR TROPICAL AQUARIA

The best average temperature for most tropical fish is 75° F. Gentle fluctuations of 10° F. above and below will be tolerated by most fish, provided that they take place very slowly. Electrical heating is the most efficient method. Immersion heaters are relatively inexpensive items, and these are available in a wide range of wattages for various sizes of aquaria. These heaters should not be placed vertically in the aquarium but should be inclined or buried in the sand. It is preferable to use two heaters for each tank, in case one of them burns out. The use of two heaters also ensures that the heat is more evenly distributed. Since $2\frac{1}{2}$ W will raise 1 gal. of water 10° F, an approximate guide to the numbers of watts required at a selected temperature is given by the following equation (after Evans, 1952):

$$\text{Wattage required} = \frac{\text{Required tank temperature} - \text{Room temperature}}{10} \times \text{Tank capacity (gal.)} \times 2\cdot5$$

A thermostat should always be incorporated in the heating system to prevent the water from overheating.

Another method of heating an aquarium is to mount the aquarium on an open wooden box of the same length and width as the aquarium, and about 5–6 in. high. The box should be fitted with two or more 60 W lamps. Again, an efficient thermostat should be incorporated in the light-heating circuit to prevent overheating. The base of the box should be made from asbestos, and the front piece of wood should have an inspection panel enabling the lamps to be examined and easily changed should they burn out.

All electrical wiring near the aquaria should be plastic covered, and should be of good quality. All wire junctions, switches, etc., should be placed where water cannot reach them. The safest type of thermostat is the type which is only partly immersed in the water. It is advisable to fit a neon pilot lamp into the circuit, so that the action of the thermostat may be easily checked. One efficient thermostat will operate several heaters incorporated in a number of aquaria of the same capacity, provided that they are to be maintained at the same temperature. If the tanks vary in size, put the thermostat into

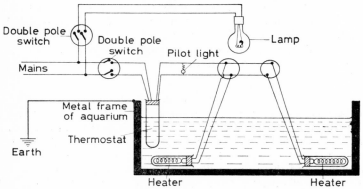

Figure 2.2   Circuit diagram for heating and lighting a tropical aquarium

the smallest tank and select heaters of the correct wattage for the other aquaria.

For perfect safety the metal frame of the aquarium should be properly earthed. The earth wire should be soldered on to a part of the frame where the paint has been completely removed.

Figure 2.2 shows a circuit diagram for heating and lighting a tropical aquarium.

AERATING THE AQUARIUM

Freshwater aquaria containing a reasonable number of aquatic plants do not need to be supplied with extra aeration. It must be remembered that although aquatic plants give off oxygen in daylight during the process of photosynthesis they also absorb sufficient oxygen from the water for them to respire, and they continue to respire in darkness. Tropical aquaria seem to benefit from extra aeration, and in the case of marine aquaria aeration is a necessity.

Aeration may be obtained in several ways, but the most efficient method is that of a reliable mechanical pump. The electrically operated 'Hy-Flo' pumps are particularly recommended. There are several models available, the smallest being capable of operating one inside filter and two diffusers, while the largest model will operate a large number of diffusers and filters. 'Hy-Flo' pumps are sold by Medcalf Bros., Hy-Flo Products, Florence Works, Florence Street, Islington, London, N.1.

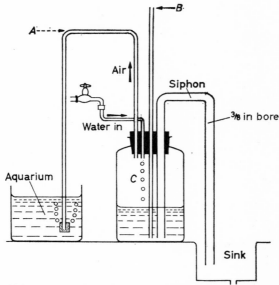

Figure 2.3. An efficient water-operated aerator, which only requires a very slow stream of water

Aerators of the electric vibrator type are less expensive, but are noisier and far less efficient. Water-operated aerators are easily constructed in the laboratory and are very efficient, but some of them use a great deal of water. Three examples of water-operated aerators are shown in *Figures 2.3–2.5*. In *Figure 2.3* the level of tube *A* must be about 1 ft. above the top of bottle *C*, and tube *B* must be about 3 in. above tube *A*. Aerators of the type shown in *Figure 2.4* need to use a large volume of water if they are to function well. *Figure 2.5* shows an aerator operating an air lift which is transferring water from the first aquarium to the second; water is automatically returned to the first aquarium by the constant-level siphon.

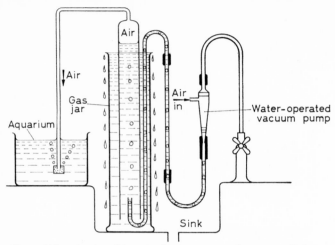

Figure 2.4. A powerful type of water-operated aerator which can supply air to a large number of aquaria

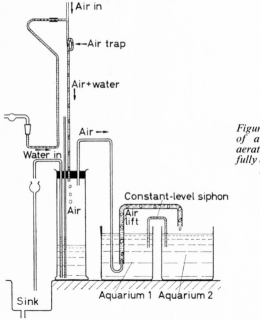

Figure 2.5. A modified version of a type of water-operated aerator which was used successfully at the Sheffield University Zoology Department

160

Aerators may also be used to operate aquarium filters. An efficient filter will save a lot of time, as the aquarium will hardly ever need to be emptied and cleaned and the water in the aquarium will remain crystal clear. Filters are easily constructed but they may be purchased from most aquarist's shops if preferred. Three types are shown in

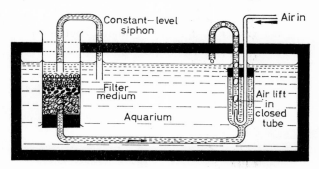

Figure 2.6. An easily constructed external type of filter unit

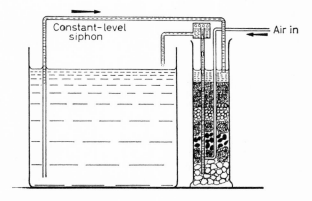

Figure 2.7. Another external type of aquarium filter which is easy to construct

Figures 2.6–2.8. As is shown in *Figure 2.7*, by using a series of constant-level siphons a single filter may be used to filter the water of a number of aquaria, but it will be necessary to change the filter medium more frequently. A few points concerning filters are as follows:

(*i*) Most of them operate on the air-lift principle. An air lift is arranged by feeding a supply of air from a small tube into a wider tube which is standing in the water. As each bubble ascends the tube, a short column of water is trapped between it and the next bubble; thus, water is lifted to the top of the tube.

(*ii*) Air lifts will not work efficiently if more than 11 in. long, and with such long tubes it is necessary to use tubing of a very small bore.

(*iii*) The best filtering medium is made of layers of glass-wool, fine shingle, coarse and medium sand, and carbon. The carbon will remove organic matter and feed the plants, but needs frequent renewal.

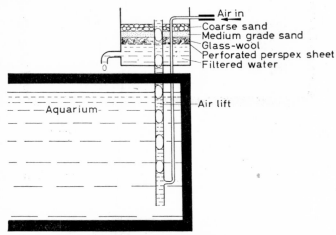

Figure 2.8. An internal type of aquarium filter, easily constructed from perspex and glass

Air should always be released into the aquarium through a diffuser which may consist of a porous stone, or a short length of bamboo cane. The stream of small air bubbles from a diffuser makes it possible for more oxygen to be absorbed and causes some circulation of the water, which prevents pockets of cold water forming in the aquarium.

AQUARIUM ACCESSORIES

The following pieces of inexpensive equipment are necessary for the aquarist:

(*i*) *Thermometers*—As well as a maximum–minimum thermometer which should be hung in the centre of the aquarium room, each aquarium should have its own thermometer. A useful type is the glass–mercury thermometer which may be attached to the inside glass of the aquarium by means of a rubber sucker.

(ii) Fish nets—These should be of a rectangular or triangular shape. One 9 in. net of medium texture and one 2 in. fine mesh net will be found most useful.

(iii) Sediment remover—Various types of sediment remover are sold by aquarists, but all that is really required is a 4 ft. length of rubber tubing to act as a siphon. This is also useful for emptying the water from aquaria. An improved sediment remover which can easily be made in the laboratory is shown in *Figure 2.9*. A finger is placed over the upper tube, and the apparatus is lowered into the

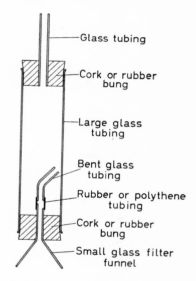

Figure 2.9. Sediment remover

aquarium until the funnel is directly above the sediment. Then the finger is removed and the sediment is drawn automatically into the large tube. The apparatus is emptied by inversion over a sink or waste bucket.

(iv) Glass scraper—The best type of glass scraper, which is used to remove encrusting algae from the glass, is a metal holder for a razor-blade which is attached to a metal handle.

(v) Tongs and forceps—These are very useful gadgets, and should be made from wood or plastic. They are particularly useful for the individual feeding of axolotls and xenopus.

(vi) Feeding rings—These are plastic bowls which are perforated, and are floated in the aquarium by means of a cork ring. Live food such as tubifex worms are placed into the bowl. Fish usually eat all

of the worms before any of them can bury themselves in the sand at the base of the aquarium.

FOODS AND FEEDING OF AQUARIUM INMATES

Since it is not possible to offer the variety of food which is enjoyed in nature, care must be taken to ensure that the food which is given has sufficient food value to make it worth giving. It is also important to supply a variety of different foods to the aquarium inmates. The exact choice for a particular animal will depend in the main on its natural diet; e.g., if the animal is mainly carnivorous, the major part of its diet should consist of live foods. A list of commonly used aquarium foods is given below:

Live foods
(1) *Daphnia* (for culture see page 85)
(2) *Artemia* 'brine-shrimp' (for culture see page 84)
(3) *Tubifex* (for culture see page 73)
(4) *Enchytraeus* (for culture see page 73)
(5) *Mytilus*
(6) *Infusoria* (cultures may be easily prepared*)

Fresh food
(7) Chopped heart
(8) Chopped liver
(9) Lettuce leaves

Dried food
(10) Dried *Daphnia*
(11) Dried *Artemia* (sometimes cooked with 2 parts of oatmeal)
(12) The fine powder of rat cake (this is a very good dried food which is suitable for a number of tropical fish)
(13) Special commercial preparations
(14) Nettle powder (this is the best food for tadpoles of many types of *Anura*)
(15) Dried egg (useful for feeding young fish)

It is important to note that it is better to give minute portions of food frequently rather than give a large portion all at once. This prevents any uneaten food from fouling the water. Uneaten food is the commonest way in which aquaria become fouled.

SAND AND STONES FOR AQUARIA

Aquaria which contain fish should have a layer of coarse sand or fine gravel on the base. Generally it should be arranged so that it is a few inches higher at the back of the aquarium than at the front;

* Culturing *Infusoria:* if some pond water is placed into a glass aquarium containing a layer of pond mud and some milk, or a crushed lettuce leaf, or an old banana skin, and is left for several days, a thick culture of *Infusoria* will usually be present.

this causes much of the sediment to gather at the front of the aquarium where it is easily removed. Water-worn natural stones may be added to improve the appearance of the aquarium. Crystalline rocks such as white spar, calc spar, gypsum, marble, alabaster or limestone should not be used as they will dissolve slowly making the water alkaline. As well as these, metal-bearing ores should be avoided. Some of the most attractive water-worn stones come from streams in Westmorland, while grey and red sandstones, Mendip rock, and various granites are all useful. They should be arranged so that they appear to be as natural as possible, with their stratum lines bearing some relationship with one another and lying horizontally.

Aquaria which contain larger amphibians such as axolotls and xenopus should have a layer of large pebbles at the bottom, but care must be taken to ensure that the animals are fed individually and that no food remains among the stones where it would decay and foul the water.

Marine aquaria do not have to be supplied with sand or stones unless the inhabitants are to be maintained for a long period of time. Stones are necessary for fish and other animals which are timid, and then they should be arranged so that they form a safe hiding place for the animals. Tube-dwelling worms should be supplied with a deep layer of marine mud, and other marine animals which like to bury themselves in mud or sand should be supplied with whatever comprises their natural habitat.

AQUARIUM PLANTS

On no account should plants be used in marine aquaria if at all possible. Seaweeds soon decay and foul the water. The feeding of all green plants is dependent on the energy obtained from sunlight, this process of feeding being known as photosynthesis. To deprive plants of light, then, is to starve them. Another requirement of plants is nitrogenous material, but this is usually present in the waste matter of the aquarium's animals. Some useful aquarium plants are listed below, together with short notes on their temperature and light preferences.

PLANTS FOR INDOOR COLD-WATER OR TROPICAL AQUARIA

(1) *Vallisneria*: Requires only moderate lighting. It is more prolific in tropical aquaria. It is easily propagated by means of runners. The variety with the twisted leaves is the most useful type, as its leaves are less inclined to spread across the surface of the water and so obstruct light from the other plants.

(2) *Sagittaria*: This does not require strong light; it is a slow grower, and is propagated in the same way as vallisneria.

(3) *Myriophyllum*: This requires strong light, and will not stand overcrowding. There is a red variety as well as the more common green variety.

(4) *Egeria densa*: This will tolerate hard water, and prefers strong light. The stems grow very long and cuttings are easily rooted.

PLANTS SUITABLE FOR INDOOR COLD-WATER AQUARIA

(5) *Elodea canadensis*, 'Canadian pond weed': This is a must for most cold-water aquaria. It is very prolific and is easily propagated by means of cuttings. It prefers strong light and hard cool water.

(6) *Ceratophyllum*, 'hornwort'; It has a very brittle stem which grows to a great length. Strong light is required.

(7) *Hottonia*, 'water violet': Requires a moderate amount of light; rooted stems are used for propagation. It is useful for its dark green bushy foliage.

(8) *Fontinalis antipyretica*: This is slow growing, and has dark green compact foliage. Suited to a shady position.

PLANTS SUITABLE FOR TROPICAL AQUARIA

(9) *Limnophila (Ambulia)*: This somewhat resembles cabomba but it is more prolific; it requires strong light and prefers soft water. Cuttings should be planted separately and not in bunches.

(10) *Cabomba*: Its requirements are similar to limnophila.

(11) *Hygrophila*: A hardy plant, which prefers strong light. Easily propagated from cuttings.

(12) *Ceratopteris*, 'Indian fern': This is a very attractive aquarium plant which produces young plants from its foliage. These become detached and float to the surface. They are easily rooted in sand. It prefers hard water and moderate light.

(13) *Fontinalis gracilis*: Grows very dense in strong light, so only moderate light should be given.

(14) *Cryptocoryne*: There are several species of this plant, all of which are useful. Propagate by dividing roots or by runners. Grows well in subdued light, and in soft water.

(15) *Echinodorus*, 'Amazon sword plant': This is best suited to a large aquarium, where it will make a splendid centre piece.

FLOATING PLANTS FOR COLD-WATER AQUARIA

(16) *Lemna*, 'duckweeds': There are several species of this useful

floating plant. The lesser duckweed *Lemna minor*, and the ivy-leaved duckweed are the most useful varieties for aquarium use. It requires strong light.

FLOATING PLANT FOR TROPICAL AQUARIA

(17) *Pistia*, 'water lettuce': Will form rosettes of leaves up to 6 in. across, so should only be used in large aquaria where some shade is required. It requires strong light.

MARINE AQUARIA

The following is a brief description of a successful marine aquarium system which is becoming increasingly popular in several of the larger university departments. In spite of the limited size of the filter bed its efficiency is increased by dividing it into a number of sections; water flows alternatively up and down through this series of filter beds. Also incorporated is a refrigerating plant which cools the sea-water to the desired temperature. Plastic piping is incorporated throughout, as sea-water will attack most metals, and many metals themselves are harmful to animals. The pump, which is used for lifting the water from the reservoir at the end of the filter bed to the high-level refrigerated supply tank, must be specially designed for this purpose. It is advisable to have a spare pump in readiness. Water from the high-level tank is fed by gravity into the various aquaria which should be earthenware sinks of varying dimensions. Water overflows from the outlet pipes of each sink into a plastic chute, which directs it into the first section of the filter bed (see *Figures 2.13* and *2.14*).

The aquaria should be fitted with loose-fitting glass covers to prevent excessive evaporation taking place. The level of water in the system should be regularly topped up with distilled water. The specific gravity of the water should also be regularly checked.

For most purposes the temperature of marine aquaria should be maintained at 10° C; it should never drop below 5° C and never rise above 14° C. Unless such a temperature can be maintained it will be of little use attempting to keep marine animals.

Supplementary aeration should be given to each of the aquaria. When marine aquaria are kept in operation for more than a few months it becomes necessary to control the chemical changes which take place in the sea-water. Full details of this control are given in Breder and Howley (1931). The main factors are discussed below.

Salinity

As water gradually evaporates from the marine aquarium system, so the concentration of salt will increase. The easiest way to correct this is to have the original level of sea-water marked on the side of the aquarium, and to periodically 'top up' the system with glass-distilled water until the original level is reached.

A hydrometer used regularly will afford a check upon the total salt concentration, and tables are available by which the conversion from density to salinity may be made rapidly. The density of sea-water should approximate 1·023 g/cm³, a value which corresponds to a salinity reading of about 29·83°/00.

Chloride Determination by Silver Nitrate Titration of Small Samples of Sea-water

The accuracies demanded by the oceanographer are unnecessary for most physiological–ecological work, and the following method will be found adequate. Use a silver nitrate solution made up according to the range of chloride values encountered (*Table 2.2*). Use the selected silver nitrate solution in a 5 ml. burette graduated to 0·01 ml. Samples of water are of 1 ml. To the 1 ml. sample add 3 drops of 5 per cent potassium chromate (indicator). Titrate, keeping the flask agitated, until the lemon colour is replaced by the faint but distinct orange colour. In the higher range of salinities it is usually necessary to break up the clots of precipitate with a small stirring rod. Do all the titrations in triplicate and take an average reading. With higher salinities, a more accurate result may be obtained by making a known dilution of the sample of sea-water.

Table 2.2

AgNO₃ *concentration*	*Equivalent to*
23·95 g/l.	5 mg chloride/ml. (for sea-water)
19·16 g/l.	4 mg chloride/ml. (for polyhaline waters)
9·58 g/l.	2 mg chloride/ml. (for most brackish waters)

The silver nitrate solutions must be stored in dark bottles

After carrying out the titration it must be standardized in order that any accuracy may be claimed. Use either the 'standard sea-water' of known chlorinity, available at many marine laboratories, or a carefully weighed-out solution of oven-dried sodium chloride with a chloride concentration of 10 mg/ml. Then calculate a correction factor for the volume of silver nitrate used in titrating.

pH of Marine Aquaria

The optimum pH for sea-water is given by Breder and Howley as between 8·0 and 8·4, preferably 8·2–8·3. They suggest the use of a colorimetric method for the period checking of the pH. A Lovibond comparator may be used in the following way: fill both tubes of the comparator to the marked level, add 10 drops of the indicator to one tube, then place both tubes in position in the comparator making sure that the tube containing the indicator is placed against the central window of the comparator. Turn the comparator disc until colour match is obtained and then read off the pH. Colorimetric methods are never very accurate with saline solutions, owing to 'salt error', but they may be regarded as being sufficiently accurate for most purposes. Alternatively, a more accurate method is to use a pH meter. If neither of these methods is possible, the pH can be roughly assessed by using indicator papers.

If the pH readings are too low the water should be titrated with N/100 hydrochloric acid, using bromocresol purple as indicator, for the bound carbon dioxide, i.e., for the total concentration of buffer salts present in the water. If the result shows that they have been greatly depleted they may be increased by the addition of a few grammes of sodium bicarbonate dissolved in distilled water. Most marine animals are very tolerant to excesses of this salt, probably because the increase in Na^+ ions is small compared with those already present. The buffer salt content may be approximately normal and yet the pH somewhat low. It is wise then to determine the free carbon dioxide value by titrating with N/44 sodium hydroxide using phenolphthalein as indicator. If there is a relatively high free carbon dioxide content it indicates that the system is inadequately aerated. When the aeration is corrected the pH should then return to normal.

THE CONSTRUCTION OF TIDAL TANKS

Although tidal tanks are not essential for maintaining animals which live in the tidal zone, they may be of use in certain experiments on such animals, and indeed some of these animals do prefer to live in a tidal tank. Two methods are shown in *Figures 2.10* and *2.11*. For convenience the supply head of water, and the pump have been omitted from *Figure 2.11*.

The rate of filling in each case is controlled by the size of the tube which admits the sea-water, and the emptying by the size of the outlet pipe and the rate at which the tank is being continually filled. The first method necessitates the boring of a hole into the side of the aquarium, into which the outlet pipe must be sealed. Both types can be made to operate a series of aquaria by using a system of constant-level siphons.

A METHOD FOR DECHLORINATION OF TAP-WATER

Tap-water contains a considerable amount of chlorine which is toxic to many aquatic animals. It is usually eliminated if the water is allowed to stand in an open container for a few days. However, it is

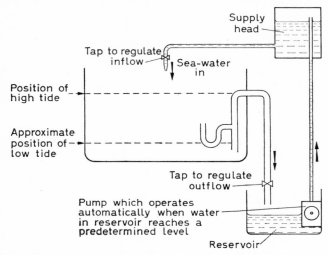

Figure 2.10. One method of constructing a tidal aquarium

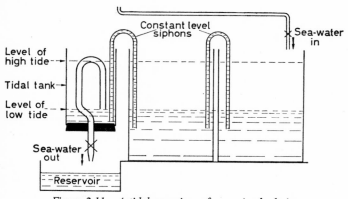

Figure 2.11. A tidal aquarium of very simple design

possible to construct a piece of apparatus which will make it possible to have a source of dechlorinated water always at hand.

The method is to pass the water through a large column of activated carbon. If the column contains about 2 ft.³ of carbon it will be possible to obtain a flow rate of dechlorinated water of about 50 gal./h. The column can be constructed from earthenware, glass or plastic pipes (large diameter plastic drain pipes are ideal). An outlet pipe is provided near to the base of the column, and the bottom few inches of the column are filled with graded gravel and sand before the activated carbon is added. This prevents the carbon from escaping from the column. The dechlorinated water is led from the

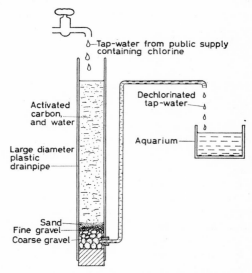

Figure 2.12. Suggested apparatus for the dechlorination of tap-water

outlet pipe up to the level of the top of the carbon column before it is finally run into the aquarium. It will be seen from the diagram of this system (*Figure 2.12*) that the column of carbon is kept full of water at all times.

THE CULTURE OF DIATOMS (PARTICULARLY NITZSCHIA) FOR REARING MARINE LARVAE

By using the method of Miquel (1890), modified by Allen and Nelson (1910, 1914) it is possible to maintain pure cultures of a variety of diatoms. Briefly it consists of adding certain nutrient salts to seawater, sterilizing, and inoculating with a single species of diatom. Two solutions are prepared separately:

Solution A
Potassium nitrate	..	..	..	..	20·2 g
Distilled water	..	..	..	..	100 ml.

Solution B
Calcium chloride (CaCl₂.6H₂O)	..	..	4 g
Disodium hydrogen phosphate crystals	..	4 g
Melted ferric chloride (FeCl₃.6H₂O)	..	2 ml.
Conc. hydrochloric acid	..	..	..	2 ml.
Distilled water	..	..	..	..	80 ml.

Dissolve the calcium chloride in 40 ml. of distilled water and add the hydrochloric acid. In a separate beaker dissolve the sodium phosphate in 40 ml. of distilled water, add the melted ferric chloride, and slowly mix the two solutions.

To prepare Miquel's solution add 2 ml. of Solution A and 1 ml. of Solution B to 1 l. of sea-water. Sterilize by bringing just to boiling point. Cool, decant or filter off the precipitate and separate the filtrate into two 1 l. flasks. Shake vigorously to aerate.

The prepared medium is poured into sterile, short-necked, wide-mouthed flasks of 125 ml. capacity and these are covered with inverted beakers. The flasks should be only half filled so that the proportion of air surface to volume is large. Inoculate each flask by adding to it 6–8 ml. of a previously obtained culture of the required diatoms. Then place the flasks in front of a window facing north, where they will be protected from direct sunlight. Light and temperature have a great effect on the propagation rate of diatoms. The best temperature appears to be about 15–16° C. Some workers prefer to provide the cultures with artificial light which can be kept at a constant level. The commonest diatom cultured in laboratories in both the U.S.A. and Europe is *Nitzschia closterium f. minutissima*. This is probably due to its small size, and its ability to remain in suspension for a long time.

VIVARIUM MANAGEMENT

A vivarium, *sensu stricto*, is a place artificially prepared for keeping animals in their natural state; but in a zoological sense a vivarium is a housing specially prepared for animals which require a damp terrestrial habitat combined with an aquatic habitat.

A vivarium is usually constructed in a large aquarium of angle iron and glass. Since it is to be divided into two separate habitats it needs to be of a greater size than that usually required for an aquarium. A tank of a convenient size for most purposes would be 36 in. × 15 in. × 12 in.

The first thing to put into the tank is the junction piece between the water and the soil. This can be made from a piece of wood which

VIVARIUM MANAGEMENT

will be attached across the tank at a slope. The two ends of the piece of wood should be attached to the glass by means of Bostik adhesive (black). The bottom edge of the piece of wood should not be made watertight, as the water which runs through this gap will keep the soil damp. If for any reason it is necessary to keep the soil portion dry, the gap between the wood and the glass base may be sealed with Bostik sealing strip. To improve the appearance of the piece of wood, it may be covered with a rough layer of plaster of Paris, which should be coloured when mixing by adding some burnt umber or raw umber solution.

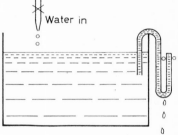

Figure 2.13.   A simple constant-level device for use with fresh water or sea-water

When the Bostik is dry, the terrestrial portion may be prepared: A layer of pebbles or pieces of broken brick should be added to a depth of 1 in. Following this a layer of course sand is added. Ideally, a layer of medium sand and then a final layer of soil are added. A light mixture of loam and peat is preferred.

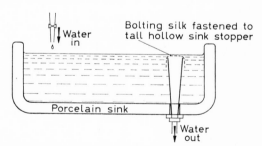

Figure 2.14.   A simple constant-level device, recommended for marine animals, which is incorporated in a porcelain sink

Some shelter for the animals should be provided. A neat way of doing this is to employ large pieces of tree bark, so arranged that the

173

animals can hide beneath them. Plant pots, laid on their sides also make good shelters. Some flat pieces of sandstone may be arranged so that they offer a dry surface over part of the vivarium.

Plants should be added to the vivarium; it is best if they are planted at the back of the vivarium, particularly with prolific and tall varieties. Hygrophytes or marsh plants should be used, the following being recommended varieties:

(1) Tradescantia: The common green variety is a very useful plant for vivaria. It requires moderate light. Readily propagated by putting cuttings into water until they root, then planting in moist soil.

(2) Sedges: Some of the shorter varieties are useful.

(3) Mosses: Although the mosses are not marsh plants, they can be grown in vivaria where they make an attractive foreground.

(4) Grass: Small plants from marshy places can usually be made to grow in a vivarium.

When the plants are all arranged in the vivarium, the water may be added to the aquatic side. The level of the water will gradually fall as the soil absorbs some of the water, but this may be adjusted after a couple of hours.

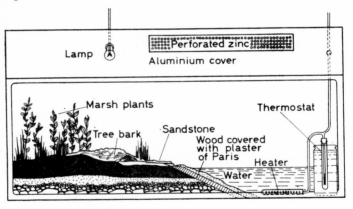

Figure 2.15. A typical vivarium

Vivaria intended for housing the usual laboratory animals, such as toads and salamanders, should be kept at normal room temperature. If a higher temperature is required, this may be done by fitting electric lamps of a higher wattage into the cover. This, of course, will illuminate the vivarium more brilliantly, so extra shade should be given to the animals. Alternatively, a radiant-heat bulb may be used. The water may be warmed with an immersion heater which should be regulated with a thermostat. If the water is shallow it will be necessary to partially submerge the thermostat in a deeper thin-walled glass vessel which stands in the vivarium water (see *Figure 2.15*).

The cover of the vivarium must be so designed as to prevent the animals from escaping, and it must also allow a free exchange of air. If the cover is fitted with an electric lamp, the cover may be made of aluminium or wood, and should have a panel of perforated zinc inset into it. *Figure 2.15* shows a suggested design for a vivarium, which would be suitable for salamanders or toads if used without the heater and thermostat.

REARING AND FEEDING OF FROGS, URODELES, AND THEIR LARVAE

Adult frogs should be maintained in large vivaria supplied with running water. The water should be kept at a depth of $1-1\frac{1}{2}$ in. by means of an overflow pipe. Shelter must be provided for the frogs; plant pots, hollow bricks and brick pipes are suitable for this purpose. The land area need only be small, but overcrowding must be avoided. Frogs will feed on mealworms, and a shallow straight-sided, dish containing mealworms should be placed on the land portion of the vivarium.

Larvae should be kept in aquaria provided with water plants. The water should be changed occasionally, but not too frequently. Tap-water may be used in some areas, but it should always be allowed to stand for several hours before admitting the larvae. If tap-water proves toxic, pond water should be used instead.

Metamorphosis is a critical stage for anuran and urodele larvae. The larvae do not feed at this time and become weak, unless they have been well fed during the period before metamorphosis. Facilities for crawling out of the water on to land must be provided, and it is better if special metamorphosis vivaria are set up when the larvae have reached this stage. Signs of metamorphosis are colour changes and lengthening of hind limbs in urodeles, and emergence of one fore limb and tail resorption in anurans. The water in these tanks should be only 1–2 in. deep, and an incline should be fitted to a dry area consisting of pebbles.

Anuran tadpoles are equipped with horny teeth and will rasp algae from the sides of the aquarium. They will also feed on small pieces of meat, liver, and frog muscle. The yolk of hard-boiled eggs is accepted and nettle powder is also a useful food, of which sufficient to make the water a pale green colour may be added every few days. Pieces of fresh lettuce leaf may also be added to the water, but care should be taken to see that the water does not become foul. Any uneaten food must be regularly removed from the aquarium.

Salamander and newt larvae begin to feed soon after they are three weeks old. They are carnivorous and should be fed on small living *Daphnia*. It is necessary for the food to be actively moving in front of their eyes before they will snap at it. Older larvae will feed on adult *Daphnia*, *Tubifex* worms, and even on small pieces of meat, as they rely more on their sense of smell. Other small crustacea and *Enchytraeus* may also be added to supplement the diet. If a supply of small *Daphnia* is scarce, then nauplii of the brine shrimp (*Artemia salina*) make an excellent food provided that they are washed well in tap-water before being introduced. This is most easily done by catching the nauplii in a fine bolting silk net, and then running tap-water through the net. Urodele larvae should either be kept in an individual aquarium or in very large aquaria, as they will snap at anything that moves and will bite off one another's gills or limbs.

Fungus infections (Saprolegnia) are fairly common in urodele cultures and are difficult to get rid of. The infection first shows itself as thin sticky threads on the gills and legs, but soon spreads all over the body. It is usually fatal. Detwiler and McKennon (1929) recommend a bath of 1:500,000–1:1,000,000 of mercurochrome (di-brom-oxy-mercuri-fluorescin). The animals are kept in this solution for several days, and the mould is said to slough off after 2–3 days.

Underfed urodele larvae and those which are slow in catching food sometimes swallow air bubbles. The air occasionally fills the stomach and the larvae then float to the surface of the water. There they will die of starvation if the air is not removed. The animal should be pricked with a sterile needle or a fine steel knife, or gently squeezed until the air is forced out. For the special care of experimental amphibian larvae which have been operated upon, see page 273.

REFERENCES

Allen, E. J. and Nelson, E. W. (1910). 'On the artificial culture of marine plankton organisms.' *J. Mar. biol. Ass.*, N.S. **8,** 421

Breder and Howley (1931). *Zoologica*, **9** (11), 403–442

Detwiler, S. R. and McKennon, G. E. (1929). 'Mercurochrome (di-brom-oxy-mercuri-fluorescin) as a fungicidal agent in the growth of amphibian embryos.' *Anat. Rec.*, **41,** 205

Evans, A. (1952). *Aquariums.* London; Foyles

Miquel, P. (1890–1893). 'De la culture artificielle des Diatomées.' *Le Diatomiste*, **1,** 73, **93,** 121, **149,** 165

3

HISTOLOGICAL TECHNIQUES

MICROSCOPES

THE COMPOUND MICROSCOPE

The ordinary compound microscopes which are made by different manufacturers vary little in general design. The foot should be large enough and heavy enough to support the microscope firmly for any inclination of the limb. The body tube is now generally 140 mm in length. The draw-tube is usually engraved in millimetres, and these graduations indicate the *mechanical* tube length. The internal diameter of the draw-tube is always 23·3 mm (as laid down by R.M.S. standard). A universal thread now adopted for microscope objective fittings is 36 threads per inch. The various parts of the compound microscope are shown in *Figure 3.1.*

THE USE AND CARE OF MICROSCOPES

Visual acuity is impaired by bodily fatigue, so care should be taken to avoid physical discomfort when using the microscope. The chair should be at a suitable height, and if the eyepiece is not inclined the instrument should be inclined to a convenient angle, unless the nature of the preparation demands that the stage be horizontal. The microscope should be placed far enough on the table to allow one's arms to be supported.

A suitable light source is required, but daylight is not recommended due to it being variable and usually of low intensity. A 60 W opal bulb, enclosed in some type of shielding to protect the observer's eyes from glare, will be satisfactory for all general work. Place the lamp in front of the microscope about 6–8 in. away from the mirror. It is important to remember that when the substage condenser is in use the plane side of the mirror must always be used, but when low power objectives (50 mm, 70 mm) are being used it may be better to dispense with the condenser and use the concave side of the mirror.

Rotate the nosepiece until the lowest power objective is in line with the body tube. Look into the microscope and adjust the mirror until the field becomes brightly illuminated. Then place a slide with the specimen on the stage and bring the substage condenser to

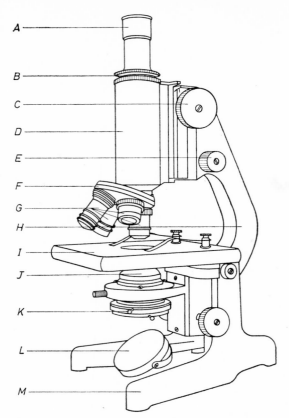

Figure 3.1. A compound microscope: A. Eyepiece
(usually a ×6 or ×10 Huygenian type); *B.* Draw-
tube; *C.* Coarse adjustment control; *D.* Body tube;
E. Fine adjustment control; *F.* Rotating nosepiece
bearing the objectives (those in most common use
have $1\frac{1}{2}$ in., $\frac{2}{3}$ in., $\frac{1}{6}$ in. and $\frac{1}{12}$ in. focal lengths. The
$\frac{1}{12}$ in. objective is an oil-immersion type); *G.* The
objectives; *H.* Limb; *I.* Stage (A mechanical stage
may be fitted as a useful optional extra); *J.* Substage
condenser (usually an Abbé type); *K.* Iris diaphragm;
L. Mirror (one side is plane and the other concave);
M. Base or foot

its highest position. Then focus the microscope, first of all by adjusting the distance of the objective from the object until it is at the
approximate focal length, and by using the coarse adjustment finally
getting it into exact focus by using the fine adjustment. (When low

power objectives are in use it is often unnecessary to use the fine adjustment.) Now put the object out of focus by racking the body, first a little above and then slightly below the point of exact focus. Should this operation cause the object to move across the field, then the mirror is not set up accurately and should be immediately readjusted.

To use the condenser, have the microscope focused on a slide using a high power objective (say 16 mm), and set the condenser at the top of its travel. Look into the microscope and hold a pencil at, or put a spot of ink on, the surface of the bulb; then move the condenser down slowly until the tip of the pencil, or ink spot, is clearly seen. Remove the pencil or ink spot and the condenser is now focused. If the bulb has a rough surface it may be better to have the condenser very slightly out of focus.

The substage iris diaphragm should now be adjusted. This is done by removing the eyepiece and looking at the back lens of the objective through the body tube with the eye about 6 in. above the microscope. Adjust the iris until about three-quarters of the back lens is illuminated. This is only an approximate setting, and the eyepiece should be replaced and the object viewed. The iris diaphragm should then be adjusted slightly to give the best results. Generally pale unstained material will require a smaller setting than well-defined and stained material. It should be noted that the iris diaphragm must not be used to regulate the light intensity. The blue filter which is usually supplied with each microscope fits into the holder below the iris diaphragm and is used to whiten the rather yellowish light from an ordinary light bulb. Other coloured filters may also be used.

Sometimes the condenser is constructed so that the top lens can be unscrewed in order that the remaining lenses will provide a large enough field of light when low power objectives are being used. On the more expensive microscopes the condenser is usually fitted with a centring mount. If fitted with this refinement, any adjustment necessary should be done at the beginning of the setting up procedure. With the condenser fully raised, set the mirror so that the field is illuminated and focus the microscope on a slide using a medium power objective (16 mm). Remove the slide and close the substage iris to a pinhole. Now, looking down the microscope rack the condenser down until the small aperture of the iris diaphragm is seen. This should be in the centre of the field, but if not the condenser may be centred by means of the substage condenser centring screws so that this bright spot is central in the field. When raising or lowering the condenser, a flare of coloured light is usually seen around the edge of the diaphragm aperture image. This flare of colour should be symmetrical; if not it is an indication that the mirror is incorrectly set. The centring mount is usually only fitted to microscopes which have other types of condensers than the Abbé, which is normally fitted to the less expensive models.

TO USE HIGH POWER OBJECTIVES

On the majority of microscopes all the objectives are parfocal (i.e., when one is correctly focused the others, when swung into position, will also be in focus—although some slight movement of the fine adjustment is usually necessary). When swinging in the higher power objectives care should be taken to see that they do not foul the stage-clips. If the condenser has already been focused for use with a lower power objective, it should not require any further adjustment, but the iris diaphragm will require some adjustment. This is carried out as in the case of the low power objective.

TO USE THE OIL IMMERSION OBJECTIVES

Oil immersion objectives are generally of 2 mm or $\frac{1}{12}$ in. focal length. Begin the operation by having the object in the centre of the field using the next highest power objective (usually 4 mm). Raise the body tube by means of the coarse adjustment and place one small drop of immersion oil over the part of the specimen to be examined. Looking at the objective from the side, rack down the objective until it just makes contact with the oil. Look into the microscope and continue to rack down very slowly until the object is seen, then immediately transfer to the fine adjustment until the object is correctly focused. Again the iris diaphragm will need readjusting, and this is done as before. Immediately after using the oil immersion objective wipe the oil from the objective with lens tissue or a piece of soft material which may be wetted with saliva. Should any oil become hardened on the objective a trace of xylene may be used, but on no account should alcohol be used. The oil should also be wiped from the slide if one wishes to revert to a lower power objective.

THE CARE OF MICROSCOPES

Microscopes require lubrication but this should not be carried out too freely or too frequently. The greases which are used by the manufacturers will last for many years. Manufacturers generally warn users against lubricating the bearings of the shafts which carry the milled heads (i.e., coarse and fine adjustments, and condenser shaft).

MICROSCOPES

Microscopes which are not in use should be kept in their cases, and should on no account be stored in a chemical laboratory or in any place where there are corrosive fumes.

Optical surfaces should be cleaned by first of all blowing away any dirt (a special blower brush is useful for this purpose), and then brushing gently with a soft camel-hair brush. Finally polish the glass with a special lens tissue or a piece of clean soft linen. Clean only exposed and readily accessible surfaces. Objectives should never be taken to pieces except by the manufacturer. Back lenses of objectives, if they require cleaning, should only be cleaned with a soft camel-hair brush. Small amounts of dust on the mirror and the condenser will not seriously affect the performance of the microscope. It is permissible to unscrew the lenses of eyepieces should grit get inside, but great care must be taken to see that the eyepiece is reassembled correctly.

THE MAGNIFYING POWER OF A COMPOUND MICROSCOPE

To see an object as large as possible with the unaided eye it is necessary to place the object as near to the eye as possible compatible with distinct vision, i.e., at the near point. This least distance of distinct vision for normal-sighted people is now conventionally given as 10 in. or 250 mm, and is frequently denoted as Dv.

The focal length of a simple magnifier, such as an eyepiece from a microscope, when divided into 10 in. or 250 mm, will give the magnifying power of the magnifier; e.g., an eyepiece of 1 in. focal length has a magnifying power $= 10/1 = \times 10$. An eyepiece of 50 mm focal length has a magnifying power $= 250/50 = \times 5$.

The magnifying power of a compound microscope is obtained by dividing the optical tube length of the microscope by the focal length of the objective and multiplying this result by the magnification of the eyepiece (or by multiplying the 'primary magnification' by the magnification of the eyepiece). For example: using an objective of 4 mm focal length, an eyepiece of 10 mm focus, and assuming an optical tube length of 160 mm, the magnification equals

$$\frac{160}{4} \times \frac{250}{10} = 40 \times 25 = 1,000$$

RESOLVING POWER OF A LENS

The resolving power of a lens may be defined as the smallest distance between two objects that the lens will render as separate images. The resolving power depends to a great extent on the numerical aperture of the objective.

NUMERICAL APERTURE, N.A.

The N.A. or numerical aperture is an optical constant depending on the apical angle of the maximum cone of light which the lens can take up from a point of the object.

It is defined as being equal to the product of the refractive index n of the medium outside the lens and the sine of half the apical angle of the cone of light taken up by the objective: N.A. $= n \sin \theta$.

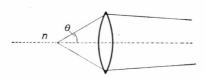

Table 3.1 gives a list of objectives of known focal lengths together with their usual corresponding approximate numerical apertures.

TABLE 3.1*

Focal Length (mm)	Numerical Aperture
75	0·10
50	0·12
38	0·15
25	0·20
16	0·25
8	0·50
6	0·70
4	0·75
3	0·90
2	1·20
1·7	1·40

*From Martin and Johnson (1958) by courtesy of Blackie and Son

PHASE-CONTRAST MICROSCOPY

The phase-contrast microscope converts differences in refractivity (i.e., refractive index × thickness) into a variation in intensity of light appreciable to the eye. It depends on a phase difference between the direct light and diffracted light passing through the microscope objective. This phase difference, in practice, is generally about a quarter of a wavelength of light. The system is made so that the beams of direct and diffracted light are superimposed by the objective to form the final image, and because the direct light can be separated from the diffracted light and altered in phase by the necessary one-quarter wavelength, a transparent object can be made to give a clear, contrasty image. Any variations in the intensity in the image will correspond to variations in the refractive indices of the various structures in the object.

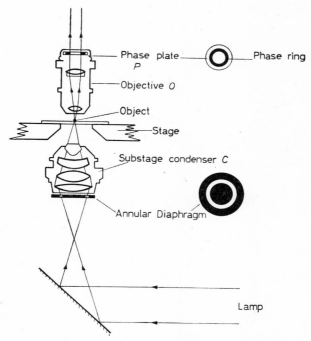

Figure 3.2. The positions of the annular diaphragm and phase plate

The phase-contrast principle was first applied by Professor F. Zernicke. Although different manufacturers of microscopes use different methods of obtaining the phase-contrast effect, they are all essentially similar. Namely, the object is illuminated by a hollow cone of light, the mean numerical aperture of which is about one-half of that of the objective. This cone of light is obtained by passing the beam of light through an annulus, which may be situated directly in front of the light source or, better still, immediately below the substage condenser. The objective is focused on the specimen, and the light which it collects is passed up through the eyepiece into the eye.

183

In the upper focal plane of the objective the image of the annular diaphragm will be formed by the condenser and objective together, and it is at this point (the upper focal plane of the objective) where the phase plate is inserted. This is a glass plate supporting a ring of

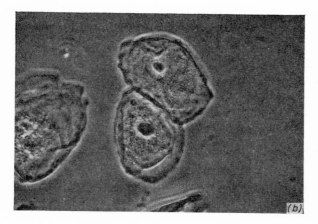

Figure 3.3. Unfixed squamous epithelial cells viewed by (a) direct illumination, and (b) phase-contrast illumination

material exactly matching the image of the annular diaphragm in size and which accelerates the phase of light passing through it by a quarter wavelength relative to any light passing through the supplementary area of the phase plate. The result is that all direct light passing through the object must also pass through the phase ring. Also, the diffracted (scattered) light from the object which has been collected by the objective will, except for a very small amount, pass through the supplementary area of the phase plate. Hence, the direct light has been separated from the diffracted light and speeded up by one-quarter of a wavelength. Maximum contrast only occurs when the two beams are of the same intensity, and because in practice the direct light is always more intense, a neutral filter (a deposit of a thin layer of metal) is placed over the ring on the phase plate.

METHODS FOR EXAMINING TISSUES AND CELLS

DISSOCIATION OF CELLS

The technique of dissociation or maceration of tissues has been much neglected during recent years, but it is of immense value for the study of isolated cells. The processes, of which there are many, all take the following form: tissues are soaked in a suitable fluid for a considerable length of time, which loosens the connections between the cells and allows them to be easily separated for microscopical study. Some methods are given below:

(1) Fresh hydra may be completely dissociated by placing them in a 0·001 molar solution of the tetra sodium salt of ethylene diamine tetra acetic acid (M.W. = 382·20). The process takes several hours.

(2) Nervous tissue: Addison (1937) recommends Gage's fluid, which is 2 ml. formalin in 1 l. normal saline. After this treatment large ventral horn cells can easily be dissected out with the aid of a binocular microscope, and stained with carmine, picrocarmine, or any aniline dye.

(3) Thyroid follicles: These can be freed from surrounding tissue and can be examined individually after maceration in:

Concentrated hydrochloric acid	..	..		3 parts
Distilled water	..	..	..	..	1 part

The time required is about 24 h. Thorough washing should follow the maceration treatment.

(4) Smooth muscle of bladder: this is well dissociated in 10–20 per cent nitric acid. The resultant fibres are suitable for class use (Dahlgren (1937)).

(5) Epithelia which have a free surface may be dissociated by soaking the tissue in a saturated solution of boric acid in 0·75 per cent saline to which has been added some Lugol's iodine (about 2 drops per 25 ml.). After thorough impregnation, transfer the tissue into the plain solution without the iodine and leave to soak for

several days. An average time is three days. The iodine must be added to the first solution immediately before use. For marine invertebrates, the boric acid should be made up in sea-water. The method is suitable for dissociating hydra, intestinal cells of earthworms and many other tissues (Goodrich, 1941–42).

SMEAR TECHNIQUE

The material is examined, after smearing it on to a slide, using a second slide or a platinum loop. Alternatively, to give what is termed an 'imprint or impression smear', the tissue may be pressed against a slide with a coverslip. After making the smear or imprint it is fixed and then stained.

THE PREPARATION OF A BLOOD SMEAR

Two slides are carefully cleaned. The blood which is obtained for the smear should be free flowing and should on no account be squeezed from the wound. One small drop of blood should be placed on to one of the slides about $\frac{3}{4}$ in. from one end. The second slide, held at 45 degrees to the first slide, is brought back so that the blood runs along the edge of the second slide, in the acute angle so formed. This slide is then quickly and firmly pushed along the first slide, dragging the blood into a thin even smear. The smear should be waved vigorously in the air to dry the blood film in the shortest possible time, so avoiding crenation of the corpuscles.

Important: The slides must be perfectly clean and free from grease. Better smears are made if the slide used for dragging the blood is one with polished edges.

THE STAINING OF BLOOD SMEARS

(1) *Leishman's stain*

Solution required:

Leishman's stain (powder)	..	..	..	0·15 g
Pure methyl alcohol (acetone free)		..	..	100 ml.

Dissolve the stain in the alcohol by grinding it in a pestle and mortar with some of the alcohol, then pour this stained alcohol into the bottle prepared for the stain. Add more alcohol and repeat the procedure until all the powder is dissolved. Stopper the bottle and leave it to stand overnight (some workers put it in an incubator at 37°C during this time). Filter the stain, then dilute a few drops of it with distilled water and pour it on to a clean slide; unless a metallic scum forms on the surface of the stain it is unfit for use.

Method: (*i*) Add just sufficient stain to cover the blood smear, and leave to fix for 1 min; (*ii*) To this stain add an equal quantity of pH 7·0 buffered distilled water, mixing carefully with a pipette. Allow the diluted stain to act for 10 min; (*iii*) Tip off the staining solution, and rinse the slide in the buffered distilled water until the smear appears pink to the naked eye. This usually takes about 10 sec; (*iv*) Blot dry with a filter paper.

When perfectly dry the smear may be examined using an oil immersion objective, or may be first mounted in D.P.X. or another neutral mountant.

(2) *Giemsa stain*

Solutions required:

(*a*) Giemsa stock solution.

Giemsa's stain, powder..	..	..	..	3·8 g
Glycerol (pure) ..	..	..	..	125·0 g
Pure methyl alcohol (acetone free)	..	..		375·0 g

Warm the glycerol to about 60°C, add the Giemsa's stain powder and shake thoroughly. Add the methyl alcohol, stir and allow to stand at room temperature, with occasional shaking, for 24 h. Filter.

(*b*) Buffer solution pH 7·0.

Method: (*i*) Fix the blood smear in pure methyl alcohol for 3 min; (*ii*) Stain in a mixture of 1 part Giemsa's stock solution and 20 parts of pH 7·0 buffer for 1 h or longer, depending on the effect required; (*iii*) Wash and differentiate in pH 7·0 buffer solution for 30 sec; (*iv*) Blot and allow to dry.

It is advisable to place the slide film downwards in a Petri-dish of stain in order to prevent any deposition of precipitated stain on the preparation. Small pieces of glass rod should be attached to the bottom of the Petri-dish to prevent the smear from touching the glass.

'IMPRINTS' OR IMPRESSION SMEARS

These are prepared by squashing very small pieces of the tissue to be examined between two slides. The slides are then separated, and the material fixed prior to staining. A quick and reliable method is the Wright–Giemsa technique. This is recommended for impression smears of bone-marrow and lymph nodes. It may also be used on blood smears.

Method:

(*a*) Air dried smears should be fixed in either (*i*) pure methyl alcohol for 5–10 min, or (*ii*) undiluted Wright's stain; about 1·5 ml. being added to the slide and allowed to fix for 1–1½ min.

(b) If fixed by method (i) then flood the dry slide with 3 ml. mixture of Wright's stain (1 part) and diluted Giemsa (1 part). Add the Wright's stain to the already diluted Giemsa. Stain for 20 min. (Diluted Giemsa is prepared by diluting 1 volume of Giemsa stain with 3 volumes of pH 7·2 buffer. Mix well and use immediately.) If fixed by method (ii) add 1·5 ml. of diluted Giemsa to Wright's stain. Mix by gentle rocking and allow to stain for 20 min.

(c) Flush off the stain vigorously with pH 6·8 buffer, and allow to differentiate for ½–1 min.

(d) Drain the slides, then blot or air-dry. When dry, mount in a neutral medium.

VITAL STAINING

Certain dyes (vital stains) are taken up by some living cells where they colour elements within the cells, e.g. mitochondria. Certain other cells (phagocytic cells) will engulf certain dye particles, which can then be seen within the cells, e.g. some elements of the reticulo–endothelial system. If vital staining techniques are carried out within the body they are referred to as *intravital*, but if carried out on living cells outside the body they are then referred to as *supravital*.

SUPRAVITAL METHOD FOR DEMONSTRATING MITOCHONDRIA

When cells are suspended in a natural body-fluid it is possible to dissolve certain supravital stains directly in this fluid without using any artificial saline. To do this the dyes are precipitated in a dry form on to a slide, and blood is then applied to the prepared slide. The following is a modification of Sabin's method. Solutions required: (1) Saturated solution of neutral red iodide in absolute alcohol; (2) One-tenth saturated solution of janus green in absolute alcohol.

Method: Clean a slide in xylene and thoroughly dry. Lay it flat on a staining rack. Put a few millilitres of absolute alcohol into a measuring cylinder and add 2·2 ml. of the neutral red iodide solution and 3·2 ml. of the janus green solution, and make up to 20 ml. with absolute alcohol. Take 0·2 ml. of this solution and spread it evenly on the entire upper surface of the slide. Allow the alcohol to evaporate, then put a drop of blood on to the slide, apply a coverslip and seal it with soft paraffin. After about ¼ h the slide should be ready for examination. The neutral red iodide stains the neutrophil granules of the polymorphs and the vacuoles of the monocytes salmon pink, while the eosinophil granules are stained yellow. The janus green stains mitochondria very sharply by this method, particularly those of the lymphocytes.

TRYPAN BLUE INJECTION METHOD FOR DEMONSTRATING CERTAIN ELEMENTS OF THE RETICULO-ENDOTHELIAL SYSTEM OF MAMMALS

Prepare a 0·5 per cent solution of trypan blue in sterile distilled water (not saline) and warm it to body temperature. Inject 1 ml. per 20 g body weight subcutaneously. This should be repeated daily until the skin is coloured blue. Kill the animal and fix the organs such as spleen and kidney in 10 per cent formal–saline or in Heidenhain's 'Susa'. Paraffin sections are prepared and the nuclei may be stained with safranin.

N.B. The injections must be performed by a licensed person.

INTRAVITAL METHYLENE BLUE METHOD FOR INVERTEBRATES

Solution required: Reduced methylene blue solution (i.e., reduced to its leuco-base).

To 100 ml. of 0·5 per cent methylene blue in distilled water, add 3 drops of 24 per cent hydrochloric acid. Mix well and filter. To 10 ml. of the filtrate add 2 ml. of 12 per cent rongalit solution in distilled water. Warm over a slow flame. Do not boil. Stir until the solution turns to a dirty-green colour. Remove from the flame and continue stirring until it becomes a clear yellow solution containing a white flocculent precipitate. Cool and filter. During the filtering process the solution should be covered to prevent the oxidation of the leuco-base. The prepared solution lasts for only a few days.

Method: Place the animal or tissue in about 25 ml. of water and add 1–2 ml. of the stain (the water will become milky-blue then dark blue in colour). Staining times vary from a few seconds to two hours. Nerve cells stain purply-blue.

SECTIONAL METHODS

These are certainly the most important of the established histological techniques. With very few exceptions, sections are always prepared from 'fixed' material.

FIXATION

Let it be said right away, that unless material is properly fixed, good histological results cannot be obtained. The aims of fixation are to prevent autolysis (the lysis or dissolving of cells by enzymic action from within themselves) and post-mortem decomposition (putrefaction) from taking place. (Putrefaction usually occurs in the alimentary tract where there is normally a high bacterial content. It causes tissue breakdown, usually with the evolution of gas.) It is essential that fixation should preserve the tissues in as lifelike a condition as possible. Fixation is also necessary to harden the tissue sufficiently to make it possible to be sectioned, and also to render the tissue insoluble during subsequent treatment. Some cells or cell components are more easily seen after fixation due to the fact that their refractive indices are changed. Fixatives usually have an effect on subsequent staining reactions. More often they act as mordants, but occasionally they may inhibit certain stains.

Common Reagents Employed in Fixing Solutions
Formaldehyde (H.CHO)

A gas soluble in water to approximately 40 per cent W/W. This saturated solution is sold commercially as 40 per cent formaldehyde or *formalin*. Hence 10 *per cent formalin* solution consists of:

Formalin (40 per cent formaldehyde solution)   10 ml.
Distilled water ..   ..   90 ml.

Commercial formalin is usually acid, but is easily neutralized by the addition of sodium carbonate or calcium carbonate. It may be convenient to store it over calcium carbonate, which will keep it approximately neutral.

Mercuric Chloride (*Corrosive-sublimate*) ($HgCl_2$)

Soluble in water at room temperature to 7 per cent. It is a powerful protein precipitant, which penetrates and hardens tissues rapidly. However, penetration is slowed down to a marked degree once the outer few millimetres of tissue have been fixed. Therefore, tissues to be fixed should be kept as small as possible. Because mercuric chloride hardens tissues, the correct fixation times should be strictly observed. Tissues fixed in any fixative containing mercuric chloride will require special treatment to remove the brown deposit which results. This is done by treating the tissue with iodine, either during the dehydration process or by treating the individual sections before staining. If the former method is used, then the iodine solution is 0·25 per cent in 70 per cent alcohol. If the individual treatment of sections is preferred then the following procedure is recommended: (1) Place sections in 0·25 per cent iodine in 70 per cent alcohol for 5 min; (2) Rinse in water, then remove iodine colour from tissue by (3) Placing in 2 per cent aqueous sodium thiosulphate solution for 3 min; (4) Wash in running water for a few minutes.

Picric Acid ($C_6H_2(NO_2)_3OH$)

Normally employed as a saturated aqueous solution (approx. 1 per cent). Owing to its explosive nature when dry, picric acid should be kept damp, preferably under a layer of water. It is a protein precipitant and combines with them to form soluble picrates. After fixation in solutions containing picric acid it is necessary to render these picrates insoluble by transferring the tissue to 70 per cent alcohol, before putting it into water.

Potassium Dichromate ($K_2Cr_2O_7$)

This chemical has a strong fixative action on certain lipoids and is frequently used in the study of myelinated nerve fibres. After fixation in solutions containing potassium dichromate, tissues should be washed for about 12 h in running tap-water before dehydration. Unless this is done it will result in the formation of a lower oxide which cannot be removed.

Chromic Acid

This is prepared by dissolving crystals of chromium trioxide in water, and is conveniently stored as a 2 per cent solution. It is a powerful oxidizing agent and should not be mixed with reducing agents such as formalin until immediately before use. Tissues fixed in solutions containing chromic acid must be washed in running water for the same reason as for those fixed in potassium dichromate.

Osmium Tetroxide (OsO_4)

Frequently, though incorrectly, referred to as osmic acid. It is sold in ampoules containing 0·5 or 1 g, or in ampoules containing various quantities of 1 per cent or 2 per cent solutions. It is very volatile, and has a very dangerous vapour which can cause conjunctivitis. Store in a cool dark place. It fixes lipids (e.g., golgi apparatus and mitochondria). The vapour alone may be used to fix very small pieces of tissue.

Ethyl Alcohol (C_2H_5OH)

Alcohol used alone is of little use as a fixative. It tends to harden tissue and penetrates slowly. It should not be mixed with osmium tetroxide, potassium dichromate or chromic acid in solutions which will be kept as stock. It precipitates glycogen and leaves most enzymes in their original state.

Acetic Acid (CH_3COOH)

Never used alone because it swells tissues, particularly collagen fibres. It is frequently mixed with other chemicals which cause shrinkage in order to counteract their effect. Nucleoproteins are precipitated by acetic acid.

Compound Fixatives

Choosing a Fixative

The choice primarily depends on what parts of the tissue are to be

191

investigated. If the various parts of the tissue or animal are to be shown in their correct relationship with one another, then a micro-anatomical fixative should be employed. If intracellular structures are to be demonstrated then a cytological fixative must be used. Cytological fixatives may themselves be grouped into two types, nuclear and cytoplasmic.

Micro-anatomical Fixatives

Formol-saline	Formalin	..	..	..	10 ml.
	Sodium chloride		..	..	0·9 g
	Distilled water		..	to 100 ml.	

This is the most popular and useful of all fixatives. Tissues left in it for long periods suffer very little from its effect, except that a pigment (formalin pigment) sometimes occurs. This may be removed by treating sections with 1 per cent alcoholic sodium hydroxide solution. Fixation is usually complete after 24 h.

Zenker's fluid	Mercuric chloride	..	..	5 g
	Potassium dichromate		..	2·5 g
	Sodium sulphate	..	..	1 g
	Distilled water	..	to 100 ml.	
	Immediately before use add			
	Glacial acetic acid	..	..	5 ml.

This is a very useful routine fixative, which penetrates rapidly and evenly. Fixation time is about 12 h.

Zenker Formol (*Helly's fluid*): This is prepared in a similar way to Zenker's fluid, except that formalin is substituted for glacial acetic acid immediately before use. It is a good general fixative and of particular value in the fixation of blood-containing organs. Fixation takes about 24 h to complete.

Heidenhain's 'Susa'	Mercuric chloride	..	4·5 g
	Sodium chloride	..	0·5 g
	Trichloracetic acid	..	2 g
	Glacial acetic acid	..	4 ml.
	Formalin	..	..	20 ml.
	Distilled water	..	to 100 ml.

This fixative gives excellent cytological detail, and penetrates evenly and rapidly. Tissues of 7–8 mm thickness are fixed in 12–24 h. Small pieces less than 3 mm in thickness are fixed in 2–3 h. Tissues should be transferred direct to 96 per cent alcohol in order to avoid swelling of the tissues.

Bouin's fluid	Picric acid (saturated aq. soln.)	75 ml.
	Formalin	..	..	..	25 ml.
	Glacial acetic acid	..	..	5 ml.

This fixative penetrates rapidly and evenly and causes little shrinkage. Tissue must be transferred to 70 per cent alcohol in order to render the picrates insoluble. Sometimes difficulty is experienced in preparing serial sections of material which has been fixed in Bouin's fluid. This is because such material sometimes becomes electrostatically charged.

Cytological Fixatives

(1) *Nuclear Fixatives*

Newcomer's fluid	Isopropanol	..	..	60 ml.
	Propionic acid	..	..	30 ml.
	Petroleum ether	..	..	10 ml.
	Acetone	..	..	10 ml.
	Dioxane	..	..	10 ml.

This fixative penetrates rapidly and was devised for the fixation of chromosomes. Feulgen's reaction is improved after fixation in this fluid. Tissues less than 3 mm in thickness are fixed in 2–3 h. Thicker pieces of tissues require 12–18 h in the fixative.

Carnoy's fluid	Absolute alcohol	..	..	60 ml.
	Chloroform	..	..	30 ml.
	Glacial acetic acid	..	..	10 ml.

Carnoy's fluid penetrates very rapidly, and gives excellent nuclear fixation, with preservation of glycogen and Nissl substance. Little cytoplasmic material is left after fixation in Carnoy's fluid.

(2) *Cytoplasmic Fixatives*

Champy's fluid	3 per cent potassium dichromate	..	..	7 ml.
	1 per cent aqueous chromic acid..	..	..	7 ml.
	2 per cent aqueous osmium tetroxide	..	..	4 ml.

This solution does not keep and must be prepared immediately before use. Gives better results with mitochondria than Flemming's fluid without acetic acid. It penetrates poorly and unevenly and only small pieces of tissue must be used. It preserves fat, lipids and yolk as well as mitochondria. After fixation wash the tissue in running water for 12 h. Fixation takes about 12 h.

Zenker-formol (*Helly's fluid*): This has already been described as a micro-anatomical fixative. It gives particularly good preservation of cytoplasm particularly of bone marrow and blood-forming organs. When used for mitochondria it is necessary to *post-chrome* the fixed tissue in 3 per cent aqueous potassium dichromate for 6–8 days. Alternatively, the sections may be treated in the dichromate solution for 24 h prior to staining.

Formol-saline: This has been described as a micro-anatomical fixative, but when followed by *post-chromatization* it gives good cytoplasmic fixation.

Schaudinn's fluid

Saturated aqueous mercuric chloride ..	2 parts
Absolute alcohol	1 part
(Glacial acetic acid to 5 per cent is usually added just before use.)	

Gives excellent results with wet smears, particularly those of Protozoa. It should not be used to fix pieces of tissue.

Caution: All fixatives should be treated as poisonous solutions. Always put the fixative into the container before adding the tissue. Always use about 20 times the volume of fixative as that of the tissue to be fixed. Wide-necked glass-stoppered bottles are ideal for fixation purposes. Metal caps should be avoided when fixatives contain mercuric chloride. Remember to wash out potassium dichromate from the tissue before proceeding. The precipitate formed by mercuric chloride must be removed with iodine and the latter removed with sodium thiosulphate.

DECALCIFICATION

It is impossible to use routine methods for sectioning material which contains calcium salts unless these salts are completely removed by a process termed decalcification. An acid is always incorporated in the decalcifying solution, and the other substances are there to prevent distortion. The tissue to be calcified (a thin slice taken with a fine hacksaw) should be suspended in the fluid by means of a waxed thread. The degree of decalcification should be tested daily, either by means of an x-ray test (if this is readily available) or by means of the following test:

(*i*) Into a clean test tube measure 5 ml. of the used decalcifying solution, and add a small piece of blue litmus paper which should turn red.

(*ii*) Add 0·880 ammonium hydroxide drop by drop until the litmus just turns to blue.

(*iii*) If the solution becomes cloudy, calcium is present in considerable amount, and the tissue should be reimmersed in fresh decalcifying solution. If, however, the solution remains clear, add 0·5 ml. of saturated aqueous ammonium oxalate and allow to stand for 30 min. If a trace of cloudiness appears, decalcification is still incomplete. If it remains clear it may be regarded as complete.

Recommended Decalcifying Solutions

Gooding and Stewart's fluid

Formic acid	5–10 ml.
Formalin	5 ml.
Distilled water	to 100 ml.

Decalcification is usually complete in 2–7 days.

Formol-nitric acid

Formalin	5 ml.
Nitric acid (S.G.:1·41)	10 ml.
Distilled water	to 1 l.

The addition of urea to 0·1 per cent prevents the tissue from becoming stained yellow by the nitric acid. Decalcification usually takes from 1–3 days.

Perenyi's fluid

10 per cent nitric acid	
(stabilized with 0·1 per cent urea) ..	40 ml.
Absolute alcohol	30 ml.
0·5 per cent chromic acid	30 ml.

These solutions should be mixed immediately before use. Decalcification takes from 2–14 days. It has little adverse effect on tissue and is in common use. Unfortunately the chemical test for decalcification cannot be carried out with this fluid, and the x-ray method or pricking with a needle, at a position where it does not matter that the tissue be damaged, must be employed. Perenyi's fluid is useful for softening chitinous material.

Neutralizing of the tissue—After the tissue is decalcified it should be neutralized by putting it into 5 per cent sodium sulphate for 12 h. The tissue is then ready for processing.

Preparation of bone for decalcification—Thin slices of bones should be cut from the main piece of bone by using a *fine* bone-saw or hacksaw. After decalcification the rough sawn edges should be trimmed with a sharp scalpel.

Chelating Agents

In recent years the use of chelating agents for the decalcification of tissues has become more popular. Hillman and Lee (1953) described the use of the disodium salt of E.D.T.A. (ethylene-diamine-tetra-acetic acid) (= Sequestrene) for decalcification purposes.

The advantage of this method is that tissues so treated show a minimum of artefact, and can be treated by most staining methods with good results. The disadvantage is that the tissue tends to harden and the method is slow.

Following fixation in 10 per cent neutral formol-saline, tissue is transferred to 50 times its bulk of 5·5 per cent sequestrene in 10 per cent formalin. Tissue should be not more than 5 mm thickness and the solution should be changed every 4–5 days. After three changes, the changes should be made daily until the end-point has been determined. This may be done by x-ray or by chemical means. Following decalcification, tissues are transferred directly to 70 per cent alcohol, dehydrated via the graded alcohol, and embedded in either paraffin wax or celloidin.

N.B. The trisodium salt of E.D.T.A. is recommended for the decalcification of foraminifera.

The Preparation of Ground Sections of Undecalcified Bone

With a fine saw cut off a thin slice of the required bone. Then rub both sides of the slice on a piece of plate glass containing a small quantity of moistened carborundum powder. When the section is thin enough, wash the carborundum from the bone with copious amounts of water. Then dehydrate the section through the usual grades of alcohol, and allow it to dry. Finally mount in Canada balsam beneath a coverslip.

If it proves impossible to obtain a thin enough section in this way, the thin section should be washed, dehydrated and dried, and then attached to a piece of thick glass with some Canada balsam, or better still with Micrex or D.P.X. When the mounting medium has dried, it should be possible to continue the grinding until the section is the required thickness. It should then be washed, dried, and placed into xylene to remove the mounting agent. Then it should be allowed to dry before being finally mounted in Canada balsam beneath a coverslip.

BLEACHING METHODS FOR HISTOLOGICAL MATERIAL

Sometimes it is necessary to bleach the dark pigments, such as melanin in skin, the dark chitin of certain arthropods, and the radulae of molluscs, in order to render the rest of the material more visible or to make it more receptive to stains. Two of the commonest methods are given below:

(1) Mayer's Chlorine Bleach

This method is particularly recommended for the bleaching of sections of skin, and for bleaching heavily pigmented turbellarians, and insects.

Put a few crystals of potassium chlorate into a small dish and add a few drops of concentrated hydrochloric acid. As soon as green fumes of chlorine begin to evolve, flood with about 25–50 ml. of 70 per cent alcohol. This mixture is then used for bleaching. Histological sections will come to no harm, even if they are left in the solution for 2–3 days, though the bleaching will usually be complete after a few hours.

(2) Permanganate–Oxalic Method

Treat the fixed tissue with a 1 per cent aqueous solution of potassium

196

permanganate for one to several hours. Then transfer to a 5 per cent aqueous solution of oxalic acid until the tissue is bleached. If the bleaching is insufficient, repeat the whole procedure. This method is particularly recommended for bleaching chitinous material such as potash preparations of insects, and radulae of molluscs.

EMBEDDING AND SECTIONAL TECHNIQUES
PARAFFIN WAX METHOD

Because fixatives are immiscible with paraffin wax, the fixed tissue must be dehydrated before impregnation with wax can take place. This is usually carried out with alcohol*.

The process of dehydration usually takes place by the gradual transference of the tissue from 30 per cent alcohol to absolute alcohol, passing through 50 per cent, 70 per cent and 90 per cent grades. The final bath in absolute alcohol should have at least two changes. It is advisable to place a layer of $\frac{1}{2}$ in. anhydrous copper sulphate at the bottom of the final dehydrating bottle. The top of the copper sulphate may be covered with several layers of filter paper. When the white copper sulphate turns blue it indicates that the alcohol and copper sulphate must be renewed. For tissues of not more than 6 mm in thickness, 2–3 h in each grade of alcohol will normally be sufficient. Because alcohol itself is immiscible with paraffin wax, the dehydrated tissue must next be transferred to a 'clearing agent'. Clearing agents are solvents of paraffin wax, and are so called because in most cases they render the tissue translucent. The commonest clearing agents are chloroform, benzene, xylene and cedarwood oil.

Chloroform is probably the best clearing agent for general purposes. Tissues may be left in chloroform for 12 h without it causing undue hardness. Unfortunately it does not affect the refractive index of the tissue, and this makes it difficult to determine when the tissue is completely cleared. However, this is readily ensured by leaving the tissue in chloroform overnight. Being very volatile it is readily expelled during the wax impregnating process.

Xylene and benzene clear rapidly compared with chloroform. They both render the tissue translucent and it is therefore easy to

* The purchase of absolute alcohol is subject to many restrictions for Customs and Excise purposes. For this reason 74 O.P. spirit (absolute industrial methylated spirit) is normally used in laboratories. For the graded alcohols, these can be more economically prepared from 66 O.P. spirit. The percentage concentration of alcohol should be regularly checked by means of an alcoholometer. The British Museum (Natural History) publication *Alcohol and Alcoholometers* will be found useful because it contains a temperature correction chart as well as much other useful information.

determine when the clearing process is complete. Tissues of 4–6 mm thickness take about 2–4 h to clear.

Cedarwood oil is expensive but is very useful for clearing delicate tissues such as embryological material, for it causes little hardening of the tissues even after prolonged treatment. It penetrates slowly, so

Table 3.2. Summary of the Paraffin-wax Method
(times are for tissue about 4 mm thick)

	Fixation in:			
	10% formol-saline	Bouin's	Susa	Zenker
	(hours)	(hours)	(hours)	(hours)
Fixation time	24	24	12	24
Wash in water	—	—	—	24
30% alc.	2	—	—	2
50% alc.	2	—	—	2
70% alc.	2	2	—	2 (+ iodine)
90% alc.	2	2	2 (+ iodine)	2 (+ iodine)
Absolute alc. (1st bath)	1	1	1	1
Absolute alc. (2nd bath)	1	1	1	1
Chloroform	12	12	12	12
Paraffin wax, I	$\frac{1}{2}$	$\frac{1}{2}$	$\frac{1}{2}$	$\frac{1}{2}$
Paraffin wax, II	1	1	1	1
Paraffin wax, III	1	1	1	1

Blocking-out

Trimming of block

Attachment of block to microtome chuck

Cutting the sections

Attachment of sections to slides

tissues must be left in the oil until completely translucent, which may take a few days. It is necessary to use several extra changes of paraffin wax before all of the cedarwood oil is removed from the tissue.

Impregnation with Wax

This is carried out in an oven heated to a temperature 1–2°C higher than that of the melting point of the wax to be used. For average tissues paraffin wax with a melting point of 54–56°C is recommended. For soft tissues better results are sometimes obtained with a wax of a lower melting point, while hard tissues, e.g. fibrous tissue, benefit from the use of a wax with a higher melting point (60°C). Ceresin is usually added to the wax by the manufacturer in order to reduce the crystal size of the solidified wax. It is important that the crystal size is kept as small as possible. All wax must be filtered before use, and this is easily carried out in the embedding oven.

For routine work, tissue is transferred from the clearing agent to the first bath of molten wax, where it is left for 1–4 h and then transferred to a second bath of wax and left in this for a similar length of time. As the clearing agent is expelled from the tissue, so the wax is able to penetrate. When cedarwood oil is used, at least two changes of wax must be used, and the final wax bath should not smell of cedarwood oil. When the tissue has been thoroughly impregnated with paraffin wax it is then ready for 'blocking'.

Block Making and Block Trimming

'Blocking' is carried out by transferring the impregnated tissue to a mould containing molten wax. The most popular types of moulds are Leuckhart's L pieces (comprising two L-shaped pieces of brass, placed together to form four sides of a rectangle, and standing on a flat piece of metal or glass) and solid watch glasses. The inside surfaces of the moulds should be lightly smeared with liquid paraffin before adding the molten wax.

Blocking should be carried out as rapidly as possible. Tissue is transferred with a pair of warmed forceps, and carefully orientated within the mould. A slip of filter paper bearing the name of the tissue should be inserted near to the periphery of the wax. In order that the crystals of the wax will be as small as possible, it should be cooled rapidly. First of all blow gently on to the surface of the wax and, when a thin film has formed, direct a strong jet of cold tap-water on to one corner of the mould. This will travel horizontally across the wax surface and so strengthen the upper film of solidified wax. The mould should then be plunged into a large bath of cold water. When completely solid the wax block is removed from the mould.

Before sectioning can take place, the block must be trimmed. This should be done with a single-edge safety razor blade, and the block should be trimmed so that when a ribbon of sections is placed upon a slide the specimen will be seen the right way up under the microscope, as in *Figure 3.4*. It will be noticed that the two surfaces of the block, *AB* and *DC*, are parallel and when attached to the microtome they must be arranged so that they are also parallel to the edge of the knife. The side *BC* is cut at an angle so that the dorsal side may be easily identified, and the junctions between the individual sections in the ribbon may be readily seen. Always leave an even margin of wax around the tissue. More wax should be left at the posterior end of the tissue than at the front of the block, but sufficient should always be left in front in order that a few sections of plain wax may be cut before the actual tissue is sectioned. This allows time to do any final trimming of the block.

The trimmed block should now be attached to the chuck of the microtome. The chuck should already have a layer of wax on its

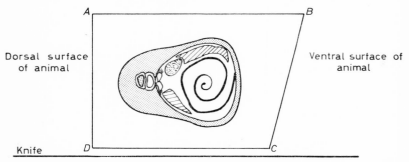

Figure 3.4. Illustrating how the block should be trimmed and arranged in relation to the edge of the knife. Note also the way in which the animal is orientated in the block, so that the sections will be viewed the right way up under the microscope

surface, and this is melted with a hot scalpel handle. The posterior surface of the block is then pressed on to this melted wax, and the hot handle run around the junction. The mounted block and chuck should then be plunged into cold water for a few minutes in order to harden the wax.

Section Cutting

This is carried out on a microtome, which is a mechanical device for cutting thin uniform sections. Paraffin sections may be cut on either a 'rocking' or rotary type of microtome. The rocking type is gradually being replaced by the smoother operating rotary microtomes. The model illustrated in *Figure 3·5* is relatively inexpensive.

However good the microtome might be, satisfactory sections cannot be obtained unless it is fitted with a sharp knife of the correct type. A certain amount of personal preference enters into the choice of knife used, but in general paraffin sections should be cut with a knife of a plane-wedge or a biconcave section (*Figure 3.6*). The care and sharpening of microtome knives is dealt with on pages 218–222.

Before inserting the knife into the microtome, the feed mechanism on the microtome should be turned back as far as it will go. Then insert the appropriate knife and tighten the securing screws. If the knife is adjustable, set it at the correct angle. Fit the mounted chuck into position and move it around until it is almost touching the knife, and the upper and lower sides of the block are parallel to the edge of the knife. Tighten all adjusting screws on the microtome, and then

Figure 3.5. A rotary microtome

(a)

(b)

Figure 3.6: (a) Section through plane-wedge knife; (b) section through biconcave knife

set the section thickness gauge to the required position. The majority of sections used in zoological laboratories are cut at 8 or 10 microns. Consistently good sections can only be prepared after the technician has had a great deal of practice. The microtome is operated until a ribbon of sections is formed. The ribbon, when about four or five sections in length, should be lifted away from the knife by means of a metal seeker, and the support maintained until the ribbon is about 1 ft. long. If more sections than this are required, for instance when one is producing serial sections, then the ribbon should be cut, leaving a few sections still adhering to the knife. The cut piece of ribbon is then placed on to a piece of paper. More sections are then cut and transferred in a similar manner to the paper, taking care to arrange them in the proper sequence. Sectioning may be continued until all the tissue has been reduced to sections. It will be noticed that the front of each section is dull whereas the reverse side is polished. A glass cover supported above the sections by a narrow wooden frame should be placed over the sections to prevent them being blown away.

Attaching the sections to the slides

The following method, which may be used for attaching serial sections as well as individual sections, is probably the best single method to learn.

Sufficient slides should be thoroughly cleaned in acid alcohol and then polished dry with a piece of silk. Arrange them in order on the bench and write the number of each slide of the series in the bottom right-hand corner, and the name of the tissue in the bottom left-hand corner, using a diamond-pencil.

Dilute 5 drops of glycerol–albumen with about 10 ml. distilled water in a test tube. Put 1 drop of this solution on to each slide and immediately spread it evenly over the upper surface of the slide with the side of the hand. Flood the upper surface of the albumenized slide with distilled water. The slides are then ready for receiving the sections.

Single or short ribbons of sections should be carefully lifted with a moistened paint brush and seeker and laid on to the water, letting one end down before the other in order to exclude air bubbles. The slides should then be transferred to a hotplate (surface temperature maintained at 45–50°C) and left until the wax expands, any creases being teased out with needles. When completely flat, remove from the hotplate and drain away the excess water, then orientate the sections into the correct position. The sections should then be put into an incubator at 37°C. It is advisable to leave them to completely dry for 12 h before using them. During the process of attachment, care should be taken to ensure that the wax does not melt. The prepared slides may be stored indefinitely in a dust-free container.

The actual arrangement of serial sections is shown in *Figure 3.7*. Care should be taken to ensure that the *ribbon length when expanded* will be short enough to be covered by the coverslip and that sufficient room will be left for a label to be attached (see *Figure 3.9*).

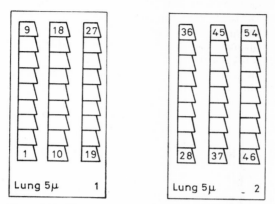

Figure 3.7. The arrangement of serial sections on slides

Vacuum Embedding Ovens

By using a vacuum embedding oven in place of an ordinary embedding oven, the impregnation time may be reduced by as much as 50 per cent. Because most of the hardening which occurs takes place during the impregnation period, it will be seen that any method which will reduce this period of impregnation will be of great value with tissues which become excessively hard. The time-saving factor alone is worth consideration before purchasing any oven. Tissues which contain air, e.g. lung, should always be embedded in a vacuum embedding oven, for by so doing the air contained in the tissue is easily removed.

The vacuum embedding oven consists essentially of an air-tight embedding oven attached to an exhaust pump, the degree of vacuum obtained being controlled by an attached mercury manometer. By reducing the pressure in the oven during the impregnation process, air bubbles and clearing agent are more readily expelled from the tissue.

The usual type of vacuum embedding oven is easily fitted up, as shown in *Figure 3.8*. This may be further simplified by using a special type of water vacuum pump (Edwards High Vacuum Ltd), fitted with a non-return valve and a reliable gauge. The method of use is as follows:

(*i*) Put the paraffin wax into small containers, which are placed on the bottom of the oven where the wax is allowed to melt.

(*ii*) The tissue is removed from the clearing agent and transferred to the first container of wax. The lid is replaced (it may be necessary to coat the washer of the lid with high-vacuum grease).

(*iii*) Close the air valve, and start the vacuum pump to reduce the pressure slowly by 400–500 mm Hg.

(*iv*) Close the stop-cock between the oven and the vacuum pump, and then turn off the pump.

(*v*) When the tissue has been impregnated for sufficient time in the bath of wax, the air valve is opened very slowly until the atmospheric pressure is restored to the oven.

(*vi*) The lid is then removed, the tissue transferred to the second bath of wax, and the whole process repeated.

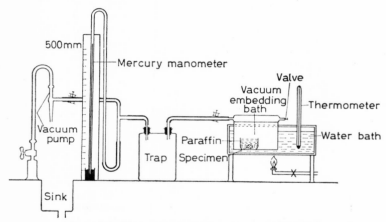

Figure 3.8. The arrangement of vacuum embedding bath

It is important that both the partial evacuation of the air and the restoration of atmospheric pressure be carried out very slowly, otherwise delicate structures in the tissue may be ruptured.

J. P. HILL'S MODIFICATION OF GUSTAV MANN'S TECHNIQUE FOR THE MASS PRODUCTION OF FINISHED SLIDES OF SECTIONED MATERIAL

When it is necessary to have one finished slide of the same material per student the following method will be found useful.

Paraffin sections of the required material are produced in the usual way and are mounted on to sheets of optically perfect mica instead of glass slides. The most convenient size for the mica is

3 in. by 1½ in. if staining jars of the necessary size are available. If not, a size of 3 in. by 1 in. may be used. The sections are mounted on to the slide in the usual manner, using glycerol–albumen, and are dried overnight in an incubator or other warm place. As many sections as possible are mounted on to each sheet.

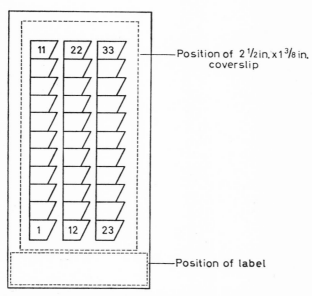

Position of 2½in. x 1³/₈ in. coverslip

Position of label

Figure 3.9. Showing a suitable arrangement for serial sections on a 3 in. × 1½ in. slide. Note the space left between the edges of the coverslip and the sections to prevent fading

When the sections are properly attached to the mica, they are processed in the usual way, treating the mica slips in the same way as slides. The processing is continued as far as the last change of xylene. The necessary number of slides are then prepared by cleaning in acid alcohol, wiping with a clean cloth, and applying a drop of thin Canada balsam or other suitable mounting medium to the middle of one side of each slide. The sheets of mica are cut up with a sharp pair of scissors so that each section is separated. Each piece of mica bearing one stained and cleared section is then put on to a slide, section uppermost, covered with another drop of mounting medium and a clean coverslip.

The amount of time saved by this method is considerable. For example, if 100 sections can be mounted on to 4 sheets of mica, it is then only necessary to process the equivalent of 4 slides.

This is a good technique to use when dealing with such difficult material as arthropods. The new formula, recommended by Steedman (1960) and produced by British Drug Houses Ltd., Poole, Dorset, is:

Diethylene glycol distearate	60 g
Glyceryl monostearate	30 g
300 polyethylene glycol distearate	10 g

The diethylene glycol distearate is sold by B.D.H. as digol distearate. To make the mixture, first melt the digol distearate, heat it until it is clear, then add the glyceryl monostearate, and when dissolved add the 300 polyethylene glycol distearate. Filter through a Barcham Green 904 filter paper. This wax, which has a melting point of 45–47°C, will ribbon well at temperatures up to 28°C. Should the room temperature be unusually high, the tropical mixture should be used instead. This is prepared as follows:

Diethylene glycol distearate	60 g
Glyceryl monostearate	30 g
Triethylene glycol monostearate	10 g

This tropical ester wax has a melting point of 50°C.

There are several methods of infiltration with ester wax, but only two will be described here.

Method 1: (*a*) Bring fixed, washed tissues into 70 per cent alcohol; (*b*) Transfer to a mixture of equal parts 70 per cent alcohol and 'cellosolve' (ethylene glycol monoethyl ether); (*c*) Transfer to pure 'cellosolve'; (*d*) Transfer to a mixture of equal parts of ester wax and 'cellosolve'; (*e*) Transfer to each of three separate baths of molten ester wax kept in an embedding oven at 48°C; (*f*) Make a block as for paraffin wax.

Method 2: (*a*) Bring fixed, washed tissues into 95 per cent alcohol; (*b*) Transfer to a mixture of equal parts 95 per cent alcohol and ester wax, in an oven at about 35–40°C; (*c*) Transfer to pure ester wax in an oven at 48°C; (*d*) Make a block. It is important that a fresh quantity of ester wax be melted prior to the preparation of the blocks. Ester wax should not be kept molten for long periods of time.

While the block is cooling surround the sides of the mould with iced water, but keep the surface of the wax liquid by means of a hot spatula. This allows the block to solidify from the bottom and sides. Unless this is done, air will be drawn into the block.

Cutting the Block

Attach the block to the chuck as for paraffin wax. Sectioning may be assisted by gentle warming of the block. Cut at a speed of about 30–50 sections per minute.

Section Flattening

Ester wax sections are flattened and attached to slides in a similar manner to paraffin sections, but the temperature required for flattening is about 45°C. The slides should be dried at a temperature of 40–45°C. Xylene will remove ester wax, as with paraffin wax.

POLYESTER WAX 90/10 METHOD

Due to the low melting point of polyester wax the proteins of any fixed material which is embedded in it are subjected to less heat denaturation than when paraffin wax is used. The method described here is the improvement by Steedman (1960) of his original formula. The improved formula is:

400 polyethylene glycol..	90 g
Cetyl alcohol (technical)	10 g

Its melting point is 38–40°C, and it is soluble in a wide range of reagents. The recommended antemedium ('clearing agent') is 96 per cent ethanol.

During the flattening process, polyester wax sections tend to take up a small amount of water, and as they are dried at room temperature or up to 30°C the protein of the section does not harden; nor does the albumen adhesive. Therefore, a carbohydrate adhesive such as amylo-pectin should be used for attaching the sections. However, with the shrinkage and hardening being reduced, normally difficult material becomes much easier to section.

Infiltration with Polyester Wax

(1) Bring fixed, washed material through the graded alcohols to 96 per cent alcohol.

(2) Transfer to a mixture of equal parts by volume, 96 per cent alcohol and polyester wax.

(3) Transfer to two separate baths of pure polyester wax at 38°C.

Block Making

Block out the specimen as for paraffin wax, but allow the wax to cool slowly. Do not plunge into cold water, or place in a refrigerator.

The wax gradually hardens and will cut more easily if it is allowed to stand for 1–4 days at a room temperature of about 20°C.

Section Cutting

Attach the block to the chuck as for paraffin wax. Cut at a speed of 80–100 sections per minute. Excellent ribbons may be obtained using a razor-blade microtome knife adaptor.

Section Flattening

Prepare a quantity of amylo-pectin adhesive: (1) Boil 1 l. of water and add to it while still boiling 1·5 g of Nipa ester No. 82121; (2) Cool 200 ml. of this solution to room temperature and add 2 g of Amylo-pectin. Stir until the powder forms a suspension, and then pour it into the other 800 ml. which should be boiling during the addition; (3) Cool, and then the reagent is ready for use. It should not be filtered.

To use the adhesive, shake the suspension before using and add a few drops to the clean slide. Flatten the sections on the liquid and drain away all of the surplus adhesive; arrange the sections in position and leave to dry at room temperature for about 12 h. When dry, the wax should be removed with xylene or absolute alcohol, from which stage it can be treated as an ordinary paraffin wax section.

CELLOIDIN METHOD

After fixation in any desired fixing solution, the tissue must be thoroughly dehydrated. Frequently the piece of tissue to be embedded in celloidin will be of a larger size than would be the case with paraffin wax; consequently the time for dehydration will be correspondingly increased. The tissue is taken through a similar series of graded alcohols, and is then transferred to a mixture of absolute alcohol and ether (equal parts). When fully saturated the tissue should then be impregnated with celloidin.

Impregnation with Celloidin

(1) Transfer the tissue to 2 per cent celloidin in alcohol and ether (equal parts).

(2) Transfer to 4 per cent celloidin in alcohol and ether (equal parts).

(3) Transfer to 8 per cent celloidin in alcohol and ether (equal parts).

(4) Transfer to 14 per cent or 20 per cent celloidin in alcohol and ether (equal parts). The final strength chosen depends on the degree of hardness required in the finished block.

Impregnation with celloidin is very slow and a specimen 20 mm thick will require at least three or four days in each solution.

Block Making

A paper boat must be constructed, and *Figure 3.10* illustrates the method of folding. The folds should, of course, be made at both ends.

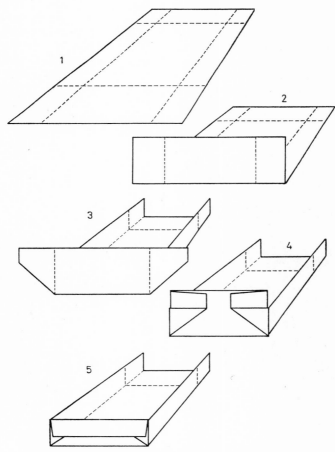

Figure 3.10. Method of making a paper boat

Into the paper boat pour the strongest solution of celloidin to a depth of ¼ in. Allow this to gel in an atmosphere of chloroform vapour. This can be simply carried out by using a desiccator, standing the mould on a perforated gauze over cotton wool soaked in chloroform. When gelled, remove from the desiccator and pour in sufficient celloidin to completely immerse the specimen, which is placed in position taking care to avoid any admission of air bubbles. Replace in the chloroform vapour until gelled. Then transfer to 75 per cent alcohol after removing the paper boat.

When required for sectioning the block must be securely attached to a wooden or plastic chuck, the surface of which should be crisscrossed with a number of saw cuts. The side of the celloidin block that is to be attached should be levelled by rubbing on coarse sandpaper, and then scratched with a scalpel. Thick celloidin is used to glue the block to the chuck, and this is allowed to gel by putting it into the chloroform vapour.

The block should be trimmed to a rectangular shape, and then one corner cut off to simplify positioning of the sections.

Figure 3.11. A sledge microtome

Section Cutting

Celloidin sections are best prepared with a sledge microtome (*Figure 3.11*) but may be cut on certain rotary microtomes. The knife which is most commonly used is the plano-concave type, with the concave side uppermost, but some workers prefer a knife of the plane-wedge type. Whichever knife is used it should be longer than that used for paraffin work, as the entire length is employed during sectioning. This is because the angle of cutting stroke is about 10 degrees in contrast with that of 90 degrees when sectioning paraffin wax (there it was important that the edge of the block be parallel with the edge of the knife). The sections should curl when cut, and the cutting angle should be adjusted until this occurs. Celloidin blocks may be cut in two entirely different conditions, namely in a wet state or in a so-called dry state.

Wet Method

Most workers prefer this method of sectioning.

(1) Arrange a Petri-dish of 70 per cent alcohol near to the microtome, or if serial sections are required it is more convenient to have a large number of rectangles of polythene sheet cut to a suitable size together with a deep dish filled with 70 per cent alcohol.

(2) Using a large camel-hair brush, flood the upper surface of the knife with 70 per cent alcohol and at the same time brush the surface of the block.

(3) Having raised the block by the appropriate amount, make the cut with a slow movement.

(4) Using the wet brush, lift off the section and place into the Petri-dish of 70 per cent alcohol or between two sheets of polythene, storing these in 70 per cent alcohol.

Dry Method

The block is treated thus:

(1) Transfer from 70 per cent alcohol to 90 per cent alcohol plus 5 per cent chloroform.

(2) When impregnated transfer to a mixture of equal parts 90 per cent alcohol and chloroform.

(3) Transfer to pure chloroform.

(4) Transfer to chloroform and cedarwood oil, equal parts.

(5) Allowing the chloroform to evaporate slowly, add more cedarwood oil daily until mixture is about 95 per cent cedarwood oil.

(6) Allow the block to dry in air after wiping surface.

(7) Attach block to chuck with some 10 per cent celloidin, keeping it pressed into position with a rubber band, and allowing it to gel in chloroform vapour for about 2 h.

(8) Cut on sledge microtome, painting the block with a little

cedarwood oil between each cut. Place the sections into cedarwood oil.

(9) When required for staining the sections must be transferred to xylene and then to a mixture of equal parts absolute alcohol and chloroform. After this transfer to 90 per cent alcohol with 5 per cent chloroform, and then to 70 per cent alcohol, and finally into water.

The process of infiltration with cedarwood oil may take from three days to a month depending upon the size of the block.

Attaching the sections to slides

Celloidin sections are generally stained by carrying them separately through the necessary reagents and attaching them to the slides immediately before mounting. The commonest way of doing this is to use the following method.

Creosote Technique

(*i*) Dehydrate the stained sections through the graded alcohols to 90 per cent alcohol.

(*ii*) Treat the sections with 95 per cent alcohol for 2–3 min.

(*iii*) Place the sections in the following fluid for not longer than 5 min:

Xylene	1 part
Chloroform	1 part
Absolute alcohol	1 part

(*iv*) Transfer the sections to pure beechwood creosote. They should flatten out in this solution. Do not exceed 7 min.

(*v*) Float section on to a clean slide.

(*vi*) Blot the section with a cigarette paper.

(*vii*) Pour xylene on to the slide; drain it off, and repeat several times.

(*viii*) Drain off surplus xylene and mount in Canada balsam.

When a large number of sections has to be treated, as in the case of serial sections, it is more convenient to employ a method for attaching the sections to slides before staining. This technique (Richardson, 1952) consists essentially of pressing the celloidin sections against a slide which has been coated with a liberal quantity of albumen. After baking at 57°C the celloidin may be dissolved without the section becoming detached. The method of procedure is as follows:

(*i*) Apply a liberal amount of undiluted Mayer's albumen or Baker's adhesive albumen to a clean slide.

(*ii*) Using a small brush apply a layer of pure turpentine to the albumenized surface.

(*iii*) Take the sections from 70 per cent alcohol, and arrange them in order on the slide, making sure that they are flat. Apply some more turpentine to the upper side of the sections.

(*iv*) Lower gently from one end of the slide a piece of cellophane (non-waterproof) which has been soaked in distilled water, so that it covers the sections like a coverslip. Smooth it down with a finger until all air bubbles are excluded. Considerable pressure should be used.

(*v*) Place a piece of newspaper, slightly larger than the size of the slide, on to the cellophane, and soak this with turpentine, then apply a second slide and bind tightly together with string, or more conveniently use a large spring clip. If care is taken it is possible to use this second slide for mounting a further set of sections, and in this way as many as 10 slides may be bound together.

(*vi*) Place the bound slides into an embedding oven at 57°C and leave them to bake for 1 h. During this time the albumen will coagulate but the sections will not dry out.

(*vii*) On removal from the oven, run some water on to the projecting newspaper, and then carefully lift off the slide and both of the papers. Immediately plunge the slide, with attached sections, into a mixture of equal parts of ether and absolute alcohol, and leave for 2 min.

(*viii*) Transfer to acetone in order to remove the celloidin. This will take several minutes. The sections are then taken down the graded alcohols and treated in a similar way to paraffin sections. However, a little more care should be taken as they are more easily detached than paraffin sections.

The staining of celloidin sections is dealt with on page 228.

DOUBLE-EMBEDDING (CELLOIDIN–PARAFFIN) METHOD

Professor Richardson devised the following method of double embedding for the successful cutting of thin sections of material (5–25μ).

Material is embedded in celloidin in the usual way. The block is then transferred to pure chloroform and left for about 12 h to harden. It is then transferred to benzene for several hours. The cleared block is then transferred to a mixture of 7 parts of paraffin wax (45°C) and 1 part of liquid paraffin which is placed into an incubator at 37–40°C. The container should be covered. After several days in this mixture it is then transferred to molten 45°C paraffin wax, in which it is left for an hour or so. The block is then removed and is wiped dry with a clean cloth. The block is then attached to a chuck and cut on a sledge (sliding) microtome as for celloidin sections. The sections, if small, can usually be attached with albumen as for paraffin sections, but if they are large the turpentine method which is used for attaching celloidin sections should be used.

Tissues may be frozen and sections of the frozen tissue, which is embedded in ice, cut on a special freezing microtome. This method is used for the rapid preparation of sections for diagnostic purposes and also for demonstrating fat and other special tissue components. Frozen sections are rarely as satisfactory as paraffin or celloidin sections, but usually allow an accurate diagnosis to be made.

It is preferable to fix the material for at least a short time before sectioning, and this is usually done in 10 per cent formol saline. If the fixative is preheated to 60°C the time required for a small piece of tissue will be 10 min. If possible all other fixatives should be avoided, but if this is not possible then the tissue must be washed in running water for several hours before sectioning. Many workers soak the tissue in a thick aqueous solution of gum arabic for several hours prior to sectioning, but this is rarely necessary.

Friable material should be embedded in gelatin, using the following procedure: (*i*) Fix the tissue in 10 per cent formol saline and then wash in running water for several hours to remove all traces of the formalin; (*ii*) Transfer the tissue to 10 per cent gelatin in 1 per cent phenol, and keep at 37°C for 24 h; (*iii*) Transfer to 20 per cent gelatine in 1 per cent phenol for 12 h at 37°C; (*iv*) Embed in 20 per cent gelatine in a glass mould and allow to set in a refrigerator or cool place. Trim the block leaving a few millimetres of gelatine on all sides of the tissue except that which will be attached to the microtome chuck; (*v*) Immerse the trimmed block in 10 per cent formalin in order to harden the gelatine. This will take about 24 h.

Because gelatine tends to inhibit freezing, the pieces of tissue should never exceed 3 mm in thickness. A disadvantage of this method is that the gelatine stains very heavily and this causes the section to be somewhat obscured. This can only be overcome by using the following technique: (*i*) Omit stage (*v*) in the embedding procedure; (*ii*) Float out the sections on to very cold water and transfer them immediately to albumenized slides; (*iii*) Drain off the surplus water and heat gently in order to coagulate the albumen. This cannot be done when demonstrating lipids; (*iv*) Place the slides in warm water to remove the gelatin.

Section Cutting

This should be carried out on a freezing microtome. Although other types of microtomes can be adapted for cutting frozen sections, the type shown in *Figure 3.12* is preferable.

The microtome is attached to the edge of a bench, and the chuck which is hollow and bordered peripherally by large holes is attached to a cylinder of carbon dioxide (CO_2). Because liquid CO_2 must reach the valve in the chuck, it is important that the cylinder be supported upside down and with the cylinder valve above the level of the microtome chuck. This does not apply to a new type of cylinder, now available, which is fitted with a central tube and which may be used with the valve uppermost, as the pressure inside the cylinder is

Figure 3.12. A freezing microtome

sufficient to force the liquid CO_2 up into the chuck from the bottom of the cylinder. The connecting tube supplied with the microtome should always be examined for damage before using the microtome. All joints should be thoroughly tightened, and the cylinder valve should only be opened when the microtome is in use. Always check that it is turned off before loosening any of the connections.

A plane-wedge knife is always used for cutting frozen sections. A special knife-cooling system is usually incorporated in the microtome, and if this is used it delays the thawing of the sections on the knife which makes it easier to transfer them to slides.

Frozen sections or gelatin sections which are not attached to slides have to be floated through a series of solutions in watch glasses. They are very fragile, and must be handled with extreme care. Glass hockey-sticks make convenient tools for the transfer of the sections. These are made from 3–4 mm glass rod. A 6 in. long piece of rod is heated at both ends until they are round, and then heated 1 in. from one end. This last inch is allowed to fall so that it lies at about 108 deg to the remainder of the rod. The bent part is pushed under the section and when lifted the section drapes itself over the rod without creasing. When put into the next solution the section should float off with ease (Culling, 1957). The staining of frozen and gelatin sections will be dealt with on page 229.

A recent invention, which employs a novel way of freezing the tissue, makes it seem very likely that the use of carbon dioxide cylinders with freezing microtomes will soon be a thing of the past.

This novel method of cooling arises from a phenomenon known as the Peltier effect. When direct current is passed across the junction of two dissimilar metals, heat is emitted or absorbed according to the direction of the current. Thermoelements of considerable refrigerating capacity are now being produced. Several of these thermoelements are built into a compact assembly, with metal plates bonded to the surfaces of the elements. This resultant thermo-module is attached by its hotplate to a water-cooled chamber, which is able to dissipate the resulting heat. With cooling water at a temperature of $+ 15°C$ the operating face of the module is capable of providing temperatures down to $- 20°C$. The operating temperature may be constantly varied by controlling the d.c. electricity to the module.

This new type of freezing stage is available in at least two sizes and may be adapted to fit any type of freezing microtome. The main advantage, apart from the need for CO_2 cylinders, is that the tissue may be frozen to the required degree, and as it is being cut the temperature may be gradually reduced. This makes it possible, at long last, to prepare serial sections of frozen material. One such thermo-module is manufactured by C. W. Brown (Engineers) Ltd, Thermoelectric Division, 422 Ware Road, Hertford. It is known as the Pelcool freezing microtome stage and is supplied together with the necessary power pack.

This type of freezing stage is easily fitted to a sledge microtome, which is usually a far better machine than a freezing microtome, and gives a greater choice of section thickness.

Another type of machine for cutting frozen sections is a cryostat. This type of machine is essentially a slightly modified Cambridge rocking microtome housed in a deep-freeze compartment, with all the necessary controls remotely placed outside the compartment. The microtome is viewed through a transparent window. The main advantage of a cryostat is that very thin sections of unfixed tissue may be prepared. A special anti-roll mechanism is fitted to stop the cut sections from curling, but the adjustment of this mechanism needs very careful attention. As each section is cut, a coverslip is introduced into the compartment and is brought up close to the section. Due to the fact that there is a considerable difference in the temperatures of the section and the coverslip, the section will jump across and adhere to the coverslip. The coverslips with attached sections are then processed. A fuller description of the operation of cryostats can be found in Culling (1963).

PETREFI'S CELLOIDIN–PARAFFIN WAX EMBEDDING METHOD

Some small and delicate structures, especially embryos, undergo distortion or rupture when embedded by the ordinary paraffin wax method. This can be overcome by using Petrefi's method. It consists essentially of initially impregnating the dehydrated tissue with celloidin before embedding it in paraffin wax.

The method is as follows: (*i*) Dehydrate in absolute alcohol, after having taken the tissue through the usual ascending grades of alcohol; (*ii*) Transfer to 1 per cent celloidin in methyl benzoate for 3–5 h (run the solution to the bottom of the alcohol and let the specimen sink before removing the alcohol); (*iii*) Transfer to fresh 1 per cent celloidin in methyl benzoate for a further 12–24 h. It is sometimes possible to store material in this solution without it causing much hardening; (*iv*) Transfer to benzene for 15 min; (*v*) Transfer to fresh benzene for a further 15 min; (*vi*) Transfer to a small bath of benzene saturated with paraffin wax and placed on top of the embedding oven (about 30°C). Leave in this solution for about 30 min; (*vii*) Transfer to pure paraffin wax for the usual time; then block out the tissue as for paraffin material.

For yolk-laden eggs and cells the following method is recommended: (*i*) Dehydrate via 30 per cent, 50 per cent, 70 per cent and 95 per cent alcohol ($\frac{1}{2}$ h in each); (*ii*) Transfer to 1 per cent celloidin in methyl benzoate for 1–2 h; (*iii*) Transfer to benzene for 10 min; (*iv*) Transfer to soft wax (M.Pt. 45°C) in embedding oven for $\frac{1}{2}$ h; (*v*) Transfer to a fresh change of soft wax for a further $\frac{1}{2}$ h; (*vi*) Embed in the usual way.

DOUBLE EMBEDDING METHOD FOR SMALL OBJECTS

This method, by Wilson (1933), is carried out in the following way: a treacle-thick solution of celloidin in equal parts of alcohol and ether is prepared. To this add an equal volume of clove oil, and stir the mixture thoroughly. Place in the warm, and stir occasionally until all smell of ether has vanished. Thin down the mixture with clove oil so that the viscous residue is a little more fluid than treacle (a 0·1 g lead shot should sink 1 in. in 1 min at room temperature).

If the specimen is very small it can be rendered more visible if it is stained with eosin (in absolute alcohol). Some viscous celloidin syrup is poured into a supported test tube to a depth of about 1 in. On top of this layer, a ½ in. layer of the celloidin–clove oil mixture is poured. Following this a ½ in. layer of pure clove oil is added, and finally this is topped with some stained absolute alcohol containing the specimen. Stopper the tube.

Allow the object to sink through the various layers until it has reached the bottom layer of celloidin in alcohol and ether—this will take several days—then pipette off the solutions above the object.

Fix a ring of glass, cardboard, or metal about ½ in. dia. by $\frac{1}{16}$ in. high to a slide flooded with a layer of molten paraffin wax. Place the slide in a Petri-dish, and fill the ring with celloidin solution. Transfer the specimen to the celloidin and orientate it under a microscope. Transfer the Petri-dish containing the slide to a chloroform desiccator and allow the celloidin to harden. When hard, fill the Petri-dish with xylene. This dissolves the paraffin wax and clears the celloidin block and specimen. After 1–2 h, transfer the celloidin block to cedarwood oil. When thoroughly impregnated with cedarwood oil, cut a rectangular block of celloidin with a vertical surface parallel to the future cutting plane. To indicate the position of the object in the block cut off the edges to a point at the opposite, bottom, right-hand end from the specimen.

Embed the block in hard paraffin wax, then trim this parallel to the enclosed block. Orientate the block correctly and affix it to the microtome chuck for sectioning.

The sections can be mounted in the usual way, but the flattening should be completed by exposing the drying slides to ether vapour. The drying should be carried out very slowly to avoid crinkling of the celloidin, and for a long time to ensure proper adhesion of the sections.

THE CARE AND MAINTENANCE OF MICROTOMES AND MICROTOME KNIVES

Microtomes are precision instruments, and should always be treated with the greatest care. When not in use they should be kept under a plastic or other type of cover. All moving parts, such as the slides, should be rubbed with a thin film of oil after use to prevent the formation of rust; this is particularly important after celloidin sections have been cut on a sliding microtome using the 'wet method'.

A good microtome is of no use without a sharp knife. A jagged edge on a knife only results in tears or striations in the prepared sections. Even a small defect invisible to the naked eye will be very obvious when the section is examined under a high power microscope. A good knife edge should look perfect under a ($\times$ 50) low-power microscope.

TYPES OF KNIVES

All good microtome knives should have a broad base so that vibration will be reduced to a minimum. Within reason, the longer the knife the better, because as one portion of the knife becomes blunt the knife can be adjusted so that another part of the cutting edge is brought into play.

(1) PLANO-CONCAVE (SLIGHTLY CONCAVE) KNIFE

This type of knife may be used for cutting paraffin sections on a sliding microtome. It may also be used for paraffin material on a rotary microtome, but is not as useful for this purpose as the biconcave knife.

(2) PLANO-CONCAVE (VERY CONCAVE) KNIFE

This type of knife is used only for celloidin work because the blade is extra thin and it would not be rigid enough for harder material. They are usually longer than the other types of microtome knives.

(3) PLANE-WEDGE KNIFE

Although many textbooks state that this knife is only used for the cutting of frozen sections, long knives of this type make excellent knives for celloidin work (Best et al, 1956). It may also be used for cutting giant and ordinary paraffin sections.

(4) BICONCAVE KNIFE

This type of knife is recommended for the cutting of paraffin sections on rocking, sliding and rotary microtomes.

(5) SAFETY RAZOR-BLADES

These may be used for light paraffin and frozen work. Most microtome manufacturers supply special holders for razor-blades, which fit into the usual slots which hold the ordinary knife. They are excellent for the cutting of very thin sections of small pieces of material. They are so inexpensive that it is hardly worth the trouble of sharpening the blades when they become blunt.

After use, clean off any paraffin wax with xylene, then dry the knife by drawing it through a clean soft duster. Knives which have been used for cutting wet celloidin sections and frozen sections should be wiped dry, then lightly smeared with fine machine oil. This oil should be removed, just before use, with a little xylene. Some workers advocate the use of two knives, one for fine work, and the other for rough work.

SHARPENING OF MICROTOME KNIVES

After a knife has been used it will tend to become blunt. If it is just blunt, but has not developed 'teeth', it is usually only necessary to strop it. For very fine work it is advisable to strop the knife after each block has been sectioned. After prolonged use, 'teeth' may develop and the knife will then require honing. After honing the knife should always be stropped.

(1) HONING

Hand honing is generally carried out by drawing the knife edge against a special type of stone, a hone. There are several types of hone, but the best is known as the Belgian black vein. This hone consists of a yellow coloured stone backed with a black stone; only the yellow side should be used for honing. A less expensive stone which is also very good is known as a Tam o'Shanter scotch hone. Plate-glass hones may be used when an abrasive such as aloxite is added to the surface. One advantage of the glass type of hone is that its abrasive power may be adjusted by the type of abrasive powder which is used. Hones must be lubricated before use. Light oil or soapy water should be used as the lubricant. In the case of plate-glass hones, the abrasive powder is made into a paste with a little water.

It is important to remember that every knife must be fitted with its own back before it is honed, and in the course of time this back should be renewed as the honing will gradually wear away the back, so changing the cutting angle of the knife. The knife should also be fitted with a handle.

The method of honing is as follows: place the hone on a non-skid surface so that it will not move during the honing process. Then pour a small amount of lubricant (oil or soapy water) on to the surface of the hone, smearing it across its entire surface. Rest the knife complete with handle and back on to the near end of the hone, with its cutting edge facing away from the operator, and its heel roughly in the centre of the near end of the hone. Then with a smooth easy action push the knife towards the far end of the hone in a diagonal direction so that it finishes with the end of the knife at the centre of the far end of the hone. The knife is then turned over on its back, and moved across so that the heel is at the centre of the far end of the hone. Then the knife is drawn towards the operator. It is again turned over on its back and moved across so that it is in its commencing position. This procedure is repeated several times until all irregularities are removed from the knife's edge. The honing process is more easily understood from the accompanying diagram (*Figure 3.13*).

Note carefully: Only the concave side of a plano-concave knife must be honed, though it is permissible to hone the plane side once or twice, using a very gentle pressure, to remove any burrs which may occur during the honing of the concave side.

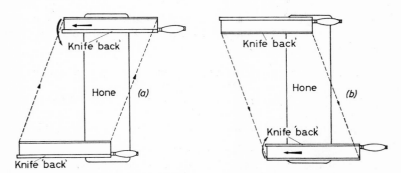

Figure 3.13. Method of honing microtome knives: (a) *forward stroke;* (b) *return stroke. N.B. Always turn knife over on its 'back'*

(2) STROPPING

When the knife has been honed, or when it has become only slightly blunt, it is necessary to polish the cutting edge. This polishing is done by a process known as stropping. The best type of strop is that made from the hide from the rump of a horse and is usually marked 'shell horse'. Some workers prefer the rigid type of strop while others prefer the flexible hanging type. Whichever type is preferred the strop must be kept free from dust, and the hide should be kept soft with regular applications of light oil to the back of the leather. Small quantities of 'strop dressing' may be applied to the surface of rigid strops. The method of stropping is almost the same as for honing, but the knife itself is in the reverse position; i.e., the knife is placed on the near end of the strop with the cutting edge towards the operator, and is dragged away, and on the return troke the cutting edge is still away from the operator. At each end of the strop the knife is turned over on its back. Note that when stropping a knife (except biconcave Heiffor knives) the special back must be in position.

KNIFE-SHARPENING MACHINES

These machines are becoming increasingly popular in many laboratories. They certainly save a great deal of valuable time in a department which has a large number of microtomes in continuous use.

There are various designs of these machines, but the type which is fitted with an eccentrically revolving lapping plate, seems to be the best. The plate is usually of plate glass, and various grades of suitable abrasives are added to the plate with a small quantity of oil or water. The various sizes of knife require their own holders. The honing angle is adjustable and it is important that this position is noted and rigidly adhered to for any particular knife. Periodically, the lapping plate is levelled off by putting a lapping bar into the holder instead of a knife.

THE RELATIONSHIP BETWEEN THE MICROTOME KNIFE AND THE OBJECT

The relationship between the knife and object is obviously of the greatest importance when sectioning. The following notes and accompanying diagrams show the most important relationships.

Angle of Cutting Stroke or 'Slant'

The slant is the angle along which the knife edge attacks the block

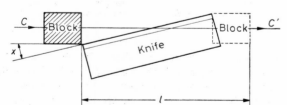

Figure 3.14. The angle of cutting stroke (slant) of a celloidin knife (after Hallpike, 1956). C—C', line of cutting stroke; x, angle of cutting stroke (slant); l, length of cutting stroke

of tissue. For paraffin sections the knife edge is used parallel to both the upper and lower surfaces of the block, in which position it enables ribbons of sections to be cut. For celloidin sections a slanting or oblique knife is used (i.e., the angle of cutting stroke is about 10 degrees). (See *Figure 3.14*, which shows a base-sledge microtome in use, but would be essentially the same for the more commonly used sliding microtome.) This small angle of cutting stroke results in a decrease of the effective cutting angle.

Tilt

Bolles Lee defines tilt of the knife as 'the angle that a plane passing through its back edge makes with the plane of the section (or the greater or less degree of elevation of the edge above the back)'. There seems to be a difference in the interpretation of this statement by

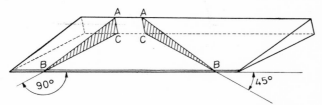

Figure 3.15. Variation of effective cutting angle (ABC) with angle of the cutting stroke (after Best et al., 1956)

various histologists and authors. Here, it is taken as being the angle between the plane of the section and the plane which bisects the cutting angle. The latter plane does not necessarily pass through the centre of the back; e.g., plano-concave knives. Generally the tilt is increased when hard tissue is being cut.

Clearance Angle

This is the angle formed by the plane of the section and the bevel nearest to the block (see *Figure 3.16*). The clearance angle is usually between 5 degrees and 15 degrees.

Top Rake Angle

This is the obtuse angle formed by the plane of the section and the bevel farthest from the block. (Best et al., 1956) states that rolling of celloidin sections (rolling is recommended) occurs when the top rake angle falls below 135 degrees.

It will be obvious that should the back of a knife become worn during honing, the cutting angle will change. This frequently happens with the biconcave knives (Heiffor) which are used with 'rocking' microtomes, and which are not usually supplied with honing backs. On the old type of rocking microtome the knife tilt could not be adjusted, and when old knives had become worn at the back cutting became impossible due to there being no clearance angle. On newer models, the knife tilt is adjustable so that the necessary clearance angle can be obtained.

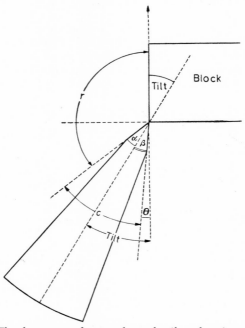

Figure 3.16. The clearance angle, top rake angle, tilt and cutting angle of a microtome knife: α = β; θ, *clearance angle*; r, *top rake angle*; c, *cutting angle*

STAINING TECHNIQUES

BASIC STAINING AND MOUNTING PROCEDURES

APPARATUS REQUIRED

The staining bench should be about 6 ft. in length, and should have a sink at one end. A slide washing rack should be placed across the sink. This rack is easily constructed from two pieces of glass rod, joined together at both ends with a piece of rubber tubing. A better type should be made from glass rod which is clamped into two metal blocks, these blocks being fitted with levelling screws. The type of staining jar to use will depend on the frequency with which that particular solution is used. If the stain is only occasionally employed a dropping bottle is probably the best to use, but for solutions which are in constant use Coplin jars or ground-glass staining jars are preferred. Some thought must be given to the size of slide which will be used. As most histological work which is carried out in zoology departments involves the preparation of serial sections, large slides are often used. Glass jars with ground-glass stoppers make good containers for coverslips which should be cleaned and put into absolute alcohol. The arrangement of the apparatus on a typical bench will be described for the staining and mounting of paraffin, celloidin and frozen sections.

Paraffin Sections

The basic procedure for the staining and mounting of paraffin sections is as follows: (1) The removal of the paraffin wax with xylene; (2) Hydration, taking the sections down to water through the graded alcohols; (3) The staining process; (4) The gradual dehydration by taking the sections up through the graded alcohols; (4) Clearing of the sections in xylene; (5) Mounting the sections beneath a coverslip in a special mounting medium.

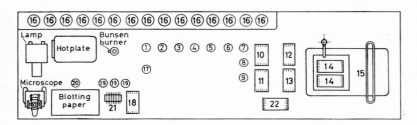

Figure 3.17. Suggested bench lay-out when staining paraffin wax sections

1. Xylene (for dewaxing);
2. Second xylene bath;
3. First absolute alcohol bath;
4. Second absolute alcohol bath;
5. 90 per cent alcohol;
6. 70 per cent alcohol;
7. 50 per cent alcohol;
8. Acid alcohol;
9. Alkaline alcohol;
10. Lugol's iodine;
11. 2 per cent sodium thiosulphate;
12. Ehrlich's haematoxylin;
13. Aqueous eosin;
14. Slotted dishes in a deeper dish, to act as slide washing tray;
15. Rack above sink. Use when staining with less common stains;
16. Raised shelf with bottles of graded alcohols, stains, etc.;
17. Xylene;
18. Final xylene bath;
19. Small bottles containing different sizes of coverslips;
20. Mountant;
21. Rack holding cleaned coverslips (corrugated paper);
22. Distilled water

[1–9, and 17 should be round, straight-sided glass staining jars with ground-glass lids; 10–14, 18 and 22 should be rectangular, slotted staining jars, capable of taking 10 slides of 3in. × 2in. size; 16, Glass bottles of varying size according to frequency with which the solution is used]

Arrange the jars of reagents on the bench in a convenient fashion. Such a layout is shown in *Figure 3.17*. The details of procedure which are required for staining paraffin-wax sections with Ehrlich's haematoxylin and aqueous eosin are now given. Once this procedure is learnt thoroughly, the technician will find that it is a relatively simple matter to carry out many other seemingly more difficult techniques.

(*i*) Dewaxing

The slide with the attached sections should be placed on to the hotplate for a few minutes, before being put into the first bath of xylene, where it is left for at least 2 min. This should remove all the wax and make the tissue transparent.

(*ii*) Hydration

The slide is then transferred to a bath of absolute alcohol, where the sections should become opaque. If any wax appears to be left on the slide, it should be returned to the xylene. After 30 sec transfer the slide to the second bath of absolute alcohol, where it should be left for about 1 min. It is then transferred to 90 per cent alcohol for a further minute.

If the tissue was fixed in fixative containing a mercuric chloride, the deposit should be removed at this stage. This is done by transferring the slide to a bath of 0·25 per cent iodine in 70 per cent alcohol for 5 min. The iodine is then removed by transferring the slide to 2 per cent sodium thiosulphate solution, after giving it a quick rinse in water. The iodine should be removed with 3 min immersion in the 'hypo'. It should then be washed in running water for several minutes and given a final rinse in distilled water.

(*iii*) Staining

The slide may be transferred directly to the dish of Ehrlich's haematoxylin from the 90 per cent alcohol or from distilled water. Some workers transfer to haematoxylin from 70 per cent alcohol. The slide should be left in the stain for at least 30 min.

After draining off any excess stain, the slide is transferred to a slide-washing tray, and is left in the running tap-water until the sections are blue (when first removed from the stain they are a red colour). This 'blueing' reaction takes about 10 min in mildly alkaline tap-water. A drop of ammonium hydroxide solution or lithium carbonate may be added to the water if it is insufficiently alkaline.

After blueing has been carried out, the underside of the slide should be wiped dry and the sections examined with a microscope. In most cases the cytoplasm will have taken up some stain, which will have to be removed. This is done by giving the slide a quick rinse in acid alcohol (1 per cent hydrochloric acid in 70 per cent alcohol), a process which is known as differentiation. On removal from the acid alcohol, the slide should then be given a quick rinse in running water, and then left to 're-blue' in the slide-washing tray. This again will take about 10 min. The slide should once again be examined, and if more differentiation is required this is carried out and the slide again re-blued. If it is necessary for the staining to be carried out quickly, the blueing may be done with alkaline alcohol (1 per cent ammonium hydroxide in 70 per cent alcohol).

(iv) Counterstaining

After rinsing in distilled water the section is then counterstained by transferring it to 1 per cent aqueous eosin Y solution for $\frac{1}{2}$–1 min. The eosin should colour the general cytoplasm pink. To some extent the degree of cytoplasmic staining is a matter of personal preference, but it should be noted that overstaining with eosin will mask the nuclear staining, a thing to be avoided.

(v) Dehydration

After counterstaining, the slide should be rinsed in distilled water and then transferred to 70 per cent alcohol where it is left for 30 sec. After this time it is transferred to 90 per cent alcohol for another 30 sec, and then to the first bath of absolute alcohol where it is left for 1 min. It should then have a further $\frac{1}{2}$ min in the second bath of absolute alcohol.

(vi) Clearing

The slide is transferred to the first bath of xylene and left to clear for several minutes. It should then be transferred to a final bath of xylene, where it may be stored with other stained slides for as long as an hour. This will enable the mounting of several slides to be carried out as a separate process.

(vii) Mounting

Sufficient coverslips (which have been stored in absolute alcohol) are wiped dry with a piece of silk, and stood on edge in a suitable rack. A rack is easily made by attaching a piece of corrugated paper to a small piece of wood. When ready, the slide is removed from the xylene and allowed to drain for a second or so. The underside is then wiped dry on the piece of blotting paper. The clean dry coverslip then receives one drop of mountant (e.g., Canada balsam), and the coverslip is placed on to the section so that the mountant will spread to its sides. Gentle pressure may be applied to the coverslip. The technician should practise mounting until he or she knows just how much mountant is required for a particular size coverslip. Large coverslips are a little more difficult to use than the usual ⅞ in. sq. type, but if a strip of mountant is applied down the centre of the coverslip, starting and finishing about ¼ in. from the ends, they are easily applied. For paraffin sections and any other thin sections the mountant should have a thin consistency. A good guide is that it should easily run off from the glass rod, with which it is usually applied.

Celloidin sections

As already stated celloidin sections are sometimes attached to slides before staining is carried out. In this case the staining procedure is similar to that just described for paraffin sections. However, celloidin sections may be much thicker than paraffin sections, and the time required in each solution will have to be increased.

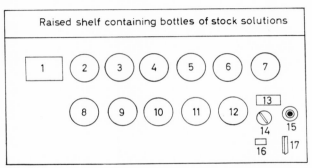

Figure 3.18. Suggested bench lay-out when staining celloidin sections with Ehrlich's haematoxylin and eosin

1. Dish of 70 per cent alcohol containing the sections;
2. Petri-dish containing 70 per cent alcohol;
3. Petri-dish containing very dilute haematoxylin;
4. Petri-dish containing acid alcohol;
5. Petri-dish containing alkaline alcohol;
6. Petri-dish containing distilled water;
7. Petri-dish containing 1 per cent eosin (aq. soln.);
8. Petri-dish containing 70 per cent alcohol;
9. Petri-dish containing 90 per cent alcohol;
10. Petri-dish containing 95 per cent alcohol;
11. Petri-dish containing alcohol, chloroform, xylene (equal parts);
12. Petri-dish containing beechwood creosote;
13. Prepared slides;
14. Jar containing Canada balsam or other mountant;
15. Dropper-bottle containing xylene
16. Clean coverslips;
17. Cigarette papers

The majority of celloidin sections are stained separately and only attached to the slides immediately prior to mounting. The staining is usually carried out by floating the sections through the various reagents in Petri-dishes. *Figure 3.18* shows a suggested arrangement

STAINING TECHNIQUES

of the Petri-dishes and other apparatus necessary to stain celloidin sections with Ehrlich's haematoxylin and eosin.

The procedure for staining is as follows: the sections should be transferred from the dish of 70 per cent alcohol, in which they have been stored, to a Petri-dish full of fresh 70 per cent alcohol.

(*i*) *Staining*

Transfer the section to a Petri-dish containing Ehrlich's haematoxylin diluted with 100 parts of distilled water, where it is left for 12 h. After this time the nuclei should be perfectly stained, and the section should require no differentiation. If, however, it does require differentiation, this is carried out by transferring it to acid alcohol for a few seconds. The section in either case should then be 'blued' in alkaline alcohol. This may take up to 10 min if the sections are very thick. Then transfer the sections to distilled water.

(*ii*) *Counterstaining*

The cytoplasm is then stained lightly with 1 per cent aqueous eosin Y for about $\frac{1}{2}$–1 min.

(*iii*) *Dehydration*

After counterstaining, the section is transferred to 70 per cent alcohol for 3 min, and then transferred to 90 per cent alcohol. From this point the best method of treatment is the beechwood creosote technique which has already been described (p. 212). However, the section may at this stage be flattened on to a slide. It should then be carefully blotted with a fine filter paper. The section is then flooded with absolute alcohol from a drop bottle, left for 1 min and again blotted dry. Absolute alcohol is again added and the section blotted dry.

(*iv*) *Clearing*

Xylene is then added to the section, which should be blotted dry and then resoaked in xylene until the section is perfectly clear.

(*v*) *Mounting*

A coverslip should be wiped dry of absolute alcohol using a piece of silk, and should then be placed on the rack. Sufficient balsam is then added to the section, and the coverslip applied. It should be lowered gradually so that no air bubbles are trapped beneath it. The slide is then ready for labelling. If it is placed in a warm place, such as an incubator, the mountant will dry more quickly.

Frozen Sections

The basic procedure for staining and mounting frozen sections, using Erhlich's haematoxylin and eosin, is now described. It resembles the method used for separate celloidin sections, in that the sections are floated through baths of the various reagents. Small Petri-dishes are probably the most convenient containers. A suggested arrangement of the Petri-dishes and other necessary apparatus is shown in *Figure 3.19*. As already mentioned, frozen sections are sometimes attached to alluminized slides before being stained, in which case the staining procedure is similar to that used for paraffin sections. The method for separate sections is to transfer the sections from the microtome knife to a dish of distilled water, using a camel-hair brush or a glass hockey-stick. Selected sections are then transferred to a dish of 70 per cent alcohol.

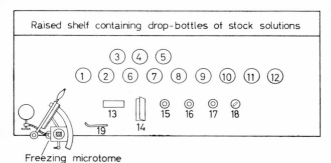

Figure 3.19. Suggested bench lay-out when staining frozen sections with Ehrlich's haematoxylin and eosin

1. Watchglass containing distilled water;
2. Watchglass containing 70 per cent alcohol;
3. Watchglass containing 90 per cent alcohol
4. Watchglass containing absolute alcohol } Used only when excess fat has to be removed
5. Watchglass containing xylene;
6. Watchglass containing half-strength Ehrlich's haematoxylin;
7. Watchglass containing tap-water;
8. Watchglass containing acid alcohol;
9. Watchglass containing alkaline alcohol;
10. Watchglass containing eosin (1 per cent aq. soln.);
11. Watchglass containing tap-water;
12. Watchglass containing 70 per cent alcohol;
13. Clean slides;
14. Cigarette papers;
15. Drop-bottle containing 90 alcohol;
16. Drop-bottle containing absolute alcohol;
17. Drop-bottle containing xylene;
18. Jar containing Canada balsam or other suitable mountant;
19. Section lifter

(i) Removal of Excess Fat

If the sections contain an excess of fat which is not required, then this should be removed by transferring the section to 90 per cent alcohol for 1 min, followed by 1 min in absolute alcohol. The fat is then removed by immersing the section for several minutes in xylene. When this has been done, the section is taken down the alcohols again to 70 per cent alcohol. It is then ready for staining.

(ii) Staining

The section is then transferred to a dish of Ehrlich's haematoxylin, diluted with an equal volume of distilled water, for 15 min. The section should then be 'blued' by transferring it to a dish of tap-water (a drop of lithium carbonate solution may be added to the section if it is insufficiently alkaline). When it has been blued, it should be differentiated by transferring the section to a dish of acid alcohol for 1–2 sec. It is then immediately transferred to a fresh dish of alkaline tap-water, in order to be 're-blued'.

(iii) Counterstaining

The section is transferred to 1 per cent aqueous eosin for 1 min. After counterstaining the section is rinsed for about 2 min in tap-water. It is then transferred to 70 per cent alcohol. At this stage it is usually put on to a slide, where it should be drained and blotted carefully with a cigarette paper. Ninety per cent alcohol is then added from a drop bottle, and is left for 15 sec. It is then drained and blotted. This process is repeated twice with absolute alcohol, then xylene is added until the section is perfectly clear. If some white opaque patches remain then more treatment with absolute alcohol must be given, followed of course with xylene. When clear, any excess xylene should be wiped away and the section mounted with a coverslip using any desired mounting medium, e.g., Canada balsam.

STAINING *

The true theory of staining probably lies in a combination of the absorption and chemical theories. The absorption theory is that a large body attracts to itself small particles from a surrounding medium. This action may be selective under certain circumstances (e.g., it is affected by the pH of both substances), and it seems to be the most likely physical explanation of the action of stains. The chemical theory is that there is an actual chemical combination between the tissue and the dye. This is, however, far from being the complete truth in spite of the fact that, generally, acid dyes stain basic elements such as cytoplasm, and basic dyes stain acidic elements such as nuclei. For example, haematoxylin, which is an acid dye, does not stain the cytoplasm, but when combined with a mordant it is one of the most commonly used nuclear stains.

Biological stains are little different from commercial dyes, which are produced mainly for the textile industry. They are, however, refined and contain few impurities. This, however, is often a handicap, as many impurities act as mordants. Some of the Grubler dyes, which were manufactured before World War I, contained many impurities but gave brilliant results, which are rarely equalled with most modern dyes.

PRINCIPLES OF DYE CHEMISTRY

A brief study of the chemical structure of the 'coal-tar dyes', which

* Mainly after Culling (1963).

are all derivatives of benzene, will assist an understanding of modern dye chemistry. As their name implies, these dyes are all derived from coal-tar, and include the well-known aniline dyes which comprised the majority of early dyes.

Benzene

The molecule of benzene is formed by six carbon atoms and six hydrogen atoms so arranged that the carbon atoms form a ring. This benzene ring is usually drawn as a simple hexagon.

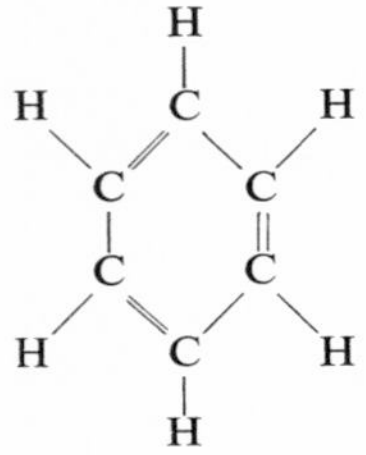

As the carbon atom has four valency bonds, the hexagon arrangement allows each carbon atom to have a double bond on one side and a single bond on the other. Therefore, if two of the hydrogen atoms are replaced by oxygen, a readjustment of the double bonds takes place and a new compound, quinone ($C_6H_4O_2$) is formed. Quinoid compounds are of importance in that they have absorption bands in the visible spectrum and are coloured. Benzene derivatives, on the other hand, absorb light only in the ultra-violet band and they are colourless.

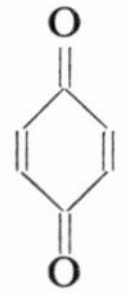

Quinone

Chemical structures that confer colour are known as chromophores. The quinoid arrangement (shown above) is a chromophore and the presence of one quinoid ring in a compound containing several rings will confer colour to that compound. The nitro group (NO_2) is also a chromophore, and when three nitro groups replace three hydrogen atoms in a benzene molecule the result is tri-nitro benzene which is yellow. Such a compound containing a chromophore is called a chromogen. Although these chromogens are

232

coloured they are not dyes since they have no affinity to textile fibres or tissue constituents.

To be a dye a compound must contain, in addition to a chromophoric group, another group which gives the compound the power of electrolytic dissociation; such groups are known as auxochromes. If an hydroxyl group (OH), which is an auxochrome, is added to the chromogen tri-nitrobenzene the chromogen will be converted to a dye–picric acid.

Picric acid is capable of forming a salt with a base and has an affinity for fibres and certain tissue constituents from which it is not easily removed. There are several auxochromic groups. Some are acidic, such as the hydroxyl group, while others are basic, such as the amino group (NH_2). There are, in addition, a few chromophoric groups which are slightly auxochromic in nature.

The sulphonic group (SO_3H) is important in dye chemistry because it forms acid salts. It is only slightly auxochromic and is used chiefly to make an insoluble dye soluble in water, or to convert an otherwise basic dye into an acid dye. For example, basic fuchsin is converted to acid fuchsin by the introduction of a sulphonic group.

An understanding of the conversion of certain dyes into colourless compounds (leuco-base) is useful as these leuco compounds are of great importance in the modern histological laboratory. Although the chromophoric groups differ in many respects, they share the property of being easily reduced, i.e. they have unsatisfied affinities for hydrogen. For example, the double bonds in the quinoid ring may break and the valencies become attached to hydrogen. When a chromophore is destroyed the compound loses its colour and it is called, for example, leuco-fuchsin. Certain dyes become colourless on removal of their acid radical, as in the case of the triphenyl methanes (basic fuchsin) and the xanthenes (phenolphthalein) and, since this reaction is normally freely reversible, such dyes are useful as indicators of the hydrogen ion concentrations (pH).

CLASSIFICATION OF DYES

Dyes are classified by the chromophoric group present and not by their colours. The main groups are given below, but further details are given by Conn (1946).

(i) Nitroso group.
(ii) Nitro group.
(iii) Azo group.
(iv) Thiazol group.
(v) Anthraquinone group.
(vi) Quinone-amine group.
(vii) Phenyl-methane group.
(viii) Xanthene group.

Natural Dyes

In spite of the fact that the majority of dyes in use today are synthetic, a few natural dyes are still used, some of which are the most important of all dyes. They are haematoxylin, cochineal (carmine), orcein, litmus and indigo.

Haematoxylin

The most commonly used dye. It is extracted from the heart wood of the logwood tree (*haematoxylon campechianum*) which grows in Campeche, Mexico. Haematoxylin has no staining properties until it has been 'ripened' by oxidation into haematein. This ripening is either carried out by exposing the prepared solutions to air and sunlight for several weeks, or by adding an oxidizing agent such as sodium iodate or potassium permanganate. In ripening, the haematoxylin ($C_{16}H_{14}O_6$) loses two hydrogen atoms to become haematein ($C_{16}H_{12}O_6$), which has a quinoid arrangement in one of the rings.

Haematoxylin

Haematein (*the quinoid arrangement is shown in the lower ring*)

If the process of oxidation continues a colourless compound is formed, and it is for this reason that most workers prefer the slow method of ripening rather than the addition of an oxidizing agent. The latter method converts all haematoxylin to haematein immediately, and further natural oxidation shortens the life of the stain.

Ripened haematoxylin is rarely used alone since it has little affinity for tissue constituents. A mordant is usually added. Such mordants are salts of metals and are either used prior to staining or are incorporated with the haematoxylin.

Carmine

Carmine is produced from cochineal after treatment with alum. The cochineal itself is extracted from the female cochineal insect (*Coccus cacti*). Carmine is only slightly soluble in neutral water, and is usually employed in strongly acidic or alkaline solutions. Like haematoxylin it is of little use unless it is used with a mordant.

Orcein

Extracted from certain lichens, orcein is used as a specific stain for elastic tissue.

Litmus

This is also extracted from certain lichens, and is a commonly used indicator.

Acid, Basic and Neutral Dyes

All other stains are salts, composed of an acid and a base.

Acid Stains

In acid stains the acid component is coloured, while the base is colourless; e.g., acid fuchsin is composed of rosaniline trisulphonic acid which is coloured red, and sodium which is colourless. They are usually used for staining basic components such as cytoplasm.

Basic Stains

In basic stains the base contains the colouring substance which is combined with a colourless acid radical. For example, basic fuchsin consists of the base rosaniline, which is coloured, combined with the acid radical Cl, which is colourless. Basic stains usually stain acid components, such as nuclei.

Neutral Dyes

Neutral dyes are so called because they contain base and acid, both parts being coloured. They are usually prepared by mixing together aqueous solutions of certain acid and basic dyes in specified quantities, the resultant precipitate being a neutral dye. Neutral dyes are usually only soluble in alcohol. The best known neutral dyes are the Romanowsky dyes which are formed from the inter-action of polychrome methylene blue and eosin. Neutral dyes stain selectively both basophilic and acidophilic structures, as well as other neutrophilic structures.

Mordants

If tissues or sections of tissue are put into certain solutions of such dyes as the 'coal-tar derivatives', they become stained. This type of staining reaction is known as simple or 'direct' staining.

Other stains, particularly haematoxylin, will not stain tissue in a simple solution but only when a third element is present. This third element is known as a mordant and forms a link between the tissue and the stain. The combination of the dye with the mordant is often referred to as a 'lake' and is capable of attaching itself to the tissue. Some lakes are unstable and it is then necessary to soak the tissue in the mordant before applying the stain. Such is the case with Heidenhain's iron haematoxylin. The term mordant should only be applied to salts and hydroxides of divalent and trivalent metals and should not be applied to other substances which improve or aid staining in some other manner. These latter substances are known as accentuators and accelerators. The commonest mordants are the salts and alums of aluminium and iron (ferric).

Accentuators

Accentuators are substances which appear to act as catalysts in that they increase the selectivity or staining power of certain dyes without actually taking part in the formation of lakes, or actually combining chemically in any way (these dyes are already capable of staining without the addition of an accentuator).

Accentuators which have been used in the impregnation of the nervous system with metallic salts, are usually called accelerators. For some reason not understood, these accelerators are generally hypnotics.

Two examples of accentuators are: (a) potassium hydroxide, when used with Loffler's methylene blue, and (b) phenol, when used with thionin to give carbol-thionin.

One example of an accelerator is veronal which is used in Cajal's method for axis cylinders.

Metachromatic Stains

Certain coal-tar dyes stain particular tissue elements a different colour from that of the basic colour of the dye. For example, mucin will stain red with toluidine blue, while the rest of the tissue will stain various shades of blue. Thionin which is blue will stain cartilage a purple colour, and safranin which is red will stain cartilage a yellow colour. Tissues which react this way are said to exhibit metachromasia, and this type of staining reaction is known as metachromasy.

Metachromatic staining must not be confused with double staining which sometimes occurs when impurities are present in some dyes. For example, lignin pink is usually present in small quantities in most batches of chlorazol black.

THE PREPARATION OF STAINING SOLUTIONS

The following points should be strictly observed:

(*i*) All glassware should be thoroughly clean, and should be rinsed with distilled water and then dried. It should then be plugged with cotton wool.

(*ii*) The distilled water used must always be neutral (unless otherwise stated). Tap-water should only be used when specifically stated in the formula. The correct solvent must always be used.

(*iii*) The separate constituents of stains should always be mixed in the order given in the formula.

(*iv*) Unless otherwise stated, the solid dye should first be mixed into a paste with a little of the solvent, before adding the remainder of solvent and any other ingredients.

(*v*) All solutions, particularly alcoholic solutions, should be kept in glass-stoppered bottles.

(*vi*) When alcohol is specified as a solvent for a particular dye, it is understood to mean absolute ethyl alcohol, and no other type of alcohol should be used unless it is known to have no adverse effect upon the staining reaction.

When methyl alcohol is specified, as in the preparation of any Romanowsky stains, it should be of a specially purified type, which is free from acetone.

(*vii*) Sometimes the formula will state that the dye must be dissolved in *aniline water*. This is prepared by adding 5–10 ml. of aniline oil to 500 ml. of hot distilled water in a flask. This mixture should be well shaken and then allowed to cool to room temperature. When cool it is filtered and is then ready for use.

The solubility of a number of dyes is given in *Table 3.3*. The solubilities are expressed as grammes per 100 ml. of solvents, distilled water and ethyl alcohol at room temperature. The figures are only a guide, as room temperatures vary and affect the solubility, and different batches of stain may vary slightly in solubility.

237

Table 3.3. Approximate Dye Solubilities

	Percentage in water	Percentage in 66 O.P. spirit
Alizarin red S	7·7	0·2
Aniline blue W.S.		
syn. cotton blue	4·5	0·3
Auramin O.	0·7	4·5
Aurantia	nil	0·3
Benzopurpurin 4B	nil	0·1
Biebrich scarlet	nil	0·05
Bismarck brown	1·2	1·0
Carminic acid	8·2	nil
Chromotrope 2R	19·3	0·2
Congo red	nil	0·2
Crystal violet (chloride)	1·7	13·9
Crystal violet (iodide)	0·04	1·8
Eosin Y (Na salt)	44·2	2·2
Erythrosin (Na salt)	11·1	1·9
Ethyl eosin	0·03	1·1
Fluorocein (Na salt)	50·2	7·2
Fuchsin, acid	12·3	0·2
Fuchsin, basic		
Pararosanilin (chloride)	0·3	5·9
Pararosanilin (acetate)	4·2	13·6
Rosanilin (chloride)	0·4	8·2
New fuchsin (chloride)	1·1	3·2
Haematoxylin	1·2	34·5
Indigo carmine	1·7	0·01
Janus green	5·2	1·1
Light green	20·4	0·8
Martius yellow (Na salt)	4·6	0·2
Methyl orange	0·5	0·1
Methyl violet 6B	4·2	6·2
Methylene blue (chloride)	3·5	1·5
Neutral red (chloride)	5·6	2·5
Nile blue sulphate	1·0	1·0
Oil red O*	nil	0·4
Orange G	10·9	0·2
Phloxine	50·9	9·0
Picric acid	1·2	9·0
Pyronin Y	9·0	0·6
Safranin	5·5	3·4
Sudan III†	nil	0·2
Sudan IV	nil	0·1
Tartrazine‡	11·0	0·1
Thionin	0·3	0·3
Toluidine blue	3·8	0·6
Victoria blue 4R	3·2	20·5

* Also used at 0·1 per cent in isopropyl alcohol
† Also used at 0·2 per ceet in propylene glycol
‡ Also used at 2·3 per cent in cellosolve

Some common staining techniques for paraffin sections are now described. There are many modifications of some of these techniques, but the ones given here are those which the author prefers and which

STAINING TECHNIQUES

give consistently good results with a wide variety of animal material. The methods will be described in a brief form. The times quoted are for 8–10 μ sections.

(1) EHRLICH'S HAEMATOXYLIN AND AQUEOUS EOSIN

Preparation of the Stains
(a) *Ehrlich's Haematoxylin*

Haematoxylin..	..	..	..	..	2 g
Absolute ethyl alcohol	..	..	..	100 ml.
Glycerol	..	..	..	..	100 ml.
Distilled water	..	..	..	..	100 ml.
Glacial acetic acid	..	..	..	..	10 ml.
Potassium aluminium sulphate	..	in excess
					(about 3 g)

Dissolve the haematoxylin in the absolute alcohol, and then add the other ingredients in the order given. Stopper the bottle and put aside in daylight for several weeks until the solution has 'ripened'. When 'ripe' the solution should be a dark port wine colour and should smell like wine. As this is a very commonly used stain, a fresh stock solution should be prepared well in advance, and one bottle should be ripening while another is in use.

(b) *Aqueous Eosin Solution*

Eosin (water soluble)..	..	..	..	1 g
Distilled water	..	..	..	..	100 g

Staining Procedure
(*i*) Dewax the section in xylene.

(*ii*) Hydrate the sections via the graded alcohols. (Some workers transfer the slide to the staining solution from 90 per cent or 70 per cent alcohol.)

(*iii*) Transfer the slide to Ehrlich's haematoxylin (for at least 30 min).

(*iv*) 'Blue' the section in alkaline tap-water.

(*v*) Rinse for 1 sec in acid alcohol to differentiate the stain.

(*vi*) 'Re-blue' the section in alkaline tap-water.

(*vii*) Transfer the slide to the eosin solution (for ½–2 min).

(*viii*) Rinse the slide in tap-water, then dehydrate the section via the graded alcohols.

(*ix*) Clear the section in xylene.

239

(*x*) Mount the section in Canada balsam, D.P.X., or Micrex.

(2) MAYER'S HAEMALUM AND EOSIN

Preparation of the Stains

(*a*) *Mayer's Haemalum* (modified)

Haematoxylin	1 g
Distilled water	1 l.
Ammonium or potassium alum	50 g
Sodium iodate	0·2 g
Citric acid	1 g
Chloral hydrate	50 g

Dissolve the haematoxylin in the distilled water, using gentle heat if necessary. Add the alum, shaking to dissolve, and again using heat if necessary. When dissolved, add the other chemicals in the order given. This modification which uses haematoxylin in place of haematein is recommended because of its improved durability.

(*b*) *Aqueous Eosin solution:* 1 per cent solution of eosin (water soluble) in distilled water.

Staining Procedure

(*i*) Dewax the section in xylene.

(*ii*) Hydrate the section via the graded alcohols to distilled water.

(*iii*) Transfer to Mayer's haemalum. When used as a progressive stain, the staining time is about 15 min. When used as a regressive stain, the staining time is from 40 to 60 min.

(*iv*) 'Blue' the sections in tap-water or alkaline alcohol.

(*v*) If stain was used progressively, counterstain with eosin directly after blueing the haematoxylin (if used regressively differentiate in acid alcohol, then 're-blue' in tap-water or alkaline alcohol).

(*vi*) After counterstaining with eosin for 20–60 sec, dehydrate the sections via the graded alcohols, clear in xylene and mount in Canada balsam.

(3) HEIDENHAIN'S IRON HAEMATOXYLIN

Preparation of the Solutions

(*a*) *Heidenhain's Iron Haematoxylin* (*Stock solution*)

Haematoxylin	5 g
96 per cent alcohol	100 ml.

(This solution should be allowed to 'ripen' for a few weeks before use.)

(*b*) *Actual staining solution:* This is prepared by diluting 5 ml. of

240

the stock solution with 45 ml. of distilled water, immediately before use.

(*c*) *Mordant solution:* 3 per cent aqueous solution of iron alum.

(*d*) *Differentiating solution:* 1·5 per cent aqueous solution of iron alum.

Staining Procedure

(*i*) Dewax the section in xylene.

(*ii*) Hydrate the section to water via the graded alcohols.

(*iii*) Mordant the section in the 3 per cent iron alum for 30–45 min at 56°C, or 12–24 h at room temperature.

(*iv*) Rinse rapidly in water.

(*v*) Transfer to staining solution at the same temperature and for the same time as that used for the mordanting process.

(*vi*) Rinse rapidly in water, then differentiate the section carefully, examining it every few minutes under a microscope.

(*vii*) Wash the section in running water for 5 min to remove the iron alum.

(*viii*) Dehydrate, clear, and mount in Canada balsam, D.P.X., or Micrex.

Results

If the method of fixation has preserved them, and the correct degree of differentiation is obtained, the following elements may be demonstrated: mitochondria, ground cytoplasm, nuclear membrane, yolk, chromosomes, chromatin, centrioles and nucleoli, also the cross-striations of muscle fibres, but these latter structures are better demonstrated if the haematoxylin is differentiated with two-thirds saturated picric acid in 96 per cent alcohol. Sometimes another stain such as Orange G, or Van Gieson is used as a counterstain, but this often detracts from the result.

(4) WEIGERT'S HAEMATOXYLIN AND VAN GIESON'S STAIN

Preparation of the Stains

(*a*) *Weigert's Iron Haematoxylin*

Solution A

| Haematoxylin.. | .. | .. | .. | .. | 1 g |
| Absolute alcohol | .. | .. | .. | .. | 100 ml. |

(Allow this solution to 'ripen' for a week or two before use.)

Solution B

30 per cent aqueous solution of ferric chloride	4 ml.
Distilled water	..	..	..	..	100 ml.
Hydrochloric acid	..	..	..	..	1 ml.

The staining solution is prepared immediately before use by mixing equal parts of Solutions A and B. They will mix more readily if Solution B is added to Solution A.

(*b*) *Van Gieson's stain*

Saturated aqueous solution of picric acid	..	100 ml.
1 per cent aqueous acid fuchsin solution	..	10 ml.

Staining Procedure

(*i*) Dewax the section in xylene, then bring the section to water via the graded alcohols.

(*ii*) Stain in Weigert's haematoxylin for 40 min.

(*iii*) 'Blue' in tap-water (the nuclei will be stained black).

(*iv*) Differentiate in acid alcohol if necessary.

(*v*) 'Blue' in tap-water.

(*vi*) Counterstain with Van Gieson's stain for 3 min.

(*vii*) Rinse rapidly in water to differentiate the acid fuchsin.

(*viii*) Dehydrate in 90 per cent alcohol, then absolute alcohol to which a few drops of alcoholic picric acid solution have been added. Then rinse rapidly in alcohol, blot, and clear in xylene.

(*ix*) Mount in Canada balsam, D.P.X. or Micrex. If the balsam is slightly acid it will help to preserve the counterstain.

Results

Nuclei	blue-black
Collagen	red
Cytoplasm, muscle, erythrocytes	yellow

(5) MALLORY METHOD
Preparation of the Solutions

(*a*) *Mordant solution*: Saturated mercuric chloride in water + 5 per cent acetic acid.

(*b*) 1 *per cent acid fuchsin* (aqueous solution).

(*c*) 1 *per cent phosphomolybdic acid* (aqueous solution).

(*d*) *Mallory's stain:*

Aniline blue (water soluble)	0·5 g
Orange G	2 g
Oxalic acid	2 g
Distilled water	100 ml.

Staining Procedure

(*i*) Dewax the section in xylene.

(*ii*) Bring the section to water via the graded alcohols.

(*iii*) Mordant the section in Solution (*a*) for 10 min.

(*iv*) Rinse in distilled water.

(*v*) Stain in Solution (*b*) for $\frac{1}{4}$–$\frac{1}{2}$ min.

(*vi*) Rinse rapidly in distilled water, then mordant collagen in Solution (*c*) for 2 min.

(*vii*) Rinse rapidly in distilled water, then stain with Solution (*d*) for 1–2 min.

(*viii*) Rinse rapidly in distilled water, then transfer to 70 per cent alcohol for about 10 sec, then differentiate the aniline blue in 90 per cent alcohol until the desired degree of staining is reached (a few seconds is usually sufficient).

(*ix*) Dehydrate in absolute alcohol, clear in xylene, and mount in Canada balsam, D.P.X., or Micrex.

Results

Nuclei	red
Collagen	blue

(6) PICRO-MALLORY METHOD

(Lendrum and McFarlane's modification of the Mallory technique.) This modification is now more popular than any of the numerous other modifications.

Preparation of the Stains

(*a*) *Celestine blue:*

Iron alum	2·5 g
Celestine blue B..	0·25 g
Glycerol	7 ml.
Distilled water	50 ml.

Dissolve the iron alum in the water overnight, then add the dye and boil for 3 min. Cool, filter and add the glycerol.

(*b*) *Mayer's haemalum* [see staining method (2)]

(*c*) *Orange G–Picric acid*

Orange G.	0·2 g
Picric acid (saturated solution in 80 per cent alcohol)	100 ml.

(*d*) *Ponceau-acid fuchsin*

Acid fuchsin (1 per cent solution in 1 per cent acetic acid)	100 ml.
Xylidine ponceau (1 per cent solution in 1 per cent acetic acid)	200 ml.
Sodium sulphate (10 per cent aqueous solution)	7·5 ml.

Staining Procedure

(*i*) Dewax the section in xylene, then hydrate the section via the graded alcohols.

(*ii*) Stain in celestine blue for 10–20 min.

(*iii*) Rinse in water, then stain in Mayer's haemalum for 5–10 min.

(*iv*) Differentiate in acid alcohol, until only the nuclei are stained.

(*v*) Rinse in 70 per cent alcohol, then stain in Orange G.–Picric acid for 1–12 h.

(*vi*) Rinse rapidly in water, then stain in Ponceau fuchsin for ½–2 min.

(*viii*) Differentiate, and mordant the collagen in 1 per cent aqueous phosphomolybdic acid solution.

(*viii*) Counterstain in 1 per cent aniline blue (water soluble) aqueous solution for 2–5 min.

(*ix*) Rinse in 1 per cent acetic acid solution.

(*x*) Dehydrate via the graded alcohols, clear in xylene, and mount in Canada balsam, D.P.X., or Micrex.

This technique gives brilliant results but requires a good deal of practice, as staining times vary considerably according to the tissue involved and the fixative used.

Results

Fibrin	red
Erythrocytes	orange
Collagen	blue
Nuclei	blue-black

(7) MASSON'S TRICHROME TECHNIQUE

There are many modifications, but the following one is recommended.

Preparation of the Stains

(*a*) *Weigert's Haematoxylin* [see staining method (4)]

(*b*) *Xylidine Ponceau-acid fuchsin:*

Xylidine ponceau	0·7 g
Acid fuchsin	0·35 g
Glacial acetic acid	1·0 ml.
Distilled water	100 ml.

Dilute 1–10 with distilled water before use.

(*c*) *1 per cent aqueous solution of phosphomolybdic acid.*

(*d*) *1 per cent solution of light green in 1 per cent acetic acid.*

Staining Procedure

(*i*) Dewax the section in xylene, then hydrate via the graded alcohols to water.

(*ii*) Stain in Weigert's iron haematoxylin for 40 min, then 'blue' in tap-water; differentiate in acid alcohol until only the nuclei are stained, then 're-blue' in tap-water.

(*iii*) Stain for 3 min in xylidine Ponceau-acid fuchsin.

(*iv*) Rinse rapidly in distilled water, then mordant in the phospho-molybdic acid solution for 3–5 min.

(*v*) Rinse rapidly in water, then stain the collagen with the light green solution for about ½ min.

(*vi*) Rinse rapidly in water, then dehydrate via the graded alcohols as quickly as possible.

(*vii*) Clear in xylene, then mount in Canada balsam, D.P.X. or Micrex.

Results

Nuclei .. .. blue-black
Collagen .. .. green
Other cytoplasmic structures .. .. pink or orange

(8) MALLORY'S P.T.A. HAEMATOXYLIN

This method is particularly useful for tissues of the nervous system. Preferably fix tissue in solutions containing mercuric chloride.

Solutions required:

A. 0·25 *per cent aqueous solution of potassium permanganate.* }Mallory's

B. 5 *per cent aqueous solution of oxalic acid.* }bleach.

C. *Mallory's haematoxylin:*

Haematoxylin .. .. 1 g
Phosphotungstic acid .. .. 20 g
Distilled water .. .. to 1 l.

Dissolve the haematoxylin and the phosphotungstic acid separately in distilled water, using gentle heat. When cool, mix the two solutions and make them up to 1 l. The solution may be ripened immediately by the addition of 1·77 g of potassium permanganate, or by exposing the solution to light and warmth for several weeks.

Staining Procedure

(*i*) Bring sections to water, and treat with iodine, followed by sodium thiosulphate.

(*ii*) Place in Solution A for 5 min.

(*iii*) Wash in water for 2 min.

(*iv*) Rinse in distilled water, then place in Solution B for 10 min.

(*v*) Wash in water for 5 min, then rinse in distilled water.

(*vi*) Stain in Solution C for 12–24 h.

(*vii*) Dehydrate through 95 per cent and absolute alcohol (do this rapidly).

(*viii*) Clear in xylene and mount in neutral Canada balsam.

Results

Nuclei, centrioles, fibroglia, myoglia and neuroglia fibres, fibrin and cross-striation of muscle fibres	blue
Collagen, reticulin, and ground substance of bone	yellow—brick red

SOME ROUTINE STAINING METHODS FOR WHOLE-MOUNT PREPARATIONS

It is just as important that material required for whole-mount preparations be as well fixed as that required for sectioning. Recommended fixation methods are given for a wide variety of material in Chapter 1.

During the staining procedure the material should be treated with the greatest care. A convenient method is to put the fixed material into a solid watch glass of a suitable size. The various solutions are then easily put onto the specimen by means of a fine glass pipette fitted with a rubber teat. The solid watch glass should be fitted with a glass lid. At any stage of the staining procedure it is a simple matter to examine the specimen by placing the watch glass on to the stage of a dissecting microscope. Dehydration in all cases should be very gradual as any distortion which occurs through shrinkage will mar the appearance of the finished specimen. Clearing should be carried out gradually and the majority of material is best cleared by transferring the specimen from absolute alcohol to cedarwood oil, in which it may remain for several hours before being transferred to xylene. Canada balsam (neutral) still remains the best mounting medium for the majority of whole mounts as it shrinks much less than such mountants as D.P.X. or Micrex. This is important because most whole-mounts are much thicker than sections, and the coverslips are further away from the slide, and there is more chance of air bubbles being drawn into the mountant. Very small specimens should be protected by mounting one or two short lengths of fine glass capillary tubing with them beneath the coverslip, so that the weight of the coverslip will not squash the specimen. For minute objects such as protozoa a piece of hair is preferable to the glass capillary. If the glass capillary is filled with xylene before being put into the mounting medium it will be almost invisible. Larger specimens require thicker material to support the coverslip, and thin strips of acetate sheeting may be used. A neater way is to prepare cells from $\frac{1}{16}$ in. or $\frac{1}{8}$ in. perspex sheet by drilling $\frac{1}{2}$ in. holes through the sheet, with their centres $\frac{7}{8}$ in. apart. When the sheet is sawn through at a position midway between each hole, a number of cells will be obtained which will be the size of a $\frac{7}{8}$ in. coverslip. Each cell should be attached to the centre of a clean glass slide using 'Glyceel' (G. T. Gurr). They may be stored in a dust-free container until they are required. When the specimen is ready for mounting the cell should be filled to the brim with Canada balsam and the specimen introduced and orientated into the correct position by means of a fine needle which should have been previously dipped into xylene. A clean coverslip is then gently lowered into position, allowing one side to descend before the other. If sufficient mounting medium has been used, some excess will flow out from the cell, but if too little has been used, air bubbles will be drawn into the cell. If this happens, remove the coverslip at once, and add more mountant, then replace with a fresh clean coverslip. The preparation should be placed in a level dust-free place where it will gradually dry at room temperature. A similar method to that just described has been used with great success for large specimens such as siphonophores and ammocoete lampreys about $2\frac{1}{2}$ in. in length. In these cases rectangular cells were made from $\frac{1}{8}$ in. perspex sheet.

The following staining methods are recommended:

(1) ANTHRACENE BLUE W.R. 'BECHER' (from G. T. Gurr)
Solutions required:
 (i) 5 per cent aluminium sulphate solution.
 (ii) Anthracene blue W.R. 'Becher' .. .. 0·5 g
  5 per cent aluminium sulphate solution .. 100 ml.

The staining solution is prepared by diluting the anthracene blue solution with the aluminium sulphate solution until a pale purple-pink solution is obtained (about 1 part stain to 20 parts aluminium sulphate solution).

The time required for staining will vary with each specimen, but an average time is about 36 h. It is unlikely that overstaining will occur, but if this should happen, excess stain may be removed by immersing the specimen in 1 per cent aqueous aluminium sulphate solution for several hours. When sufficiently stained the specimen should be washed for one hour in several changes of distilled water, and then gradually dehydrated by transferring it through the usual grades of alcohol. If a pale counterstain is required then the specimen should be transferred from 90 per cent alcohol to 0·01 per cent light green in absolute alcohol for a few seconds. Dehydrate thoroughly in at least two changes of absolute alcohol before clearing in cedarwood oil. Transfer to xylene a few minutes prior to mounting in neutral Canada balsam. This staining technique has given excellent results with chick blastoderms, trematodes, protozoa, large amphioxus, and an assortment of planktonic animals from siphonophores to molluscs. The main advantage of this stain over others is that most other stains tend to overstain the outer regions of the specimen before staining the inner parts, and subsequent differentiation usually results in the inner region becoming very much understained. This difficulty does not arise with anthracene blue (Mahoney, 1963).

(2) IRON ALUM—EHRLICH'S HAEMATOXYLIN

This quick and simple technique gives excellent results with a wide variety of animals. The technique is similar to that of Heidenhain's iron haematoxylin, but the times are much reduced and Ehrlich's haematoxylin is used instead of Heidenhain's haematoxylin. The method is to take the specimen down to water, mordant for 10–30 min in 3 per cent aqueous iron alum solution, then rinse for 10 sec in distilled water, and stain in Ehrlich's haematoxylin for 10–30 min. Rinse in distilled water, then differentiate in 1 per cent iron alum solution, changing the solution at least once. When sufficiently differentiated dehydrate slowly in the usual way, clear and mount.

(3) DILUTE HAEMATOXYLIN

The method is essentially the same as that already described for staining celloidin sections. Take the fixed specimen down to water, then transfer to dilute Ehrlich's haematoxylin (Ehrlich's haematoxylin 1 part: distilled water 100 parts). Leave to stain for 1–3 days until the desired degree of staining has been obtained. Then transfer the specimen to alkaline alcohol (1 per cent ammonium hydroxide in 30 per cent, 50 per cent or 70 per cent alcohol). Differentiation is not usually required if the staining process is carefully controlled. Should it be necessary to differentiate the specimen this is done with dilute acid alcohol, then the specimen is 're-blued' with alkaline alcohol.

This method gives excellent results with a wide variety of specimens.

(4) MAYER'S ACID HAEMALUM

This stain is a very powerful nuclear stain suitable for staining whole-mount preparations of trematodes and cestodes. Mayer's haemalum may be used as an alternative but this is a less specific nuclear stain.

Preparation of the Solutions

Haematein	1 g
90 per cent alcohol	50 ml.
Potassium alum	50 g
Distilled water	1 l.
Glacial acetic acid	20 ml.

Dissolve the haematein with moderate warmth in the alcohol. Add this to a solution of the alum in water, then add the acetic acid. Cool and filter.

Staining Procedure

(*i*) Take the fixed specimen to water.

(*ii*) Stain for several hours (1–24) in Mayer's acid haemalum.

(*iii*) 'Blue' in tap-water containing a few drops of ammonium hydroxide.

(*iv*) Dehydrate slowly through the ascending grades of alcohol.

(*v*) Clear in cedarwood oil for several hours.

(*vi*) Rinse in xylene for a few minutes.

(*vii*) Mount in Canada balsam.

(5) GRENACHER'S BORAX CARMINE

This is a very popular stain for whole-mount material, but unless carried out very carefully it will frequently give poor results. A lot of failures could be prevented by using the stain progressively, or at least by only slightly overstaining, so that differentiation is kept to a minimum. A recommended staining time for most specimens is 3–10 min, and if the material is very small, the staining solution may be diluted with an equal volume of 30 per cent alcohol. Carry out differentiation in acid alcohol, using a low-power microscope, until the desired degree of staining has been achieved. Then gradually dehydrate, clear and mount in the usual way.

The staining solution is prepared as follows: boil a solution of 3 per cent carmine in 4 per cent aqueous borax solution for 30 min. Then dilute with an equal volume of 70 per cent alcohol, and after allowing it to stand for some time, filter the solution.

(6) MAYER'S PARACARMINE

This technique is similar to the previous one, but the results are frequently superior. The staining solution is prepared in the following way:

Carminic acid	..	..	..	..	1 g
Aluminium chloride	..	..	..	..	0·5 g
Calcium chloride	..	..	..	..	4 g
70 per cent alcohol	..	:.	..	..	100 ml.

Dissolve, using gentle heat if necessary, then allow to settle, and filter. Sometimes it is necessary, particularly with large specimens, to dilute the staining solution with an equal quantity of 70 per cent alcohol, but as this sometimes causes the formation of precipitates, the solution should be slightly acidified.

(7) GOWER'S CARMINE
This is almost a purely nuclear stain, and is recommended for staining whole mounts of trematodes. It frequently gives good results with other types of animals, and is excellent for hydroids.

Before the stock solution of this stain can be prepared, it is necessary to prepare some acidified carmine. This is carried out by adding 10 g carmine to 100 ml. of 45 per cent acetic acid. Dissolve by heating, allow to boil, then cool and filter. The residue on the filter paper is acidified carmine. This should be allowed to dry, and it may be stored in a dry clean glass bottle.

The actual staining solution is prepared as follows:

Acidified carmine	..	..	..	..	1 g
Potassium alum ..	..	..	..	..	10 g
Distilled water ..	..	..	..	..	200 ml.

Dissolve the chemicals in the water, using heat, then cool and filter. Then add a crystal of thymol to prevent the growth of moulds. The staining procedure is to bring the specimen down to water and stain for 16–36 h in Gower's carmine. Then wash in several changes of distilled water; take up to 70 per cent alcohol, then destain in Mayer's bleaching solution (page 196) until the desired intensity is reached. Rinse in 70 per cent alcohol. If desired the specimen may be counterstained in Edicol Pea Green H (I.C.I.) 0·5 per cent solution in 70 per cent alcohol for approximately 5 min. Alternatively a 0·01 per cent alcoholic solution of light green may be used for a few seconds. Dehydrate, clear, and mount in the usual way.

(8) KIRKPATRICK'S CARMALUM
Gives constant results with either commercial carmine or cochineal. The solution consists of:

STAINING TECHNIQUES

Cochineal or carmine	..	..	..	..	25 g
Glacial acetic acid	..	..	..	..	25 ml.
Potassium alum ..	..	..	..	..	25 g
Distilled water ..	..	..	..	..	1 l.

Powder the cochineal or carmine in a mortar; add the acetic acid and 100 ml. of the water; allow to soak for 20 min, then boil gently for 1 h. Meanwhile, dissolve the alum in 500 ml. of the water and add it to the cooled cochineal or carmine solution. Repeat the heat treatment for 1 h. Cool and filter. Add 1 g salicylic acid (or some thymol crystals) to inhibit the growth of moulds. The solution will keep for at least one year.

Staining Procedure

Transfer the specimen to the staining solution for 12 h or more. Then destain in acid alcohol (0·5 per cent HC in 70 per cent alcohol); this may take several hours. Dehydrate through the ascending grades of alcohol. Clear in xylene, and mount in Canada balsam. The finished specimen should be a transparent red colour, with the different tissues in various shades of red.

SPECIAL TECHNIQUES
(1) SALIVARY GLAND CHROMOSOMES OF DROSOPHILA

(*a*) Select fully grown active larvae which have been well fed and raised at a low temperature. (See Drosophila Culture, page 88.)

(*b*) Dissect out the salivary glands in 0·7 per cent saline. With a pair of needles, use one to hold the larva firmly and the other to detach the head portion immediately behind the mouthparts. If the larva is very active it is advisable to use ice-cold saline. The whole of this 'dissection' must be carried out under a dissecting microscope. The salivary glands which are joined together anteriorly, are almost transparent and usually remain attached to the head portion together with a variable quantity of the fat body and fore-gut. They are most easily identified by the associated fat body.

(*c*) Remove as much of the fat body as possible.

(*d*) Transfer the glands to a clean slide and add a drop of either (*i*) Aceto-orcein (2 per cent orcein in 60 per cent acetic acid), or (*ii*) Propionic-orcein (1 per cent orcein in 45 per cent propionic acid). Allow to stain for about 5 min.

(*e*) Lower on a cover glass, then placing several thicknesses of filter paper over the cover glass apply pressure with the thumb, taking care to avoid any lateral movement of the cover glass.

(*f*) Heat gently over a spirit flame, then examine under a high-power microscope.

If permanent preparations are required, the cover glass should be removed after freezing the stain by placing the slide on to a block of dry ice (solid CO_2–Drikold), or by floating off in 45 per cent acetic acid; then the slide is dehydrated in 95 per cent alcohol, followed by absolute alcohol, finally mounting in euparal.

Giant chromosomes are also found in the nuclei of other diptera (e.g., *Chironomus*, and *Simulium*). The nuclei of these diptera, and those of *Drosophila*, start to undergo mitosis, but only reach mid-prophase, where each chromosome becomes recognizable as a separate structure. The division is then arrested, so instead of the usual spiralization giving a short fat metaphase chromosome, longitudinal splitting of the thread proceeds until about 256 threads lie side by side in each chromosome. This results in the chromosome having the usual metaphase diameter together with the prophase length, so giving a volume of about 128 times that of a normal metaphase. Such nuclei can be seen with a hand lens. The giant chromosomes have a banded appearance, each band corresponding to a chromomere on a single thread, and probably represents a gene locus, or a group of such loci (Shaw, 1960).

(2) TO DEMONSTRATE MEIOSIS IN ANIMAL MATERIAL

Insect testes are the most suitable material for demonstrating animal meiosis. The insects are only suitable at one particular time of the year. Grasshoppers have very large chromosomes and give very clear pictures of late prophase stage.

Adult male grasshoppers are dissected from June to late August. The testes are removed and prepared as aceto-orcein squashes (as for salivary glands) or they may be smeared on to a clean slide and immediately fixed in either acetic alcohol (glacial acetic acid, 1 part; absolute alcohol, 3 parts) or 2 BD fixative, which is:

Chromium trioxide	1 g
Potassium dichromate	1 g
Osmium tetroxide (2 per cent solution) ..	30 ml.
Glacial acetic acid	1·5 ml.
Saponin (optional)	0·1 g
Distilled water	230 ml.

After fixation in 2 BD or acetic alcohol, the smear should be stained by Feulgen's method.

Mammalian and other animal testes are almost certainly better examined as stained sections. Paraffin sections should be prepared, and staining with Feulgen's or Heidenhain's iron haematoxylin is particularly recommended.

(3) IDENTIFICATION OF CHROMATIN

Simple staining of the nucleus and nucleoli may be carried out by almost any of the routine staining methods, and when special care is taken to differentiate iron haematoxylin, both chromosomes of dividing nuclei, and chromatin or resting nuclei, may be readily demonstrated. Similar results may be obtained with many of the coal-tar dyes. But to stain the various components of the chromatin it is necessary to use a special histochemical technique. The chromatin of cells consists mainly of two types of nucleoproteins: (*i*) deoxyribonucleic acid (DNA) and (*ii*) ribonucleic acid (RNA). The RNA occurs mainly in the cytoplasm of the cell but it is also present in chromosomes, and in the nucleoli.

(*A*) *Technique for Deoxyribonucleic Acid* (*DNA*)

The technique makes use of the Feulgen reaction, in which aldehyde groups are released from the deoxypentose sugar of DNA when subjected to mild acid hydrolysis. The aldehydes are then detected by their reaction with Schiff's reagent (leucofuchsin), which causes them to turn a reddish-purple colour.

Fixation

Most fixatives will give good results with this technique, but the necessary hydrolysis times may vary considerably. If only nuclei are to be studied, Carnoy's fixative is recommended, while for general results formol–saline will give excellent results, and for smears of tissues methyl alcohol is recommended. Hydrolysis times are approximately 10 min in each case.

Preparation of Schiff's Reagent

First method (de Tomasi, 1936)—Dissolve 1 g of basic fuchsin in 200 ml. of boiling distilled water in a stoppered 1 l. flask. Shake for 5 min. Then cool to exactly 50°C, filter and add 20 ml. of N/1 hydrochloric acid to the filtrate. Cool further to 25°C, and add 1 g of sodium or potassium metabisulphite. Store in the dark for 18–24 h, add 2 g activated charcoal and shake the mixture for 1 min. Filter to remove the charcoal, then store in the dark at 0–4°C.

Second method (Barger and DeLamater, 1948)—Dissolve 1 g basic fuchsin in 400 ml. of boiling distilled water, cool and filter. Then add 1 ml. of thionyl chloride, stopper, and allow to stand overnight. Clear by shaking with activated charcoal, as in the first method, and filter. This solution should be stored in a refrigerator.

Preparation of the Sulphite Rinses

These must be freshly prepared each day. Add 7·5 ml. of 10 per

253

cent potassium metabisulphite solution and 7·5 ml. of N/1 hydrochloric acid to 135 ml. of distilled water. This will give a sufficient quantity to fill three Coplin jars.

Staining procedure

(*i*) Bring the paraffin sections to water, and if fixed in a solution containing mercuric chloride, treat the sections with iodine solution followed by sodium thiosulphate.

(*ii*) Wash in running water for a few minutes, then transfer to the hydrolysing bath which consists of N/1 hydrochloric acid preheated to 60°C. In most cases the required hydrolysis time will be approximately 10 min.

(*iii*) Rinse in distilled water, then transfer to Schiff's reagent for $\frac{1}{2}$–$1\frac{1}{2}$ h.

(*iv*) Without rinsing, transfer to the first bath of sulphite solution, then to the second and third baths, leaving the sections for about 5 min in each of the baths.

(*v*) Rinse well in distilled water.

(*vi*) If a counterstain is required, transfer to 1 per cent aqueous light green solution for a few seconds.

(*vii*) Dehydrate through the alcohols, clear in xylene, and mount in Canada balsam, D.P.X. or Micrex.

Results

DNA	red–reddish purple
Other constituents	pale green

(B) Technique for Ribonucleic Acid (RNA)
Pyronin–Methyl Green Stain of Unna-Pappenheim

If possible, each batch of stain should be tested by staining a known positive, and by treating a section with ribonuclease before it is used for routine purposes. There are two common methods in use: that of Trevan and Sharrock for formalin-fixed material and that of Jordan and Baker for Zenker-fixed material. The methyl green must be washed with chloroform in a separating funnel to extract the methyl violet which is usually present in every batch. The extraction is continued until the washings are free from colour. The purified stain should remain reasonably pure for 6 to 9 months, but will gradually form methyl green as a breakdown product. Pyronin Y is usually more selective than pyronin B. After carrying out a great many of the published methods, Culling (1963) states that the following technique gives the most consistent results.

254

(*a*) For formalin-fixed tissue—Trevan and Sharrock's stain:

5 per cent aqueous pyronin Y	17·5 ml.
2 per cent aqueous methyl green (purified) ..	10 ml.
Distilled water	250 ml.

Dilute with an equal quantity of acetate buffer pH 4·8.

(*b*) For Zenker-fixed material—Jordan and Baker's stain:

0·5 per cent aqueous pyronin Y	37 ml.
0·5 per cent aqueous methyl Green (purified)	13 ml.
Acetate buffer (pH 4·8)..	50 ml.

It is better to make up small quantities of stain than to store larger quantities. The technique is the same whichever solution is used.

(*i*) Bring sections to water, then pour on staining solution and leave to stain for 15–60 min.

(*ii*) Rinse rapidly in distilled water, then blot with filter paper.

(*iii*) Flood with acetone for a couple of seconds, discard, then flood again with acetone.

(*iv*) Flood the slide with a mixture of equal parts of acetone and xylene.

(*v*) Flood the slide with xylene, discard, and replace with fresh xylene.

(*vi*) Mount in a neutral mountant.

Results

Deoxyribonucleic acid (DNA)..	green
Ribonucleic acid (RNA)	red

(pH 4·8 acetate buffer is prepared by mixing 100 ml. of M/l sodium acetate solution with 40 ml. of M/l hydrochloric acid.)

(4) THE P.A.S. TECHNIQUE

This technique will give a positive staining reaction with all of the polysaccharide complexes which one is concerned with in histology. These include glycogen, hyaluronic acid, mucoproteins, glycoproteins, glycolipids and phosphatides. By carrying out several P.A.S. tests, following special supplementary tests, it is possible to identify many of these substances, but this process of identification is considered by the author to be beyond the scope of this book, and only the instruction for the P.A.S. technique itself will be given.

Fixation

For the majority of material, fixation in formol–saline or a mercuric chloride–formol fixative will give good results. Although glycogen is not fixed by formalin, it is rendered insoluble in water.

Processing the material

Routine paraffin sections are excellent for this technique.

The staining technique

(*i*) Bring sections to water.

(*ii*) Oxidize the sections for 5–10 min in 1 per cent aqueous solution of periodic acid (this converts substances with 1:2 glycol grouping to dialdehydes which will react with the Schiff's reagent).

(*iii*) Wash in running water for 5 min, then rinse in distilled water. Then immerse the sections in Schiff's reagent for 10–30 min.

(*iv*) Transfer to three sulphite rinses (2 min in each rinse). (See Feulgen technique, page 253.)

(*v*) Wash for 10 min in running water.

(*vi*) A good counterstaining method is to stain the nuclei with Ehrlich's haematoxylin, and the cytoplasm with tartrazine in cellosolve, or 2 per cent Orange G in 5 per cent aqueous *dodeca*-Tungsto-phosphoric acid.

(*vii*) Dehydrate, clear and mount.

When this technique is used for demonstrating glycogen, a control slide should be prepared, and the P.A.S. test carried out on this slide after it has been digested with diastase. This is done by flooding the slide with saliva and leaving it in a damp chamber at 37°C for 1 h.

(5) IMPREGNATION OF CELL WALLS WITH SILVER NITRATE

Preparations of pavement epithelium and similar structures showing the cell boundaries are easily prepared in the following way: rub a crystal of silver nitrate over the cornea of a frog's eye or the eye of some other convenient animal. Remove the cornea, and place it in distilled water in a watch glass. With a small brush remove the epithelium. Expose the dish to strong sunlight or at least strong daylight until the preparations have turned brown. Wash in distilled water, dehydrate through the usual grades of alcohol, clear in xylene and mount in Canada balsam. Metallic silver is deposited in the cell walls of the epithelium and fibrous layer, when the silver nitrate is reduced by the action of the light.

Other membranes similarly impregnated yield excellent results; for example, amphibia which have been kept in aquaria for some time shed pieces of their skin, and these pieces of epithelium will be found floating in the water. Other lining epithelia which may be used are the mesothelium (lining membrane of the abdominal cavity) and the endothelium of large blood vessels. The usual technique for the endothelium is to inject a 1 per cent aqueous solution of silver nitrate into the mesenteric artery of a mammal after severing the hepatic portal vein. Continue the injection until it runs out of the cut vein. Allow to stand for 2 min then inject a quantity of distilled water. Then remove a section of the artery, slit it open in a dish of distilled water, remove the membrane, spread it out and expose it to bright sunlight until it turns brown. Rinse in distilled water, dehydrate through the alcohols, and clear in xylene before mounting in Canada balsam.

(6) TECHNIQUES FOR THE DEMONSTRATION OF MITOCHONDRIA

Mitochondria are minute filamentous or granular intracellular structures. They are lipo-protein in nature, and are quickly affected by autolysis. It is therefore important that material should be fixed as soon as possible after death of the animal, in a suitable fixative.

Mitochondria may be demonstrated by vital staining. Examine dissociated cells in a solution of janus green B in isotonic saline (no stronger than 1 in 10,000). The mitochondria usually stain before any autolytic changes take place. They are at first a bluish-green in colour, but after a time the colour may fade due to the formation of its leuco-base.

For permanent preparations, thin paraffin sections should be prepared. The fixation is very important, and the best fixative appears to be Helly's fluid. Fix for 24 h, then post-chrome the tissue for 4–8 days, changing the solution at least 2–3 times. The post-chroming is done with 3 per cent aqueous potassium dichromate solution. After post-chroming wash the tissue well with running water for 12–24 h before processing. Some workers prefer to post-chrome the sections rather than the tissue. There are several staining methods which are suitable:

(A) Heidenhain's Iron Haematoxylin

This technique has already been described. If the differentiation is carefully carried out and the material has been suitably fixed, this method can give reasonably good results.

(B) Champy–Kull

This is probably the best method, but is more difficult to carry out than method (C).

(i) Bring sections to water.

(ii) Remove mercury precipitate with iodine and sodium thiosulphate.

(iii) Wash well in water, then flood the slide with aniline acid

257

fuchsin (saturated solution 14 per cent acid fuchsin in aniline water). Heat the slide and stain until steam rises, then leave to stain for a further 5 min.

(*iv*) Rinse slide with distilled water, then flood with 0·5 per cent aqueous toluidine blue solution for 3 min.

(*v*) Rinse with distilled water, then flood with 0·5 per cent aqueous aurantia in 70 per cent alcohol, for 2 min.

(*vi*) Rinse slide with absolute alcohol for a few seconds, clear in xylene, then mount in neutral Canada balsam.

N.B. If results are poor, alteration of the staining times of toluidine blue and aurantia will have to be made. If the section is too red, increase the time of staining with toluidine blue by $\frac{1}{2}$ min amounts. If the section is too blue, increase the time of staining with aurantia by similar amounts. It will be necessary to examine the mitochondria with a microscope fitted with an oil-immersion objective.

Results

Mitochondria	..	..	..	..	..	red
Nuclei	..	..	..	..	..	blue
Cytoplasm	..	..	..	..	yellow-orange

An easier method for the beginner is that of Altmann:

(*C*) *Altmann's Acid Fuchsin–Picric Acid Technique*

(*i*) Bring sections to water and remove mercury precipitates with iodine and sodium thiosulphate solutions.

(*ii*) Flood slide with 14 per cent acid fuchsin in aniline water, heat until steam rises, then leave to stain for 5 min.

(*iii*) Rinse in distilled water for 2 sec, then differentiate in Altmann's differentiator until the bright red of the section begins to fade. Altmann's differentiator is prepared as follows:

| Saturated picric acid in absolute alcohol | .. | 20 ml. |
| 30 per cent alcohol | .. | .. | .. | .. | 60 ml. |

(*iv*) Then, controlling the differentiation under a microscope, continue with a diluted differentiator (diluted with an equal volume of 30 per cent alcohol), until only the mitochondria are red and the nuclei and cytoplasm are yellow. Erythrocytes will also be stained red.

(*v*) Rinse in 90 per cent alcohol for 1–2 sec then dehydrate in absolute alcohol for 1–2 sec, clear in xylene and mount in neutral Canada balsam, D.P.X. or Micrex.

(7) CANCER DIAGNOSIS USING PAPANICOLAOU'S STAINS

G. N. Papanicolaou devised the following staining techniques for the diagnosis of malignant conditions of the female reproductive tract by the smear technique (see page 278).

Solution E.A.36 is recommended for vaginal, endocervical and endometrial smears. Solution E.A.65 is recommended for other types of smears, but either solution may be used for both groups.

Method

Fix the smear in iso-propyl alcohol, or ether/alcohol (1:1 or 1:2) for 5–15 min.

(*ii*) Hydrate the sections via the usual grades of alcohol to distilled water.

(*iii*) Stain the nuclei with Ehrlich's haematoxylin for 10 min; 'blue' in tap-water, differentiate in acid alcohol, then 're-blue' in alkaline alcohol or tap-water.

(*iv*) Dehydrate via the graded alcohols to 95 per cent alcohol, then stain in O.G.5, O.G.6 or O.G.8 for ½–2 min. Rinse in several changes of 95 per cent alcohol.

Solution O.G.5

    Orange G (0·5 per cent in 95 per cent alcohol)   100 ml.
    dodeca-Tungsto-phosphoric acid   ..   ..   25 mg

Solution O.G.6

    Orange G (0·5 per cent in 95 per cent alcohol)   100 ml.
    dodeca-Tungsto-phosphoric acid   ..   ..   15 mg

Solution O.G.8

    Orange G (0·5 per cent in 95 per cent alcohol)   100 ml.
    dodeca-Tungsto-phosphoric acid   ..   ..   10 mg

(O.G.6 or O.G.8 are recommended for normal smears, but O.G.5 is recommended for cancer diagnosis as it gives a sharper contrast of abnormal cells.)

(*v*) Stain in E.A.36 for 2 min or in E.A.65 for 1½ min. Then rinse several times in at least three changes of 95 per cent alcohol. (Use different alcohol from that used for rinsing after staining in Orange G.)

Solution E.A.36

    Light green SF solution (0·5 per cent in 95 per
      cent alcohol) ..   ..   45 ml.
    Bismark brown solution (0·5 per cent in 95 per
      cent alcohol) ..   ..   10 ml.
    Eosin yellow solution (0·5 per cent in 95 per
      cent alcohol) ..   ..   45 ml.
    dodeca-Tungsto-phosphoric acid   ..   ..   0·2 g
    Lithium carbonate (saturated aqueous solution) 0·05 ml.
                            (1 drop)

Solution E.A.65

Light green SF solution (0·25 per cent in 95 per cent alcohol)	45 ml.
Bismark brown solution (0·5 per cent in 95 per cent alcohol)	10 ml.
Eosin yellow solution (0·5 per cent in 95 per cent alcohol)	45 ml.
dodeca-Tungsto-phosphoric acid	0·2 g
Lithium carbonate (saturated aqueous solution)	0·05 ml. (1 drop)

(*vi*) Dehydrate, clear and mount in the usual way.

STAINING TECHNIQUES FOR THE CENTRAL NERVOUS SYSTEM

The use of methylene blue has already been discussed on page 189. Most other staining methods for C.N.S. tissues involve a technique whereby the various structures in the tissue are impregnated with metal. The most important of these metals is silver nitrate. Most tissues have the power of reducing silver nitrate to various degrees, and nervous tissue is capable of reducing it to a high degree. Some other tissues such as mucus cells, and some types of connective tissue, also have this power, and are all termed Argyrophyllic. The success of any silver impregnation method depends on a differential reduction potential between the nerve cells and the surrounding tissues. The reduction potential will still remain after fixation, but is modified according to the fixative used. The nature of the fixative is therefore of the greatest importance. Basically, the impregnation methods may be divided into the following four groups:

(*i*) Fresh tissue treated with a metallic salt solution; e.g., osmium tetroxide solution.

(*ii*) Fresh tissue treated with a metallic salt solution plus a reducing bath; e.g., Cajal technique.

(*iii*) Fixed tissue treated with a metallic salt solution plus a reducing bath; e.g., Bielchowsky.

(*iv*) Tissue fixed in an oxidizing agent (potassium dichromate), or fixatives containing it, then treated with silver nitrate or mercuric chloride. The chromate is deposited in the nerves; e.g., Golgi method.

The theory of the impregnation reactions is not fully understood, but it is generally agreed that (*a*) the silver nitrate consists of silver molecules formed by reduction of argentic ions; (*b*) that in the staining bath some silver is reduced and deposited as 'nuclei'. The more efficient the method, the more 'nuclei' will be produced and deposited in the nerve fibres, and less elsewhere. And (*c*) the 'nuclei' are negatively charged and absorb the positively charged argentic ions, which under the action of the reducer are transformed into insoluble silver. The stain therefore aggregates around the 'nuclei' and its extent will obviously depend on the extent of the initial 'nucleation', and also on there being sufficient argentic ions present in the tissues.

Failures may therefore be due to one or more of the following things: (*i*) lack of 'nucleation' in the fibres, or too much 'nucleation' elsewhere; (*ii*) a deficiency of argentic ions to be absorbed; (*iii*) an excess of argentic ions, so that most are not absorbed into the 'nuclei' but are deposited into the tissues, usually causing precipitation and a loss of selectivity of the staining.

The actual distribution of 'nuclei' is dependent not only on the natural distribution of reducing substances in the tissues but also on the pH. The pH is of the greatest importance in all silver impregnation methods, and if theory is lacking the optimum pH must be determined empirically.

Some useful staining techniques for C.N.S. are given below.

(1) *To Demonstrate Nissl Granules in Paraffin Sections of C.N.S. Tissue*

Fix the tissue in Heidenhain's 'Susa', formol-saline, Carnoy, or acetic-alcohol. Susa fixation is particularly recommended. After dehydrating, treating with iodine and sodium thiosulphate, the tissue should be cleared in cedarwood oil then embedded in 54°C paraffin wax. Cut sections at 10–20 μ thick. Hydrate the sections to water; stain for 1–2 min in 0·5 per cent cresyl violet acetate* solution; rinse in 70 per cent alcohol then transfer to 90 per cent alcohol. Differentiate in 1 per cent colophonium resin in 96 per cent alcohol until only the nuclei and the Nissl granules are stained. Rinse in two changes of absolute alcohol, clear in xylene, and mount in D.P.X. or Micrex.

(2) *To Demonstrate Cell Bodies, Axons, Dendrites and Neurofibrils*

Holmes technique will usually give excellent results. Solutions required:

A. 20 per cent silver nitrate solution.

B. (*i*) Boric acid	..	..	..	..	1·24 g
Distilled water	..	..	..	..	100 ml.
B. (*ii*) Borax	..	..	..	..	1·9 g
Distilled water	..	..	..	..	100 ml.

* Cresyl violet acetate (obtainable from National Aniline Division, America) is particularly recommended. The solution is prepared by boiling 0·5 g dye in 100 ml. distilled water, and adding 4 drops of glacial acetic acid.

C. Staining bath of buffered silver nitrate:

Solution B (*i*)	55 ml.
Solution B (*ii*)	45 ml.
Distilled water	392 ml.
1 per cent silver nitrate	3 ml.
Pyridine (pure white)	5 ml.

D. Reducing bath:

Hydroquinone	1 g
Sodium sulphite (cryst.)	10 g
Distilled water	100 ml.

E. 2 per cent oxalic acid solution.

F. 0·2 per cent gold chloride solution.

G. 5 per cent sodium thiosulphate solution.

Method

(1) Hydrate the sections to water and place in Solution A for 1–2 h in the dark.

(2) Rinse in three changes of distilled water for 10 min.

(3) Place in Solution C for 2–5 min at 37°C (the solution must be previously warmed).

(4) Place in Solution D at 50°C for 2–5 min.

(5) Wash in running tap-water.

(6) Rinse in distilled water for 2 min.

(7) Tone in Solution F, then rinse in distilled water.

(8) Place in oxalic acid Solution E for 2–10 min, until axons are blue-black. Then rinse in distilled water.

(9) Transfer to 5 per cent sodium thiosulphate solution, giving two changes during a period of 5 min.

(10) Wash in tap-water for 5–10 min.

(11) Dehydrate, clear and mount.

At stage 3 the pH may be altered slightly. High pH for fibres, lower pH for cells. From 7–10 ml. of pyridine sometimes improves the fibres staining, and if this is added the amount of distilled water must be decreased accordingly. At stages 7–8 these stages may be repeated if the sections are not dark enough.

(2a) *The following modification of the Holmes method was devised by A. D. Blest and gives excellent results with some invertebrate material, such as insect brains*

This modified method has been used on the brains of *Schistocerca*, *Apis*, *Antherea* and *Automeris spp*. The brains are fixed in alcoholic Bouin's solution, washed in 50 per cent alcohol, and embedded in 56°C paraffin wax, after dehydration with the graded alcohols and clearing in cedarwood oil. Sections are cut at 10µ. After dewaxing, the sections are brought to distilled water as rapidly as possible. The staining method is as follows:

(*i*) Transfer the slide to 20 per cent silver nitrate solution for 2–3 h.

(*ii*) Rinse in distilled water for 5 min.

(*iii*) Incubate in the following solution at 37°C for 16–20 h.

M/5 boric acid	27·5 ml.
M/20 borax	22·5 ml.
1 per cent silver nitrate solution	5–10 ml.
Pyridine or derivative [2:6 lutidine dimethyl-pyridine (lutidine)]	2–6 ml.
Distilled water	250 ml.

(The pH should be 8·4 at 20°C, using B.D.H. narrow-gauge indicator strips.)

(*iv*) Place, without washing, in the following solution for 3 min.

Hydroquinone	3 g
Sodium sulphite	30 g
Distilled water	300 ml.

The initial temperature of this reducing bath is 60°C, falling to 55°C at the end of the treatment.

(*v*) Wash in running tap-water for 3 min.

(*vi*) Rinse in distilled water for 3 min.

(*vii*) Tone in 0·2 per cent gold chloride solution (1–3 min).

(*viii*) Rinse in distilled water for 1 min.

(*ix*) Reduce in 2 per cent oxalic acid solution for 5 min.

(*x*) Wash in distilled water, then fix in 5 per cent sodium thiosulphate for 1 min.

(*xi*) Wash thoroughly in distilled water, dehydrate, clear and mount.

N.B. Use glass distilled water where distilled water is required. All glassware must be clean, and chemicals pure.

(3) *For Myelin Sheath Staining*

The following method, used by Professor J. Z. Young for quantitative studies on fibre diameters, etc., in small nerves, is recommended. The nerve must be small enough for the fixative to penetrate readily.

The nerve is dissected out and stuck on to a piece of card, without washing in saline, taking great care to avoid pinching or stretching. It is then fixed for 12–24 h in Flemming's solution:

1 per cent chromic acid solution	15 ml.
2 per cent osmic acid	4 ml.
Glacial acetic acid	1 drop

After fixation the nerve is transferred direct to 50 per cent alcohol, followed by 70 per cent, 90 per cent and two changes of absolute alcohol, leaving it for 10–15 min in each solution. The nerve is then cleared in cedarwood oil for 24 h.

The nerve is then transferred to a mixture of equal parts of cedarwood oil, benzene, and paraffin wax for 15 min. It is then infiltrated with wax (55°C melting point) in the embedding oven for 10–15 min. After blocking out the nerve, sections are cut at 5μ. The staining procedure is as follows:

(*i*) Remove wax with xylene, hydrate through the graded alcohols to distilled water.

(*ii*) Mordant the sections for 12 h at 37° C (or 2 h at 55° C) in 3 per cent potassium dichromate solution.

(*iii*) Rinse in distilled water, then place in Kultschitzky's haematoxylin for 12–24 h at 37°C (or 2 h at 55°C).

(*iv*) Rinse in distilled water.

(*v*) Transfer to 3 per cent potassium dichromate solution for 1 min.

(*vi*) Rinse in water, then place in 0·25 per cent aqueous potassium permanganate solution for 1 min (not longer).

(*vii*) Wash in distilled water, and differentiate with Pal's solution:

Oxalic acid	1 g
Potassium sulphite	1 g
Distilled water	200 ml.

This solution should bleach the connective tissue and leave only the myelin rings stained black.

(*viii*) Wash in distilled water for 30 min.

(*ix*) Wash in tap-water for 30 min.

(*x*) Dehydrate, clear in xylene, and mount in Canada balsam.

N.B. Stages (*vi*) and (*vii*) may be repeated if bleaching is insufficient. Kultschitzky's haematoxylin is prepared as follows:

10 per cent haematoxylin in absolute alcohol	
(ripened)	10 ml.
Glacial acetic acid	2 ml.
Distilled water	90 ml.

(The solution must be prepared just before use.)

(4) *The Differential Impregnation of Degenerating Nerve Fibres in Paraffin-embedded Material*

The following method (Guillery, Shirra, and Webster, 1961) give a dark impregnation of degenerating fibres and these stand out clearly against a background of palely stained normal fibres. The method is essentially the same as that of Nauta and Gygax (1951).

(*i*) Fix the brain by perfusion with 10 per cent formol-saline. (Add an excess of lithium carbonate to the 40 per cent formaldehyde.

This is filtered before use and taken as 100 per cent.) Store the blocks for 6 weeks to 6 months.

(*ii*) Blocks up to 1 cm across can be used. Wash for 8 h in several changes of distilled water. Dehydrate the blocks, clear in cedarwood oil (2–3 days) and transfer to equal parts of cedarwood oil, benzene and paraffin wax (M.Pt. 45°C) at 37°C for 2–3 h. Embed in 54°C paraffin. Cut the sections at 12–15μ (thicker sections may separate from the slides during subsequent treatment). Use Mayer's glycerol-albumen for mounting the sections.

(*iii*) Remove the wax with xylene and take the slides through the alcohols to distilled water.

(*iv*) Transfer for 6 h to 50 per cent alcohol, 100 parts; ammonium hydroxide (sp.gr.0·90), 1 part.

(*v*) Wash thoroughly in three changes of distilled water and transfer to 1·5 per cent silver nitrate, 95 parts, white pyridine (Analar), 5 parts. Leave the slides in the dark at room temperature for 24 h. The pyridine can be replaced by higher methylated derivatives of pyridine. Ten per cent 2,4,6-trimethyl pyridine (collidine) has been found particularly useful in that it causes more suppression of normal fibres than pyridine.

(*vi*) Without washing, transfer the slides to the following solution:

4·5 per cent silver nitrate solution	.. ..	20 ml.
Pure ethyl alcohol	.. ..	10 ml.
Ammonium hydroxide (sp.gr.0·90)	.. ..	1·8 ml.
2·5 per cent sodium hydroxide solution	..	1·5 ml.

This solution is placed into a warmed dish on a hotplate and covered. The slides are placed into the solution for 3 min, by which time the temperature of the solution should have reached 40–45°C. Do not take more than three slides through the volume given and change the solution frequently.

(*vii*) Without washing, transfer to the reducing fluid made up as follows:

10 per cent ethyl alcohol	.. ..	450 ml.
1 per cent citric acid solution ..	..	17·5 ml.
10 per cent formalin (not neutralized)	..	17·5 ml.

(*viii*) Wash the slides in distilled water.

(*ix*) Treat with 1 per cent sodium thiosulphate solution, wash, dehydrate, clear and mount.

If the sections are too dark increase the amount of ammonia in stage (*vi*), if too light, decrease the ammonia content.

Other techniques which are frequently used for staining nervous tissues include Ehrlich's haematoxylin and eosin, Weigert's haematoxylin, and Van Gieson and Mallory's P.T.A. haematoxylin. These methods are all employed as they are for other tissues.

REFERENCES

Addison, W. H. F. (1937). *McClung's Handbook of Microscopical Technique*, 2nd ed. p. 439, London; Oxford University Press

Barger, J. D. and DeLamater, E. D. (1948). *Science*, **108,** 121

Best, Fordham, Hallpike, Riddihough, Schuster and Sears (1956). 'Notes on the technique of temporal bone microtomy.' *Brit. med. Bull.*, **12,** No. 2 (Neuro-otology) 93

Blest, A. D. (1961). *Quart. J. micr. Sci.*, **102,** pt 3, 413–17

Conn, H. J. (1946). *Biological Stains*

Culling, C. F. A. (1963). *Handbook of Histopathological Technique*, 2nd ed. London; Butterworths

Dahlgren, U. (1937). *McClung's Handbook of Microscopical Technique*, 2nd ed. p. 423, London; Oxford University Press

Goodrich, E. S. (1941-42). *Quart. J. micr. Sci.* **83,** 245–258

Guillery, R. W., Shirra, B. and Webster, K. E. (1961). *Stain Tech.*, **36,** 9

Hilleman, H. H. and Lee, C. H. (1953). *Stain Tech.*, **28,** 285

Mahoney, R. (1963). *J. Sci. Tech.*, **9,** 154–5

Martin, L. C. and Johnson, B. K. (1958). *Practical Microscopy*, 3rd ed. London; Blackie

Nauta, W. J. H. and Gygax, P. A. (1951). 'Silver impregnation of degenerating axon terminals in the central nervous system.' *Stain Tech.*, **26,** 5–11

Richardson, K. C. (1952). *Quart. J. micr. Sci.*, **93,** 371

Scott, S. G. (1937). *The Microtomist's Vade-Mecum* Bolles-Lee, 10th ed., p. 119. London; Churchill

Shaw, G. W. (1960). *Modern Cytological Techniques.* Modern Science Memoirs, No. 40. London; J. Murray

Steedman, H. F. (1960). *Section Cutting in Microscopy.* Oxford; Blackwell

Tomasi, J. A. de (1936). *Stain Tech.*, **11,** 137

Wilson, D. P. (1933). *J. Roy. micro. Soc.*, **53,** 220

4

EMBRYOLOGICAL TECHNIQUES

The subject of experimental embryology is a wide one, but for the purposes of this book it will only be necessary to mention a few of the more fundamental techniques.

(*I*) VERTEBRATE EMBRYOLOGY

(*a*) FISH EMBRYOLOGY

Coregonus ('Whitefish') ova can be used for representing the meroblastic type of cleavage. The eggs of this fish are excellent for the study of cleavage stages and mitosis, the chromosomes being of large size. The whitefish live in the Great Lakes of North America and the technician of other countries will probably find it more convenient to purchase the ready prepared microscopical preparations which are sold by Turtox. However, the method of preparation recommended by Margaret H. Davidson, in *Turtox News* is described below.

The eggs are generally reared by artificial means, as under natural conditions an extremely small percentage of the eggs are hatched, and of those which hatch only a few reach maturity. The eggs are taken from a ripe female (about mid-November) and are immediately dry fertilized by the milt from a ripe male. Afterwards they are carefully washed, and placed in overflow hatching jars, where they remain until they are hatched. The current of incoming and outgoing water helps to prevent the eggs from clumping, but a careful check is made to make sure that no clumping does occur, and if any do show tendencies to clump they are gently stirred with a feather. A proper table of development cannot be given because much depends on the temperature of the water, but generally the first polar body is given off half an hour after fertilization and the blastula stage is reached within 2 days. Abnormal development occurs if the temperature of the water rises above 4–5°C.

For microscope slide preparation only the blastodisc is used, since no cleavage of the yolk occurs. But fixation is carried out on the entire egg. Allen's Formula 3 and Bouin's fluid give good results, but Davidson recommends her own formula of:

Formalin	..	..	..	..	..	20 parts
Water ..	..	..	..	..	..	30 parts
Glycerol	..	..	..	..	..	10 parts
Glacial acetic acid	..	..	..	..	10 parts
Alcohol	..	..	..	..	..	30 parts

The eggs are fixed for 24 h and can then be preserved in the same solution minus the acetic acid.

To remove the blastodisc, transfer the eggs to a dish of 50 per cent alcohol, and puncture the membrane surrounding the egg on the side away from the blastodisc. Tear away the membrane. By using two sharp needles, carefully remove the blastodisc from the yolk. This operation is simple due to the presence of many small oil droplets between the yolk and the blastodisc. The operation is made easier by lining the Petri-dish with a piece of coarse filter paper, as this prevents the eggs from rolling about freely.

The blastodisc is then dehydrated by means of the usual series of graded alcohols. Xylene or methyl salicylate in increasing concentrations may be used for clearing. Up until this stage the blastodiscs should remain for about 15 min in each solution. Impregnation with paraffin wax is carried out gradually by adding wax to a warm bath of clearing agent before transferring the blastodiscs to pure paraffin. Three changes of pure parafin wax are required over a period not exceeding 1 h.

For the general study of mitosis the material shows to best advantage if sectioned between 8 and 10 μ and cut horizontal to the surface of the blastodisc. For polar body formation vertical cuts are preferred. Staining is done using Heidenhain's iron haematoxylin, mordanting the slides for 4–6 h in 4 per cent iron alum, and leaving overnight in stain after washing the sections in running water. Destaining is carried out in 2 per cent iron alum solution. After dehydration and clearing the sections are mounted in Canada balsam.

Lepidosteus ('Garpike'). The garpike, also, is North American and spawns in the Great Lakes in late May. The eggs are deposited on to the sand flats in shallow water and there they are fertilized by the milt from the males. The eggs are more or less typical of the holoblastic cleavage, and the protoplasm of the egg is not definitely marked off from the yolk, as in the case of the meroblastic egg. It is therefore necessary to use a fixative which is adapted to both the protoplasm and the yolk. Gilson's fluid appears to be the best fixative for this purpose (see page 32). The eggs are fixed for 24 h, and are then transferred to 50 per cent alcohol. The membrane is removed in a similar manner to that described for the whitefish eggs.

The entire egg (minus the membrane) is dehydrated through the alcohol series, allowing 3 h in each solution. Terpineol or methyl salicylate is used for clearing, the clearing process taking about 8 h. Infiltrate with paraffin wax with several changes over a period of 8 h. The final change of clearing agent must be free from any smell of clearing agent. Sections vertical to the surface of the blastodisc are cut at 10–15μ. Davidson states that Harris's haematoxylin gives excellent results.

Whole-mount preparations of blastodiscs of these and other fishes are also useful for demonstration purposes. Fluid preserved larval stages of fishes should also be kept for teaching purposes.

(b) AMPHIBIAN EMBRYOLOGY

'The Common Frog', *Rana temporaria*, is almost certainly one of the most commonly used animals in embryological work. If the eggs and tadpoles are required solely for external examination, i.e., for fluid-preserved museum preparations, they may be fixed in 5 per cent neutral formalin. But when histological preparations are required a different fixative should be used. For the eggs and all tadpoles below 10 mm in length, Smith's fixative will give excellent results. Smith's fixative is:

Solution A.
1 per cent aqueous solution of potassium dichromate
Solution B.

40 per cent formaldehyde solution	200 ml.
Glacial acetic acid	50 ml.
Distilled water	1 l.

Mix equal parts of Solutions A and B just before use. Fixation is for 24 h. Then wash the material in running water for 6 h. Davidson then recommends that the specimens be transferred to 3 per cent formalin. This solution is changed several times or until it no longer becomes coloured. Store if required in 3 per cent formalin.

Tadpoles larger than 10 mm in length may be fixed in Smith's fixative but better results are obtained if fixed in Bouin's fluid, acetic alcohol, or corrosive sublimate with acetic acid. The formulae of the last two fixatives are:

Acetic alcohol

Absolute alcohol	90 ml.
Glacial acetic acid	10 ml.

Corrosive–acetic (modified)

Mercuric chloride	5 g
Glacial acetic acid	10 ml.
Distilled water	90 ml.

With both Bouin's fluid and corrosive acetic fix for 24 h, then dehydrate from 35 per cent alcohol. With acetic-alcohol fix for 8 h, then transfer to absolute alcohol for 1 h before clearing.

The gelatinous membranes surrounding the egg must be removed before the process of dehydration is carried out. This should be carried out by transferring each egg separately, by means of a section lifter or spoon, to a soft towel or piece of coarse filter paper. Roll

TABLE 4.1. The Approximate Development of *Rana temporaria* in Water at a Temperature of 18°C

Hours after Fertilization	Stage of Development
1	Grey crescent across dark side of egg
$3\frac{1}{2}$	Cleavage into 2 cells
$4\frac{1}{2}$	Cleavage into 4 cells
$5\frac{1}{2}$	Cleavage into 8 cells
$6\frac{1}{2}$	Cleavage into 16 cells
$7\frac{1}{2}$	Cleavage into 32 cells
16	Commencement of blastula
21	Segmentations of blastula are very fine
26	Early gastrula
34	Middle stage of gastrula
42	Late gastrula
50	Neural plate developed
67	Neural fold beginning to close over
84	Neural tube formed; egg rotates
90	Tail bud present
96–118 (4–5 days)	Tadpole shows muscular movement; 4 mm length
118–130	Heart starts beating; 5 mm length
140–150 (6 days)	External gills; gill circulation commences
150–162	Mouth opens: 7 mm length
185	Circulation to tail fin commences: 8 mm length
216	Operculum covers external gills; teeth present
240 (10 days)	Operculum complete: respiratory hole on right side, through which the first limb appears
288 (12 days)	Tadpole free swimming; 11 mm length

the egg along the towel or paper by means of a needle, taking great care not to damage the egg itself. Wash the egg in running water for about 3h, then pass it through 15, 30, 50, 70 and 80 per cent alcohol, leaving if for at least 3 h in each change. Transfer to 95 per cent alcohol for 2 h, then to two or three changes of absolute alcohol over a period of 1 h. Davidson recommends clearing in methyl salicylate, though xylene, chloroform and other reagents may be used. The clearing with methyl salibylate is done by passing the egg through gradually increasing strengths of methyl salicylate in absolute alcohol until pure methyl salicylate is reached, the changes being made when the material sinks to the bottom of the container. When cleared, transfer the container to an incubator at 37°C and add shavings of paraffin wax during a 3 h period. Change to a paraffin oven, and add melted paraffin to one-half the amount of liquid in the container. After 10 min pour away one-half of the liquid and add the same amount of paraffin. Allow another 10 min to elapse before transferring to pure paraffin wax. Leave in pure wax for no longer than 1 h during which time the wax should be changed three times. Sections are normally cut at 12–15 μ, and are stained with haematoxylin and eosin. If the yolk tends to detach itself from the slide during processing this may be overcome by coating the sections with a very thin celloidin solution (8 per cent celloidin . . . 50 ml.; absolute alcohol . . . 450 ml.; ether . . . 450 ml., just previous to the use of 95 per cent alcohol.

An alternative method of dehydration and embedding is the following and gives almost equal results: fixed eggs are transferred to 35, 50 and 70 per cent alcohol by easy stages. They are then taken through the following series of solutions allowing 1 h in each (no longer).

(i)	70 per cent alcohol	..	..	..	4 parts
	Normal butyl alcohol	..	..	..	1 part
(ii)	80 per cent alcohol	..	..	..	3 parts
	Normal butyl alcohol	..	..	..	2 parts
(iii)	90 per cent alcohol	..	..	..	2 parts
	Normal butyl alcohol	..	..	..	3 parts
(iv)	95 per cent alcohol	..	..	..	1 part
	Normal butyl alcohol	..	..	..	4 parts
(v)	Normal butyl alcohol				

The material is then transferred to pure toluene for a few minutes, and then to a bath containing equal parts of solid paraffin wax and toluene. This is kept warm overnight (on top of the paraffin oven). Then transfer to pure paraffin wax, after first of all allowing the mixture to reach the inside oven temperature. Give five changes at 10 min intervals. Paraffin wax of a reasonably hard consistency should be used (say 58°C melting point or higher in warm countries). Some beeswax added to the melted wax usually gives improved results.

Histological sections of tadpoles—These are easily prepared by using the following method: fix the tadpoles in Smith's formol–dichromate or in Bouin's fluid for 24 h. If fixed in the former, wash in running water for 12 h; if fixed in the latter transfer directly to 50 per cent alcohol. Dehydrate gradually via the usual grades of alcohol then embed by the Petrefi method (see page 217).

N.B. It may be necessary to decalcify older stages prior to dehydration. For this, Gooding and Stewart's decalcifier is recommended.

Whole-mount preparations of tadpoles—These should be bleached with Mayer's chlorine bleach (see page 196), then washed in running

271

water before staining is carried out. Any of the stains recommended for whole-mounts may be used (see page 246).

Early stages of eggs—These may be fixed, then embedded (after removal of the jelly membranes) in small cubes of agar agar. The agar blocks containing the eggs at various stages of development can then be dehydrated with alcohol and cleared in methyl benzoate. After a time the pigmentation of the egg will fade, but if the preparations are required for immediate examination, the eggs may be partially bleached before being embedded. The agar blocks may be examined under a low-power microscope, and are useful for showing the early cleavage stages.

AMPHIBIAN EXPERIMENTAL EMBRYOLOGY

Frog eggs up to neurula stage are not very suitable for general experimental embryological work, due to the fact that when decapsulated (vitelline membrane removed), they are very soft and delicate and usually collapse. But from late neurula stages on, all membranes can easily be removed. The vitelline membrane and a number of gelatinous membranes vary in number and consistency in different species of amphibians. Most experimental work is carried out on decapsulated eggs. For a description of various methods of decapsulating see Hamburger (1942). The following solutions are those which are in common use in experimental embryology laboratories:

(1) *Holtfreter Solution*

Sodium chloride	..	..	..	3·5 g
Potassium chloride	..	..	..	0·05 g
Calcium chloride (anhydrous)		..	..	0·1 g
Sodium bicarbonate	..	..	..	0·2 g
Glass distilled water	..	..	..	1 l.

The solution is prepared by autoclaving the mixture without the sodium bicarbonate. The sodium bicarbonate is sterilized dry and then added to avoid its precipitation.

Holtfreter solution is hypertonic, and amphibian gastrulae will exogastrulate if kept in this medium after removal of the vitelline membrane (Holtfreter, 1933). Generally a more dilute solution is used, such as one-tenth strength.

Full-strength Holtfreter solution is used while the actual operation is being carried out and while the wound is healing, or the transplant has healed in. They are then transferred to the more dilute solution.

(2) *Narcotic solutions*

Either of the following narcotizing solutions may be used, but the former is preferred.

(*i*) *M.S. 222. Sandoz* (see page 144)—Concentrations of 1:2,000 or 1:3,000 are recommended. Embryos can be kept under light anaesthesia in these solutions for several days.

(*ii*) *Chloretone*—In most cases a 1:3,000 solution in the culture medium is satisfactory. Old larvae may require a stronger solution. Narcosis becomes evident after a few minutes, and recovery takes from 5–10 min. This substance is far more toxic than M.S. 222.

(3) *Amphibian Ringer solution*

This solution is sometimes required in experimental work and has the following composition:

Sodium chloride	..	..	..	6·5 g
Potassium chloride	..	..	..	0·14 g
Calcium chloride (anhydrous)		..	..	0·12 g
Sodium bicarbonate		..	..	0·1 g
Glass distilled water ..	..	..	..	1 l.

Goerttler (1925) and Schechtman (1932), using gastrulae of different amphibians, examined the gastrulation movements of the prospective ectoderm by staining various regions of the ectoderm with dyed agar. A description of the technique is given in the work of Hamburger (1942).

The dyed agar is prepared in the following way: Nile-blue sulphate and neutral red are generally used as vital dyes for this technique. Prepare a 1–2 per cent solution of agar agar in glass distilled water. Boil briefly, then pour thin films of the agar solution while it is still warm on to very clean microscope slides or larger glass plates. Allow them to dry thoroughly for 1–3 days. Then place the agar plates in a large volume of 1 per cent Nile-blue sulphate or 1 per cent neutral red and leave them to stain for one or more days. The excess stain is then washed off, and the agar film allowed to dry. The plates can be kept indefinitely in a dustproof wrapping. Before use, a small area is moistened with a drop of water. After the agar is swollen (1–2 min) narrow strips of the film are scraped off with a scalpel. Dyed agar plates may also be stored in 70 per cent alcohol, but this must be washed off thoroughly before use.

THE CARE OF EXPERIMENTAL AMPHIBIAN LARVAE

It may be advantageous to keep amphibian larvae which have been operated upon in individual aquaria. Glass crystallizing dishes are ideal for this purpose. Until the wound has healed over, the larvae should be kept in full-strength Holtfreter solution, but after healing has occurred the larvae may be kept in either one-tenth Holtfreter solution or in amphibian ringer. Older larvae can be transferred to water.

Operated animals frequently suffer from oedema, particularly in the tail-bud stages. Oedematous blebs appear on the flank or on the ventral side. Such animals usually die after a few days, and should be fixed in the early stages of the oedema if the material is valuable. Occasionally a cure may be affected by pricking the oedematous vesicles with a sterile glass needle, but if this is attempted the larva should be previously narcotized with M.S. 222.

(c) AVIAN EMBRYOLOGY

The avian egg usually employed for embryological study is that of the 'Domestic Fowl', *Gallus domesticus*. The eggs should be obtained from a reliable dealer with a reputation for supplying a large percentage of fertile eggs. If it is necessary to store them, they should be kept in a cool place (optimum temperature about 13°C). They should on no account be stored for more than 6 days.

Incubation

There are various kinds of incubators manufactured. These can be roughly divided into two types: (*i*) still-air types (the temperature in this type of incubator will vary considerably in different parts of the machine); (*ii*) forced-air type (the optimum temperature of the forced-air draught should be 37–38°C throughout the incubation period).

It is essential that the correct degree of humidity is maintained inside the incubator, and refilling of the water pans, etc., must be carefully attended to. Generally a relative humidity of 60 per cent will be found satisfactory. The humidity of the incubator is, of course, closely related to the humidity in the room and to the ventilation inside the incubator and in the room.

The eggs should be turned twice daily (unless the incubator is fitted with an automatic tilting device). If the date is written on the eggs, when they are put into the incubator, it will act as a useful marker when turning them, as well as being a very necessary piece of information for determining the incubation period.

The natural breeding season of the fowl is February–June, and the best eggs for incubation purposes are obtained during this season. Excessive hot or cold spells of weather should be avoided. Two peaks of mortality occur during incubation, one around the 3rd and 4th days, and another around the 18th–20th day. A hatchability of about 80 per cent, which implies an even higher percentage of fertility, is considered very satisfactory.

Testing the eggs by candling

An excellent candling device is described by Stewart (1961). This device employs a Lister type of ophthalmic bulb which gives maximum light and minimum heat, enclosed in a double-walled container, the outer wall being perforated by a ring of holes at the top and bottom. This type of candler was developed for virus work and a simpler type of candler will be satisfactory for the purposes of testing for fertility. The usual candling device is used in a dark room, and is simply a 2 in. diameter hole cut in a piece of wood or metal. The hole is situated an inch or so above a 100 W lamp. The yolk-sac circulation is visible, at $2\frac{1}{2}$–3 days, as a network of blood vessels radiating from an indistinct dark spot, which is the embryo. In later days, the expanding vitelline circulation, and the chorio-allantoic circulation, can be seen. From the 3rd–7th day, dead embryos can be recognized by the 'blood ring' which settles at the periphery of the area vasculosa. From the 7th day on, the chorio-allantoic circulation can be seen in live embryos as a network close to the shell. From the 13th day on, the embryo appears increasingly dark, and the demarcation line of the air-sac becomes very distinct. In embryos which die during this period, this line becomes somewhat indistinct.

Removal, fixation and treatment of chick blastoderms

Avian eggs are meroblastic in character (cytoplasm is limited to the germinal disc which occupies a very small portion of the large-yolked egg).

The egg becomes fertilized while it is in the upper end of the oviduct. As the egg slowly descends the oviduct, layers of albumen encircle the yolk and germinal disc. Just prior to being laid the egg is enclosed with a shell (secreted by the shell glands). Naturally, all the time the egg is in the hen's body incubation is continuing and by the time the egg is laid the early or sometimes late gastrula stage has been reached. Development is halted upon laying until it is brought up to incubation temperature. It must therefore be remembered, when calculating the age of an embryo, that some incubation has already taken place, and also that about 4 h should be allowed for the egg to reach incubation temperature after being placed in the incubator. Thus, if one requires a 48 h embryo, the egg should remain in the incubator for 52 h; even then it will not be an accurate incubation time. It will be seen from this that it is not possible to draw up an accurate development chart, and the one given in *Table 4·2* is only very approximate.

The procedure for removal of the blastoderm is relatively simple and should offer little difficulty to the average technician. Before commencing, assemble all the necessary equipment ready for use. A dish about 3–4 in. deep is nearly filled with warm normal saline; a

TABLE 4.2. The Approximate Development of Chick at 37°C and 60 per cent Relative Humidity

Hours	Number of Somites	Special Features
18	0	Primitive streak, 2.2 mm; lateral spread of mesoderm
20	0–1	Primitive streak shorter; neural plate and folds visible
23	3	Neural folds meet in brain region; blood islands unite and blood corpuscles produced
25–26	5	Neural folds fuse in brain region; embryo linked to blood island system by vitelline veins; primary optic vesicles form
30–31	10	Three primary brain vesicles visible; heart develops which bends slightly to right; faint heart beats; head bends ventrally and sinks into yolk
35–36	13	Five brain vesicles visible; heart distinctly to the right; network of blood vessels in area vasculosa; torsion in head region commences, head amnion begins to grow back
39–40	17	Fore-brain at angle to hind-brain; heart is S-shaped, and blood flowing properly; cranial flexure nearly 90 degrees; head turns on to left side; head amniotic fold covers fore-brain; tail bud starts to develop from remains of primitive streak
46	21	Fore-brain at right-angles to hind-brain; heart has developed right and left auricles; one aortic arch is present; first pair of visceral clefts form in fore-gut; lens vesicles form; auditory vesicles form; as well as the head, the first 5–7 somites also exhibit torsion; head amnion covers hind brain and first few somites; tail folds of amnion begin to develop; distinct tail bud
48–50	24	Heart has a distinct ventricle and a conus arteriosus; two aortic arches present; third pair of visceral clefts begin to develop; hind gut appears: cranial flexure causes fore-brain to be brought close to the heart; lens vesicles and auditory vesicles nearly closed
50–55	27	Third aortic arch appears; liver bud appears, also tail gut and anal plate; eye still anterior to ear; cranial flexure at its maximum; cervical flexure increases; trunk flexure noticeable in region of 10th–12th somite; limb buds appear
60	30	Brain vent double by now; glomeruli present in mesonephric tubules; fourth aortic arch begins to develop (first pair may begin to atrophy); fourth pair of visceral clefts develop; liver now obvious; cloaca begins to form; eyes now lie posterior to ears; caudal flexure commences; allantois begins to develop as outgrowth of hind gut
72	36	Cerebral hemispheres develop; Wolffian duct reaches cloaca; tail gut begins to degenerate; lung buds develop; eyes well posterior to ears; tail now at right-angles to body; head and tail folds of amnion meet leaving a small oval aperture over somites 26–28; allantois gets larger; limb buds now obvious

support for the egg is useful and this can be made from wax weighted with lead, or from a ring of plasticine. A few 2 in. diameter glass watch glasses and some fine pasteur pipettes fitted with rubber teats are also required. A few crystallizing dishes filled with the chosen fixative should also be to hand. Instruments required are a pair of medium scissors, a pair of fine scissors, a pair of fine forceps, and a camel-hair brush.

Keeping the egg in the same position as when it was in the incubator, place it on the support in the dish of saline (at 37°C). If the operator is right-handed the egg should be arranged on the support so that the air-sac (blunt end) is to the operator's right-hand side. In this position the blastoderm will lie on top of the yolk and will have its posterior end farthest away from the operator. The shell is cracked at the air-sac end with the handle of the larger pair of scissors, and the upper hemisphere of shell is carefully removed after it has been cut round. The blastoderm will now be visible. If incubated for 24 h or longer the blastoderm is removed in the following way: using the fine scissors, cut right round the periphery of the vitelline membrane, or at least well away from the embryo, and then with a pair of forceps carefuly pull the embryo and membrane away from the yolk. Pull the floating blastoderm backwards and forwards in the saline so as to wash it free from any attached yolk. Then lower an upturned watch glass into the saline and bring it up under the blastoderm until out of the saline. Using the brush carefully, arrange the blastoderm so that it is on the summit of the watch glass, and then spread the membranes evenly around the rest of the watch glass. Carefully lower the upturned watch glass and embryo into a dish of fixative. After a few minutes the embryo is easily detached from the watch glass and the latter can be removed. As the whole extra-embryonic membrane is not usually required, it may be trimmed to a smaller size with a pair of sharp scissors.

With very early embryos, up to 24 h incubation, a modification of the above method may be used to advantage. When the blastoderm has been exposed, and while still in the saline, about 5–10 ml. of a formol–nitric mixture is pipetted on to the blastoderm and allowed to react for a few minutes. This hardens the tissues and makes it easier to cut the embryo off from the yolk and float it into a watch glass. From the watch glass it is transferred, by means of a section lifter, to a dish of fixative.

For these early stages, fixation in Smith's formol–dichromate gives good results, but fixation time should be kept to a minimum as the embryos tend to become rather brittle. After fixation, wash gently but adequately in distilled water for 1–2 h, then take through

35, 50 and 70 per cent alcohol. They may be stored in the latter solution, but prolonged preservation in alcohol is not recommended.

Later stages (more than 24 h) are best fixed in Bouin's solution. Fix for 24 h, then transfer to 50 per cent alcohol for 1 h. Then store in 70 per cent alcohol.

To prepare sections of chick blastoderms the fixed embryos with a minimum of attached extra-embryonic membranes, should be carefully and slowly dehydrated via the usual grades of alcohol, and then cleared for about 24 h in cedarwood oil. Then rinse in benzene and transfer to a dish of benzene which is placed on top of the embedding oven and is saturated with shavings of paraffin wax. Leave for 1–3 h according to size. Then transfer to pure paraffin wax inside the oven and leave to impregnate for 1–2 h, giving at least two changes of wax during this time. Better results are obtained if 1 per cent beeswax is added to the paraffin wax. Sections are usually cut at 8–10 μ transversely through the trunk region.

N.B. When embryos of from about 2–4 days' incubation are cut transversely through the trunk region, the sections through the head region will contain both fore-and hind-brain. Unless this is clearly understood the sections will be rather difficult to interpret.

Whole-mount preparations of early chick embryos—These may be prepared in the following manner. Material fixed in Smith's fixative must be washed in distilled water until all trace of colour has been removed. Material fixed in Bouin's solution must first of all be placed in 50 per cent alcohol (to render the picrates insoluble) and then placed in 1 per cent lithium carbonate, or 1 per cent sodium thiosulphate solution, until all trace of picric˜acid coloration has been removed. Then wash for half an hour in distilled water.

Staining is carried out in a dilute solution of anthracene blue in aluminium sulphate. The details of procedure are given on page 247. (Mahoney, 1963). Other staining methods may be used, such as borax carmine, Mayer's paracarmine, Heidenhain's iron haemato-xylin, etc., but the anthracene blue technique generally gives results which are far superior. After dehydration, clearing should be carried out in cedarwood oil, then the specimen should be washed in xylene for about 5 min prior to being mounted in thick Canada balsam. It is usually necessary to support the coverslip, and this may be done by using two thin strips of perspex (see also page 246).

MAMMALS
DEMONSTRATION OF HISTOLOGICAL CHANGES WHICH TAKE PLACE DURING THE OESTRUS CYCLE

The most convenient animal for this purpose is the mouse. The oestrus cycle has a duration of only 5–6 days. This short cycle has some disadvantages in that some of the shorter stages of the cycle may occur during the night.

Several virgin, adult female mice should be obtained. They are then kept in separate cages, or marked in some way so that they can be easily identified. Vaginal smears are prepared twice daily from each of the mice. The smears are examined, and if the mouse is at the required stage of the cycle it is killed and the ovaries, fallopian tubes,

Table 4.3. The Various Conditions of the Reproductive Organs of a Mouse During the Oestrus Cycle (there is a considerable variation with different mice)

Stage	Duration	Smear	Vaginal Epithelium	Uterus	Ovary and Oviduct
Proestrus	1 day	E+ C L	10–13 cell layers. Outer 4–5 cell layers nucleated. Under these the granulosa layer shows increased cornification. Active mitoses. Few leucocytes present	Active mitoses in epithelium. Few leucocytes. Some distension	Follicles large and distended. Few mitoses in germinal epithelium and in follicular cells
Oestrus	½ day	E++ C	Superficial nucleated layer lost. Cornified layer now superficial. Beneath this are about 12 layers of nucleated cells. Fewer mitoses. No leucocytes	Distension and mitotic activity at maximum, followed by a sudden decrease. No leucocytes	Ovulation occurs followed by distension of upper end of oviduct. Active mitoses in germinal epithelium and in follicular cells
Metoestrus (early)	1 day	C+++	Cornified layer is delaminated. Leucocytes begin to appear under epithelium	Less distension. Leucocytes penetrate epithelium	Early corpora luteum present. Eggs in oviduct. Many follicles undergoing atresia
Metoestrus (late)	1 day	C++ E++	4–7 layers of epithelial cells and many leucocytes in outer layers	Walls are collapsed. Epithelium degenerating. Mitoses rare. Many leucocytes	Growing corpora luteum. Eggs in oviduct. Few mitoses in germinal epithelium and in follicular cells
Dioestrus	2½ days	E L	4–7 layers of epithelial cells, with leucocytes in outer layers. Growth begins towards end of dioestrus stage	Anaemic. Walls collapsed. Epithelium healthy but with many leucocytes. Some secretion by uterine glands	Follicles begin rapid growth towards end of dioestrus period

E. Epithelial cells   C. Cornified cells   L. Leucocytes

uterus and vagina removed and fixed in Zenker's fluid. The remaining mice are kept alive until all of the stages of the cycle have been obtained. There are five stages which are required: proestrus, oestrus, early metoestrus, late metoestrus, and dioestrus. *Table 4·3* shows the main changes which occur in the vaginal smear, vaginal epithelium, uterus, ovary and oviduct.

The technique for the preparation of vaginal smears
A short length of glass rod, drawn out at one end into a small knob

279

of glass is dipped into normal saline and inserted into the vagina of the mouse. It is gently pushed against the walls of the vagina and then withdrawn. The end of the rod is then smeared across the centre of a clean glass slide. The slide is instantly placed into a mixture of equal parts of absolute alcohol and ether in order to fix the smear. Fix for 1 min, then transfer to 90 per cent alcohol, followed by 70 per cent alcohol. Stain the smear with Ehrlich's haematoxylin for 10 min, 'blue' in tap-water, differentiate in acid alcohol, and 're-blue' in tap-water so that only the nuclei are stained. Stain in Shorr's stain for 2–5 min, dehydrate, clear, and mount in Canada balsam (see also page 259).

Shorr's stain

Biebrich scarlet	0·15 g
Orange G	0·25 g
Light green	0·075 g
Phosphotungstic acid	0·5 g
Phosphomolybdic acid	0·5 g
Glacial acetic acid	0·1 ml.
50 per cent alcohol	100 ml.

Result

Epithelial cells	blue nuclei, green cytoplasm
Cornified cells	orange-pink—no nucleus
Leucocytes	blue nuclei, green cytoplasm

The preparation of vaginal smears is sometimes carried out in animal houses to determine the most suitable time for the mating of a particular animal.

The vagina, uterus, ovary and oviduct of each mouse is embedded in paraffin wax after the usual routine procedure. The vagina and the uterus are cut transversely, and the ovary should be serial sectioned together with the attached oviduct. Sections are cut at 8 μ and stained with Masson's trichrome stain (see page 244).

(*II*) INVERTEBRATE EMBRYOLOGY

(*a*) POLYCHAETE ANNELIDS

Nereis has been used with success to obtain the early stages in development. During late spring and summer, *Nereis* worms, in breeding condition, should be collected. The eggs and the spermatozoa are collected separately by cutting open the worms in small bowls containing about 50 ml. of sea water. The worms which must be of the heteronereis form (i.e., with larger eyes, and with body divided into an anterior atoke which is normal in structure, and a posterior epitoke which has large fin-like parapodia) contain loose masses of eggs or of spermatozoa which fill the body cavity.

Artificial fertilization is then carried out by pipetting a few millilitres of active spermatozoa soup to the container of eggs. The temperature of the dishes of sea-water containing the fertilized eggs must be kept at about 10°C and the water must be changed every few hours, especially during the first few days.

After about 3 h, cleavage can be observed. The small ciliated gastrula stage is visible after about 12 h, and the trochosphere larva will be fully developed after about 36 h. As soon as possible, the larvae are separated from the residual jelly and are transferred to clean sea-water. For about another week the larvae will grow without feeding, but when the first few segments of the body have appeared it is necessary to feed the larvae with a diatom culture (see page 171).

(b) ECHINODERM EMBRYOLOGY

(i) Asterias

The sexes cannot be determined by the external appearance, so a number of specimens must be obtained. Only fully grown starfish, with bulging skin and arms, will contain ripe gonads. They are usually in best condition from mid-May to early July.

Rinse the surface of the animals with tap-water in order to kill any sperm which may be on the outside. Then rinse again in seawater. Cut off the tip of one arm and then make a cut along the aboral side of this arm to the central disc, in order to examine the gonads. The male gonads are white or pale yellow in colour, and the gonads of female starfish are orange in colour. Put the males to one side for later use. Cut open all remaining arms of the ripe females. Then remove the entire aboral surface of the disc and that part of the arms which is near to the disc. The sides of the arms are forced apart and pinned out. Care must be taken to see that no damage occurs to the gonads or gonoducts. Wash the dissected specimens in sea-water to eliminate any body fluid, then transfer the ovaries to a container of sea-water. Take hold of each ovary near to its blunt end, by the gonoduct. Then cut away this end, as only this part contains oogonia. Transfer all the blunt ends of the ovaries to large bowls of sea-water. (All of the operations up to this point must be carried out as quickly as possible.) Then shake the pieces in the sea-water to make them shed the ova. The ova take a little while to settle owing to them having a specific gravity only slightly greater than that of sea-water. Remove the plumes (empty pieces of ovary) and pour away most of the sea-water, leaving the ova in a minimum quantity of sea-water.

The sperms are obtained in the following way: remove the testes of a male, rinse it in sea-water to remove any body-fluid, and place it into a dry vessel. The seminal fluid will soon pour out from the testes. Mix one drop of seminal fluid with 25 ml. of sea-water, and add two drops of this mixed suspension to every 250 ml. of sea-water containing the ova. The concentration of sperms is important as the ova are particularly sensitive to polyspermy. The temperature should be maintained at about 15°C. At this temperature the first cleavage should occur after about 4 h. Early stages of development can be obtained without the necessity of feeding, but when larvae are required it is necessary to feed the larvae on diatoms such as *Nitzschia* (see page 171). All sea-water containing the eggs must be carefully filtered as copepods feed on the eggs and larvae. The specific gravity of the sea-water should be kept constant, and the level should be checked daily and topped up regularly with glass distilled water. Aerate gently, and avoid direct sunlight or any bright light.

(*ii*) *Artificial fertilization of* Echinus esculentus (after Eales 1939). During the summer season, select large active specimens. Thoroughly clean several large jars (breffits are ideal) and fill them with filtered sea-water. Cut the *Echinus* into two along the ambitus (equator) and examine the gonads in the aboral halves. Ripe female gonads appear pinkish and granular and are translucent. Ripe male gonads are opaque and milky-white.

Suspend the aboral halves of the females over the mouths of the jars, gonads uppermost. Similarly suspend the halves of the males over other jars of sea-water. If the animals are mature, the ova and spermatozoa will be discharged into the water after a few minutes. The discharge will take place through the genital pores. The ova come down in small groups of isolated granules which float. Spermatozoa come down in a milky stream which soon makes the water turbid.

When both ova and sperms have been collected, remove the halves of *Echinus* from the jars, and pipette a few drops of the water containing the spermatozoa into the water containing the ova. Stir the water well. After a while, eggs which have been fertilized will sink to the bottom. Decant off the surface water with the unfertilized ova and surplus sperm. Transfer the fertilized ova to glass finger bowls containing cool sea-water. Only a few ova should be put into each bowl. Keep the bowls in a cool shady place where they should be gently aerated. Examine microscopically at frequent intervals, noting the times at which the various stages of development occur, together with the temperature of the water. When the pluteus stage is reached, they should be fed with a diatom culture (Nitzschia) (see page 171). The optimum temperatures is between 10° and 14°C.

REFERENCES

Eales, N. B. (1939). *Littoral Fauna of Great Britain.* London; Cambridge University Press
Hamburger, V. (1942). *A Manual of Experimental Embryology.* Chicago University Press
Holtfreter, J. (1933). 'Die totale Exogastrulation, eine Selbstablösung des Ektoderms vom Entomesoderm: Entwicklung und funktionelles Verhalten nervenloser Organe.' *Arch. EntwMech. Org.*, **129,** 669
Mahoney, R. (1963). *J. Inst. Sci. Tech.*, **9,** No. 4, 154
Stewart, A.M. (1961). *J. Inst. Sci. Tech.*, **7,** No. 3

5

FLUID PRESERVATION

Immersion in a preserving fluid is the usual way of storing animal material, and of these fluids, formalin and alcohol are the most popular.

Formalin

Formalin is an aqueous solution of the gas formaldehyde. It is usually purchased as a 40 per cent aqueous solution (commercial formaledhyde).

Preservation is carried out with a neutral solution of 10 per cent formalin. This solution is prepared by diluting 10 ml. of the 40 per cent formaldehyde solution with 90 ml. of distilled water. It may be neutralized by adding 0·35 g of sodium dihydrogen phosphate (anhydrous) NaH_2PO_4, and 0·65 g of disodium hydrogen phosphate (anhydrous) Na_2HPO_4, per 100 ml. of diluted formalin. Alternatively, the 40 per cent formaldehyde solution may be stored over a layer of calcium carbonate, which will keep it approximately neutral.

Marine specimens sometimes benefit if they are preserved in a 10 per cent solution prepared with sea-water in place of distilled water. If the material is to be used for dissection or display purposes only, tap-water may be used instead of distilled water.

Alcohol

Alcohol is either used directly for preserving, or material is transferred to it after being initially fixed in formalin. Pure spirit, which is specially to be recommended for the preservation of animals, consists of a mixture of ethyl alcohol and water and is often sold at a grade of 40 over-proof, or about 80 per cent alcohol by volume. It is, unfortunately, very expensive as it is subject to a heavy duty tax. For this reason, the best alcohol to use for preservation is industrial methylated spirit, which is a mixture of 95 parts of ethyl alcohol and 10 parts of wood naphtha. For preserving and for the preparation of the graded alcohols used in histology, the best grade of this spirit is 66 over-proof. (For absolute alcohol used in histology use 74 over-proof, which has been kept over anhydrous copper sulphate.) The 66 over-proof spirit contains 96 per cent alcohol by volume.

The alcohol used for preservation should be a 70 per cent solution in water. It is not necessary to make up the solution with great accuracy, but it is important for the technician to realize that the use of spirit which is too weak may entirely spoil the results of his labours, and in general that the solution used for preservation should be well over-proof (more than 50 per cent by weight of alcohol). For most purposes it is accurate enough to add 26 ml. of distilled water to each 70 ml. of 66 over-proof alcohol.

When spirit preserved specimens are being remounted, it is a good idea to check the strength of alcohol by using an alcoholometer. The best type is a volume alcoholmeter, which gives a direct reading. It is, however, necessary to apply a temperature correction to the reading. A table of temperature corrections is usually supplied with each volume alcoholometer.*

POST-FIXATION PRESERVATIVES

Animals preserved in formalin are very unpleasant to dissect, as formalin vapour irritates the eyes, and the mucous membranes of the nose and throat. During recent years a great deal of research has been carried out into the post-preservation of animal material.

Most of this work has centred around various phenyl ethers, and hydroxy benzoates. A combination of Nipa ester and propylene phenoxetol has been used by some workers with success, but the most promising appears to be ethyleneglycol-monophenylether, to which the name Phenoxetol has been given. Phenoxetol and other similar chemicals are manufactured by Nipa Laboratories Ltd., Treforest Industrial Estate, Pontypridd, Glamorganshire.

After sufficient fixation in 5–10 per cent formalin, specimens are transferred directly to a 1 per cent aqueous solution of the technical grade of Phenoxetol. This solution is prepared in the following way. The required amount of Phenoxetol is added to a quantity of boiling water and shaken until dissolved. It is then cooled and adjusted to volume. The pH will be that of the water used in its preparation, and the solution will be perfectly stable. Specimens have been kept n this solution for over two years and show no signs of deterioration.

Histological sections have been prepared of such material and the staining of the tissue has been brighter than in control specimens. It also shows some sign of preserving natural colour.

EMBALMING METHODS

Mammals which are to be kept for future dissection, remain more

* Further information about alcohol and alcoholometers will be found in the British Museum (Natural History) booklet, *Alcohol and Alcoholometers.*

supple if they are embalmed. The dry embalming method, which is commonly used for the preservation of human cadavers, is unsuitable for most other mammals. It is necessary, after perfusing the specimens with a large quantity of embalming fluid, to completely immerse the animals in a tank full of embalming fluid. The perfusion should be carried out using one of the methods described in Chapter 6. After perfusion the abdominal cavity should be opened and a quantity of embalming fluid injected into the thoracic cavity. The formula for embalming fluid is:

Phenol liquefactum B.P.	4 parts
40 per cent formaldehyde solution	1 part
Glycerol (fine pale straw)	4 parts
96 per cent alcohol	4 parts
Tap-water	12 parts

STORAGE OF SPECIMENS

Whichever preservative is chosen, the actual method of storage is of the greatest importance. Small delicate specimens are usually kept in glass jars of a suitable size, which are fitted with ground-glass lids, plastic screw caps, or rubber bungs. When the top has been finally replaced it should be dipped into molten paraffin wax to ensure that no evaporation can take place. A label, written on stiff white paper, using Indian ink, should be waxed and placed inside the tube, and a second typewritten label should be stuck on to the outside of the tube. The label in each case should give the name of the specimen, the fixative used, the storage solution (if different from the fixative) and the date on which the specimen was fixed, together with its location and any other relevant information.

Large specimens should be stored in fibreglass tanks, fitted with covers, or in earthenware or galvanized tanks if the former are not obtainable. It is advisable to wrap each specimen in a piece of muslin after it has been supplied with a waxed label. The muslin should be secured in place with waxed thread, and a second label attached to it on the end of a long thread, so that it can hang out of the tank. This method enables each specimen to be easily located. A list of all material preserved in the tank should be fixed to its lid. It will also be found useful if the capacity of the tank is written on its outside.

All stored material should be kept in a cool room, which has little fluctuation of temperature. It should also be readily accessible at all times. A regular periodic check should be carried out to ensure that evaporation is not taking place, and that the animals are pre-serving properly.

METHODS FOR THE PRESERVATION OF NATURAL COLOUR

Although other workers had experimented on similar lines, Kaiser-ling was the first person to find a satisfactory solution to this prob-lem, and although there have been many subsequent modifications his method remains the basis of present-day techniques. Unfortu-nately, these techniques have all been devised for the preservation of natural colour of human tissues, and do not give such good results with other animal tissues. Nevertheless they do give fairly good results with most mammalian tissues.

Kaiserling realized that if he could preserve the natural colour of haemoglobin, he was well on the way to answering the problem. His first method was published in 1896, and after several modifica-tions, this final formula was published in 1903:

The tissue is removed from the corpse as soon as possible after death had occurred and is placed in the following fixing solution:

40 per cent formaldehyde solution ..	800 ml.
Potassium acetate	85 g
Potassium nitrate	45 g
Distilled water	4 l.

When adequately fixed, the colour is revived in absolute, 90 per cent or 80 per cent alcohol. The colour should be restored after $\frac{1}{2}$–$1\frac{1}{2}$ h, but if the tissue is left in the alcohol solution for a longer time the colour will begin to fade. When the colour is fully restored, the tissue is transferred to the final preservative solution:

Glycerol	3 l.
Potassium acetate	2,000 g
Distilled water	9 l.

Numerous modifications of the Kaiserling formula have been pub-lished during the past 60 years. One which is a definite improvement is that of Pick–Judah:

Solution 1 (fixative)

Potassium acetate	42·5 g
Potassium nitrate	22·5 g
Distilled water	1·6 l.
40 per cent formaldehyde solution ..	400 ml.

(The salts are dissolved in hot water, and the additional water and formalin is added to the cooled solution.)

Solution 2 (colour reviver)
 96 per cent alcohol (for ½–1½ h)

Solution 3 (preservative)

Sodium acetate	36 g
Distilled water	120 ml.
4 per cent alcoholic solution of camphor ..	5 ml.
Glycerol	72 ml.

(The solution is made by adding the ingredients in the order given. At first, the camphor is thrown out of solution but redissolves on allowing the solution to stand.)

Wentworth's Hydrosulphite method

During the war years, when glycerol was particularly expensive, Wentworth devised a method which eliminated glycerol. But recently he has modified his formula to include glycerol. The method is to fix the tissue, for 1 month or longer, in the following:

Solution 1

40 per cent formaldehyde solution	100 ml.
Sodium acetate	40 g
Distilled water	1 l.

When the tissue is ready for mounting, the pH of the fluid must be taken. If more alkaline than pH 6·5, then proceed to transfer the tissue to Solution 3, but if the solution is more acid than pH 6·5, transfer the tissue to Solution 2:

Solution 2

40 per cent formaldehyde solution ..	10 ml.
Sodium acetate	40 g
Tribasic sodium phosphate ($Na_3PO_412H_2O$)	1 g
Distilled water	1 l.

This fluid has a pH of about 9·5, and the specimen should remain in it from 2–7 days, changing the solution periodically, until the pH remains constant at 8.5. The specimen is then transferred to Solution 3.

Solution 3

40 per cent formaldehyde solution ..	10 ml.
Sodium acetate	100 g
Sodium phosphate (Na_2HPO_4)	1 g
Glycerol	200 ml.
Distilled water	to 1 l.

The pH of this solution is about 7·5. If after several days immersion in this third solution the pH is still 7·5, the specimen can then be mounted in a fresh quantity of Solution 3, to which has been added 3 g sodium hydrosulphite to every kilogram weight of the specimen, immediately before the jar is sealed. This technique has not yet stood the test of time, but it seems likely that it will eventually replace the Kaiserling technique.

As previously mentioned all the methods of colour preservation concentrate on the preservation of the colour of haemoglobin. It is believed to be carried out with the following sequence of events: the first fixing solution converts all of the oxyhaemoglobin into acid haematin, the second solution changes the acid haematin into temporary alkaline haematin, and the third solution then converts this into permanent alkaline haematin.

A great deal of research still remains to be done regarding the preservation of other animal tissues in natural colour. It appears that the colours are nearly always present in the tissue after fixation, but are masked by the action of the fixative.

Promising results have been obtained by using propylene phenoxetol. The colour of several types of starfish was preserved for about a year, by placing the specimens, which had been fixed for 24 h in 5 per cent sea-water formalin, into a 1 per cent aqueous suspension of propylene phenoxetol. The suspension was prepared by shaking the required amount of propylene phenoxetol with a little absolute alcohol before mixing with the water. Unfortunately, when the specimens were finally sealed in jars, the colour faded after a few hours.

Some of the best results have been obtained by the process of freeze-drying. This technique is discussed in Chapter 7.

REFERENCES

Kaiserling, C. (1897). *Virchows Arch.*, **147**, 389–417; (1900). *Verh. dtsch. path. Ges.*, **2**, 203–7; (1902). *Ibid,.* **237**, 467–474

Wentworth, J. E. (1938). *Bull. Int. Ass. med. mus.*, **18**, 153; (1939). *Ibid.*, **18**, 79; (1942). *J. Path. Bact.*, **54**, 1, 137–8; (1957). *J. Med. Lab. Tech.*, **14**, No. 3, 194–5

6

INJECTION AND CORROSION TECHNIQUES

Injection and corrosion techniques may be used for investigating the capillary circulation of cleared and mounted sections of injected and processed tissues, or to demonstrate the venous, arterial and the capillary circulation, and such structures as the bronchial tree in gross specimens.

Injections should always be carried out as soon as possible after death, and a preliminary injection of 0·25 per cent sodium nitrite is recommended to dilate the blood vessels before injecting the actual mass. The injection mass must be in colloidal solution, since, if it is in true solution it will diffuse through the vessel walls.

A BRIEF DESCRIPTION OF THE METHOD USED TO INSERT A CANNULA INTO A BLOOD VESSEL

This method can only be carried out in detail with animals which are large enough to allow artery forceps to be introduced.

(1) As shown in *Figure 6.1(a)*, a length of selected blood vessel (as long as possible) is cleared of all surrounding connective tissue, and two ligatures are passed beneath the freed portion, then tied loosely with one-half of a reef-knot.

(2) A pair of artery forceps is clamped on to the blood vessel at the end of the exposed portion which is to receive the injection mass [*Figure 6.1(b)*].

(3) Blood is squeezed into the blood vessel and the ligature furthest from the forceps is pulled tight and tied with a reef-knot [*Figure 6.1(c)*].

(4) A small cut is made in the upper surface of the blood vessel, and the cannula is immediately inserted into this hole, pointing it towards the forceps. The remaining ligature is then tied so that the cannula is held firmly in place [*Figure 6.1 (d)*]. The artery forceps are removed and the injection may then proceed.

INJECTION TECHNIQUES USED FOR DEMONSTRATION OF THE VASCULAR SYSTEM IN SECTIONED TISSUES

(1) *Fischer's method*

Inject the selected organ, via the main artery, with normal saline

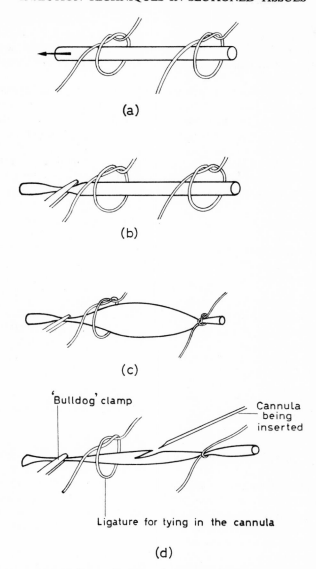

(a)

(b)

(c)

'Bulldog' clamp

Cannula
being
inserted

Ligature for tying in the cannula

(d)

Figure 6.1. Inserting a cannula into a blood vessel

until the solution issuing from the main vein is free from blood.
Without detaching the cannula, inject the organ with milk or 20

per cent lard in ether. When the milk (or lard solution) flows from the main vein, tie both artery and vein with a ligature. Fix the organ in 7·5 per cent aqueous formalin in which 1·5 per cent acetic acid has been added. Cut frozen sections to a thickness of 15–20 μ and stain with a solution of oil red 0 for 10–15 min.

The staining solution is prepared by diluting 6 ml. of a saturated solution of oil red 0 (0·25–0·5 per cent) in isopropyl alcohol with 4 ml. of distilled water, and after allowing it to stand for 10 min. it is filtered. This diluted solution will only keep for 1–2 h. Differentiate in 60 per cent alcohol to clear the background, then wash in water. Counterstain the nuclei with Ehrlich's haematoxylin, then 'blue' in tap-water or 1 per cent disodium phosphate. The sections should then be floated on to slides and mounted in glycerin jelly.

Results

Lipids	..	..	..	..	..	bright red
Nuclei	..	..	..	..	..	blue

Any other fat stain may be used instead of oil red, but the above method is especially recommended (Culling, 1963).

(2) *Gelatin method*

Gelatin is frequently avoided by many workers due to the mistaken belief that it must always be injected hot. There are a few methods for retarding the gelling action, two of which are given below, but the apparatus required to inject hot gelatine is so easy to construct that the technician should not be deterred from using this excellent method. Gelatin-injected material may be processed and histological sections prepared with no difficulty at all.

The gelatin used should always be of the best quality, sheet gelatin being superior to powder gelatin. To prepare a solution of gelatin, soak the required amount of sheet gelatin in cold distilled water for about 10 min (the gelatin will swell and become soft). This softened gelatin is then dissolved in the required amount of hot distilled water. The usual strength for injection purposes is 5–10 per cent gelatin (the weaker strength for capillaries), and unless one of the special formulae is used, the mass must be kept at 60°C throughout the injection procedure, and it is advisable to immerse the animal or organ in a bath of saline at the same temperature to avoid setting of the gelatin in any of the smaller vessels.

The gelatin mass may be coloured by adding one of the following colouring agents. The standard colours are red for arteries, blue for veins, and yellow for the hepatic portal vein.

Red: Carmine gelatin—Mix 5 g of carmine with 10 ml. of distilled water in a stoppered flask, and add 100 ml. of strong ammonia

(0·880 s.g.). Shake well, and allow to stand for $\frac{1}{2}$–1 h. Shake well again and filter through glass wool. To the filtrate add 15–20 g of gelatin and a few crystals of thymol. Stopper the flask, and keep at 37°C until the gelatin has dissolved. Remove the stopper and keep at 37°C until the smell of ammonia has disappeared. Make up to 150 ml. with warm distilled water and the mass is ready for use; it should be stored in a refrigerator.

Blue: Ranvier's Prussian blue—This is prepared by adding a saturated aqueous solution of ferric sulphate to a saturated aqueous solution of potassium ferrocyanide. The resultant blue precipitate is

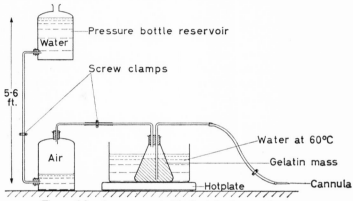

Figure 6.2. Apparatus suitable for injecting a gelatin mass

well washed in a Buchner funnel. This pigment may be used in aqueous colloidal solution or in a gelatin mass.

Yellow: chrome yellow—This pigment may be mixed with molten gelatin until the colour is sufficiently dense when viewed in a glass capillary tube. A simpler method of colouring is to use I.C.I. Monolite and Monastral dyes, which are available as solutions in red, blue, yellow and green colours. These dyes are particularly recommended for use with rubber latex.

The two methods for retarding the setting of gelatin are:

(1) *Metagelatin*

If a slight proportion of ammonia is added to a molten solution of gelatin and the whole is heated for several hours, the gelatin solution passes into a state of metagelatin. This may be thinned if necessary by adding some 30 per cent alcohol. After injection the specimens are immersed in absolute alcohol or 3 per cent aqueous chromic acid which sets the mass. This method is tricky to carry out as each batch of gelatin varies, and the required amount of ammonia and heating will vary accordingly.

(2) *Mozejko mass*

The addition of 10 per cent sodium salicylate will retard the setting of gelatin for several hours. When setting is required, this is accomplished by immersing the specimen in 4 per cent formalin. The apparatus required to carry out the above procedures is shown in *Figure 6.2.*

INJECTION MASSES USED FOR THE DEMONSTRATION OF VASCULAR SYSTEMS IN GROSS SPECIMENS

The following are a few of the many methods which have been devised for displaying the vascular systems of animals:

(1) *Latex*

This is by far the best mass to use when the injected animal is to be dissected. The injected vessels will be stronger than usual and will be elastic in nature once the latex is set. There are two types of latex suitable for injection purposes:

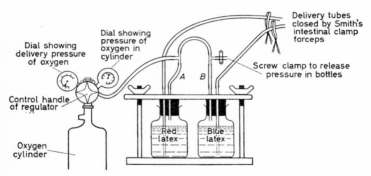

Figure 6.3. Apparatus for injection of rubber latex [from Tompsett, by courtesy of E. & S. Livingstone] 1956)

Note the simple and secure way of holding the rubber stoppers in the bottles. If only one colour is being used the rubber tubing is also clamped at either point *A* or *B*

(*i*) *Revultex* (Revertex Ltd.)—This is an 80 per cent solution of latex in ammonia with an added vulcanizer. It should be diluted with 5 per cent ammonia solution until it is thin enough to flow through a No. 20 hypodermic needle.

(*ii*) *Neoprene latex* (Imperial Chemical Industries Ltd.)—This is a synthetic latex and should be used as supplied. Both of these latex solutions should be coloured by adding a quantity of the appropriate Monolite or Monastral dye (I.C.I.).

(2) *Starch mass*

This is prepared as follows:

Water	100 ml.
Glycerol	20 ml.
40 per cent formaldehyde solution ..	20 ml.
Household starch	85 g
+ colouring matter	

The starch mass was very popular before the use of latex became

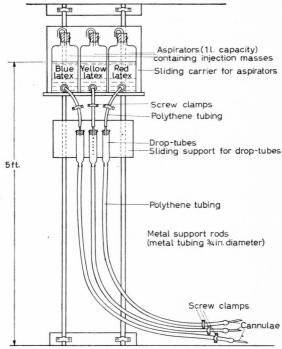

Figure 6.4. Apparatus for injection of coloured latex masses

This apparatus has been used successfully by the author for several years. The carriers for the aspirators and drop-tubes are fitted with locking wing-nuts so that they may be held at any desired height. A height of 5–6 ft. should give sufficient pressure to inject most animals met with in a laboratory.

common practice. Latex is a far superior injection mass and should always be used in preference to starch when at all possible.

(3) *Joseph's albumen mass*

This is recommended for injecting the vascular systems of invertebrates, but even for this purpose it has no advantages over latex.

The filtered white of an egg is diluted to 1–5 per cent with aqueous carmine suspension. It will remain liquid while cold, but will coagulate, yet remain transparent, when put into 2 per cent nitric acid.

SOME METHODS FOR OBTAINING THE NECESSARY PRESSURE FOR MASS INJECTIONS

(1) HYPODERMIC SYRINGES

Fitted with very fine hypodermic needles, e.g., No. 20, hypodermic syringes are ideal for injecting coloured masses into small animals such as crayfish and mussels. They are of more use if the needle is attached to a short length of polythene tubing and this attached to the syringe. This allows the needle to be held at a different angle to that of the syringe.

(2) FINE GLASS PIPETTES; FITTED TO RUBBER TEATS

The fine glass pipette is constructed in the following way: pull out a normally fine pipette from a piece of glass tubing, but while the stretched part is still hot bend it into a sharp U shape. This bent tube is then suspended from a length of wire which is fixed between two retort stands. A micro-burner flame is held against the pulled-out length of glass until the pipette falls with its own weight on to a pad of cloth. This method can be relied on to produce ultra-fine pipettes (see *Figure 6.5*). The other end of the pipette should be

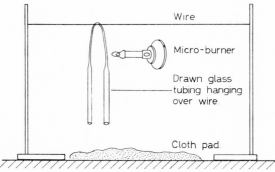

Figure 6.5.   A simple method of making ultra-fine pipettes suitable for mass injections into small animals

flamed until it is smooth. It is then attached to a short length of polythene tubing which in turn is connected to a rubber teat (about 50 ml. capacity) by means of a short length of glass tubing.

This simple apparatus is ideal for injecting very fine vascular systems of chick blastoderms, and the excretory system of liver flukes. Fitted with a No. 20 hypodermic needle in place of the glass pipette, this apparatus is ideal for injecting the arterial system of frogs, a task which can easily be performed by a competent technician.

(3) GRAVITY METHODS

There are many ways in which the apparatus can be constructed, but in all of them the pressure is obtained by having a reservoir full of liquid held at a height of several feet above the specimen and connected to the specimen by means of a flexible tube. In all cases the

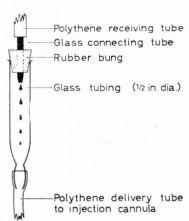

Polythene receiving tube
Glass connecting tube
Rubber bung

Glass tubing (1/2 in. dia.)

Figure 6.6. An easily constructed drop-tube for determining the rate of flow of injection masses

Polythene delivery tube to injection cannula

delivery tube should be interrupted with a drop-tube (similar to that fitted to a blood transfusion set); this allows the rate of injection to be observed, and one is able to observe that the flow has been stopped should a blockage occur. An easily constructed drop-tube is shown in *Figure 6.6*.

RECOMMENDED INJECTION ROUTES FOR SOME COMMON LABORATORY ANIMALS

Liver fluke (*Fasciola hepaticum*)

With practice it is possible to inject the excretory system of the liver fluke via the excretory pore which is at the posterior end of the animal. If possible inject whilst the animal is still alive.

Earthworm (*Lumbricus terrestris*)

The blood vascular system can be injected, via the dorsal blood vessel, making the injection towards the prostomium. The injection should be carried out as soon as possible after death.

Crayfish (*Astacus fluviatilis*)

The injection of the blood vessels is made through the heart which is situated just beneath the median dorsal part of the carapace. The live crayfish should be held in the hand and the needle inserted into the heart by pushing it between the carapace and the first abdominal segment at an angle of 30 degrees. The injection usually requires about 1–2 ml. of solution.

Lobster (*Homarus vulgaris*)

The injection of the blood vessels is made in a similar way to that used for crayfish, but the needle is inserted directly through the carapace.

Starfish (*Asterias rubens*)

The injection of the water-vascular system may be carried out, in a freshly killed starfish, by removing the madreporite and inserting the needle into the stone canal. The injection is continued until the tube feet are slightly distended with the injection mass. A similar method is applicable for many other echinoderms.

Dogfish (*Scylliorhinus canicula* and *Squalus* (*Acanthias*) *vulgaris*)

The afferent branchial system is injected, via the ventricle or the conus arteriosus, in an anterior direction. This is usually injected with a blue mass to indicate that the blood in the vessels is deoxygenated. The efferent branchial artery, as well as all remaining arteries, is injected via the caudal artery, again making the injection in an anterior direction, using a red mass. The venous system is injected via the ductus cuvieri, making the injection laterally from the heart towards the side of the fish. This injection, using a blue mass, requires a relatively large volume of liquid as most of the vessels are wide sinuses. The hepatic portal system is injected through the hepatic portal vein towards the alimentary canal using a yellow or green mass.

A method for demonstrating the parts of the internal ear of the dogfish (*Squalus* (=*Acanthias*) *vulgaris*) has been described in *Turtox News*, by H. B. Lovell.

Injection usually results in a rupture of the delicate walls of the semicircular canals. The preparation is obtained by application of the physical principle of capillary attraction, a method made possible by the small diameter of the semicircular canals. The procedure is as follows. Cut the anterior vertical canal and apply to the upper end a pipette containing a few drops of stains (such as carmine). Capillary attraction draws the coloured fluid into the canal and around into the utriculus. No pressure is necessary. Next, cut the horizontal canal and apply pipette to the posterior end of the duct; this stains the posterior arm of the utriculus. The utriculus will now be found to be an elongated tubular structure narrowing antero-ventrally at which point it connects with the ampullae of the anterior vertical and horizontal ducts, and broadening postero-dorsally where the upper ends of the same two canals join. Through the small slit-like opening from the ventral end of the utriculus some of the stain will fall into the recessus utriculi, and from there (if too much stain is used) it will flow into the anterior end of the sacculus.

The posterior vertical duct does not connect with the utriculus at either end in the spiny dogfish. It makes a complete circle with the median end communicating with the posterior side of the sacculus through a single aperture. Sever this canal and allow capillary action to draw up a darker stain from the pipette. This stain gradually enters the sacculus and works anteriorly causing this chamber to be sharply differentiated from the utriculus.

Frog (Rana temporaria)

The arterial system is easily injected via the ventricle or by inserting the needle into the conus arteriosus. This usually requires from 2–3 ml. of liquid. The venous system is injected via the femoral vein, making the injection in an anterior direction. The femoral vein is easily found if the skin on the dorsal surface of the right thigh is incised, and the muscles, triceps femoris and ileo-fibularis are pulled aside. About 2 ml. of injection mass is required. The vessels in the web of the feet are so fine that very few injection masses will enter them. When these are to be demonstrated, the arterial system should be injected with mercury. It is usually necessary to squeeze the injected limb towards the foot in order to force the mercury into the blood vessels of the web.

Mud-puppy (Necturus maculatus)

The following method for triple injection of the mud-puppy is applicable to all salamanders. The body cavity is opened from the pelvic girdle to the pectoral girdle, about ¼ in. to the left of the mid-ventral line, to prevent the cutting of the abdominal vein and the small branches of the hepatic. The viscera are displaced as far as possible to the right-hand side to expose the blood vessels.

The postcaval vein and tributaries are the first blood vessels to be injected. A No. 16 needle is inserted into the posterior portion of the postcaval, and about 8–10 ml. is injected in an anterior direction until the vessels in the liver are filled. Just before completing this injection the small finger of the left hand is placed on the postcaval where it enters the liver, momentarily checking the flow of the blue mass into this organ and forcing it into the posterior cardinals.

The needle is removed and a clamp placed over the injection site.

The arteries are injected via the aorta, inserting the needle about $\frac{1}{2}$ in. anterior to the coeliaco-mesenteric artery. The aorta is first injected in an anterior and then in a posterior direction. The mass is forced through the No. 18 needle until the pulmonary arteries are well filled and the external gills assume a reddish tint. The injection in the posterior direction is continued until the arteries of the intestine and pelvic region are filled. A clamp should be put on to the injection site on removal of the needle.

The third injection fills the hepatic and renal portal systems. A No. 19 needle is inserted into the mesenteric vein, a branch of the hepatic portal vein, and a yellow mass is forced into the vessel until all the banches of the mesenteric vein are completely filled. The injection site should be clamped on removal of the needle, and this clamp as well as the other two should be left in position until the injection mass as been solidified.

Mammals

The following method for carrying out a triple injection is applicable to all mammals: the freshly killed animal is pinned out ventral side uppermost and the abdomen is opened up by making a medium incision from the xiphisternum to a point a few inches in front of the genital aperture, and by cutting down each side of the body wall just posterior to the diaphragm.

It has been found by experience that the hepatic portal system should be the first to be injected. This is done by inserting a thin polythene cannula into the hepatic portal vein just posterior to the liver, making the injection away from the liver. During the injection procedure, the intestines should be carefully moved about by hand (this enables the mass to penetrate all parts of the system). The injection is usually complete when the vessels from the rectum and stomach have been filled with the yellow mass. After withdrawing the cannula, the hepatic vein is ligatured.

The venous system is the second to be injected, and it has been found that in all animals which have a jugular anastomosis (including rabbits, rats and guinea-pigs) the injection is made into the right jugular vein making the injection in an anterior direction (i.e., away from the heart). A hypodermic needle or a polythene cannula may be used for this injection. It may be necessary to massage the neck gently during the first part of the injection procedure to force the mass across the anastomosis. The injection is taken to be complete when the hind-limb veins have been filled with the blue mass. When completed, the jugular vein is ligatured at two places (immediately anterior and posterior to the injection site).

Lastly, the arterial system is injected with a red mass, using a hypodermic needle. The needle is inserted into the left ventricle, care being taken to ensure that the aperture of the needle is not pressed against the inside wall of the ventricle. Watch the flow indicator, and move the needle carefully until the mass is flowing readily. The injection is taken to be complete when both the eyes and limb extremities have taken on a rosy hue. If any of the red mass has leaked into the thoracic cavity during the injection process, or after removal of the needle, this should be mopped up with gauze before the mass is allowed to set.

INJECTION MASSES USED FOR DEMONSTRATING THE VASCULAR SYSTEMS AND OTHER SYSTEMS SUCH AS BRONCHIAL TREES AFTER SUBSEQUENT CORROSION OF THE SURROUNDING TISSUE

In 1882 Paul Schiefferdecker described a technique which employed celloidin (cellulose nitrate) dissolved in ether. The evaporation of the ether left a cast of celloidin in the vessels. The surrounding tissues could then be corroded away in concentrated hydrochloric acid which did not attack the cast. As ether is immiscible with water, the evaporation was slow, and because the celloidin cast was very brittle it was necessary to keep it immersed in a fluid.

In 1899, Carl Storch introduced the use of celluloid (cellulose acetate) in place of celloidin, and substituted acetone for ether. Casts prepared in this manner could be produced more quickly, and could be kept dry. The use of camphor to accelerate the hardening was also recommended.

N.B. Many writers have confused the terms celloidin with celluloid, but as most of the writers referred to 'Used x-ray films' as part of their technique there can be no doubt that they used celluloid rather than celloidin. Modern x-ray film is of no use for this purpose and some other form of cellulose acetate must be used.

In 1936, Narat introduced the use of a vinyl resin called Vinylite dissolved in acetone. In 1948, the cold-setting polyester resins, Marco Resin and Castolite were introduced. These resins opened up entirely new possibilities in the field of anatomical casting, as they made it possible to produce rigid and beautifully coloured casts of any anatomical cavity. The shrinkage during the setting process is small, and when fully hardened the casts are relatively strong and do not warp. Transparent casts may be produced or the casting material may be coloured by the addition of special pigments. Small and delicate coloured casts may be embedded in blocks of transparent resin.

Most of the improvements to the technique of corrosion casting are due to Tompsett. A detailed description of the technique required for the production of these casts is given in Tompsett (1956). This book together with the various published improvements to the technique (Tompsett, Bartlett and Wyke, 1961–63) should be carefully studied before any serious attempt is made to produce any of these casts. A brief description of the technique is given below.

PREPARATION

A short length of flanged polythene tubing (Portex polythene tubing, or Portex vinyl VY standard tubing for sizes larger than 7·5 mm diameter) is tied securely into each of the main vessels or ducts of the organ which are to be injected. The polythene tubing is then connected to a length of rubber tubing, which in turn is connected to the fixation or injection apparatus.

The organ is immersed in a bowl of cold water and is carefully manipulated so as to eliminate any air which is trapped in the vessels or cannulae. Adjustable screw clamps are fitted to the rubber tubing attached to each cannula, and these are tightened.

FIXATION

Washing the blood out of the organ is usually combined with fixation by connecting the rubber tubing leading to the main artery to a 15 l. aspirator filled with 2 per cent or 4 per cent formalin (made up with deaerated water). The fixative is allowed to flow into the vessels by gravity, and the blood and fixative allowed to escape via the veins. If the organ is liable to become waterlogged before the blood is washed out, 2 per cent sodium chloride should be added to the formalin solution. In some cases it may be necessary to make the vessels turgid with the formalin fluid, and this is done by making the initial injection with an enema syringe.

The tissue should not be waterlogged when the resin is injected as this prevents the resin from filling the vessels fully. Waterlogging can be prevented by stopping the perfusion 24 h before the resin is introduced, so that excess fluid has time to escape. Some additional treatment, such as gentle squeezing of the organ, or the siphoning of excess fluid from the arteries, may be called for. With organs such as lung and liver, where the fixed tissue is readily permeable to water, this extra treatment is not usually necessary.

302

THE RESIN INJECTION

The recommended mixture for all vascular injections is:

Marco resin 26C	.. ..	100 g
Monomer C ..	.. ..	30 g
Catalyst HCH	.. ..	6 g
Accelerator E	.. ..	6 ml.

For large structures, such as adult human bronchial tree, a more viscous solution should be prepared by using half the quantity of monomer C in the above formula (see also page 317).

The resin may be coloured red by adding red toner H 5480; blue by adding cobalt blue 3196; or yellow by adding cadmium light yellow DC 547. The pigment powder should be used sparingly as

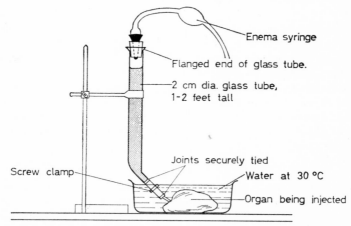

Figure 6.7. Standard injection apparatus for injecting organs with resin
(from Tompsett, 1956)

excessive quantities may either hasten or retard the setting of the resin. Before adding the pigment powder to the bulk of the resin mixture, the powder should be ground into a paste with a small quantity of the resin mixture.

The resin injection should be made within 3 days of fixation. The injection is made using the simple apparatus shown in *Figure 6.7.* The organ is placed in a bowl of water maintained at 30°C, so that it is just touching the bottom of the bowl. It must be left in the water until it is thoroughly warmed before the injection is made. Injection pressure is applied as necessary using the enema syringe. Tompsett (1959) recommends that the systems be injected one at a time, usually commencing with the blood vessels followed by the other systems.

The injection must be made as late as possible before the resin solidifies. If the above mixture is used there will be a marked rise in temperature a few minutes before the resin begins to set. The temperature of the resin mixture minus the accelerator is adjusted until it is the temperature of the room. The accelerator is then added, and the mixture left to stand in a beaker until the temperature has risen 4–8°C, according to circumstances. It is then poured into the apparatus and the injection is carried out. This usually takes less than the 3 or 4 minutes which the mixture will take to polymerize.

Care must be taken to ensure that no air is trapped in the apparatus between the resin and the organ. If air is present it may prevent the resin from entering some of the vessels, or it may cause weaknesses in the cast where there is a thin wall of resin surrounding an air bubble.

CORROSION
Leave the injected organ in a water bath for at least eight days before corroding the tissues. By means of a perspex tray, fitted with long handles, immerse the organ in a large bath of concentrated hydrochloric acid. At first the organ will float, but it will eventually sink. Cover the acid with a lid. The organ should be left in the acid for the minimum time which ensures complete maceration of the tissues.

When corrosion is complete, the organ is carefully removed from the acid bath and immersed in cold running water, where it is subjected to a jet of cold water directed from above the water level so that air bubbles and water play on the cast. This is continued until the cast is clean. Masses of resin-impregnated tissue indicate that the organ has been over injected. Such masses must be removed by dissection.

PRUNING
Extensive pruning is usually required, though sometimes fine branches can be removed, without damaging the larger ones, by using the jet of water. Resin which has entered the very fine vessels has to be removed in order that the larger vessels can be seen. This pruning is a slow and laborious procedure and should on no account be hurried. If any large branches are accidentally broken, they may be reattached using a viscous mixture of the resin ingredients thickened with some powdered Vinylite VYHH resin (obtainable from Bakelite Co. Ltd.) immediately after the addition of the accelerator.

CLEANING
After pruning, the cast may require cleaning. This may be done by giving it a short wash in 95 per cent ethyl alcohol followed by

benzene, or by immersion in a dilute solution of hydrogen peroxide for several hours. The final appearance of the cast is greatly improved by spraying it with a Marco Resin 28C mixture (see *Anatomical Techniques* for details).

MOUNTING

The finished cast must be securely mounted. A brass rod is suitable for this, as brass is fairly rigid and can be easily bent to the desired shape. The rod can be attached to a brass plate and this secured on to the base of a perspex case.

REFERENCES

Last, R. J. and Tompsett, D. H. (1962). 'Corrosion casts of the blood-vessels of stillborn babies.' *Acta. anat.*, **51**, 338–348

Tompsett, D. H. (1956). *Anatomical Techniques.* Edinburgh and London; Livingstone

Tompsett, D. H. (1958). 'Casts of the arterial tree of the brain.' *Brit. J. Radiol.*, **XXXI** (Feb. 1958)

Tompsett, D. H. (1959). 'Improvements in corrosion casting techniques.' *Ann. R. Col. Surg.* **24**, 110–123

Tompsett and co-authors. (1961–63). Improvements and additions to *Anatomical Techniques*: (*i*) 'Mounting of specimens,' Tompsett, D. H. and Bartlett, S.C., *Ann. R. Col. Surg.*, **28**, (March 1961); (*ii*) 'Further preparations from temporal bones', Tomsett, D. H., *Ibid.*, **30** (March 1962); (*iii*) 'Casts of the cerebrospinal fluid system of the brain', Tompsett, D. H. and Wyke, B., *ibid.*, 32 (April 1963)

7

MUSEUM TECHNIQUES

THE ORGANIZATION OF A ZOOLOGY–TEACHING MUSEUM

The majority of University Zoology departments possess large collections of animal material compared with the small, but often very good, collections in technical colleges and schools.

Before deciding on the way in which the material is to be stored and displayed it is necessary to consider the purposes for which the material is to be used, the existing display and storage space, and the available finance.

Taking the case of a large university collection, the curator must realize that the vast majority of the material must be clearly displayed, and in many cases the teaching staff will consider it necessary for the students to handle much of the material. Handling by students obviously results in a fair amount of damage, and should be discouraged where possible, but of course in many cases it cannot be avoided. This problem is best solved by displaying the specimens in such a way as to reveal all their important distinguishing features.

Display, unfortunately, takes up considerable space, and most departments have little space to spare. However, by carefully selecting the animals to be displayed and putting the rest of the material into an efficient store, a good teaching museum can be built up without taking up too much room. Many departments have their collections dispersed in a number of cupboards throughout the building; with a little rethinking one room could be put aside for display and the cupboards put to another use, without causing very much hardship, and the benefit which the students would obtain from having the material on permanent display would undoubtedly be considerable.

THE STRUCTURE OF THE MUSEUM

Many university buildings are old, have full interiors and do not lend themselves well to museums. However, much can be done to improve the part to be set aside for the museum. At the present time, several new universities are being built, and others rebuilt, and it may well be worth considering a few obvious requirements which could be installed.

LIGHTING

Natural light is not necessary for a zoology museum, and indeed strong sunlight must be avoided as it causes specimens to fade. The main advantages of artificial light are that it can be obtained at the necessary intensity and directed where it is required. Concealed strip lighting is probably the best.

AIR-CONDITIONING

If air-conditioning is fitted in the museum it should be possible to black-out all of the existing windows and use the acquired window space for display. Air-conditioning is recommended for several reasons besides making it possible to do away with natural light: temperature and humidity are easily controlled, and if special filters are fitted into the system, the museum will be a much cleaner place and the specimens will require less attention. If air-conditioning is not available every effort should still be made to maintain the museum temperature at a comfortable, even level. This will result in much less evaporation of the liquid from museum jars taking place. If only the museum is supplied with air-conditioning, and not the rest of the department, it will be necessary to fit double self-closing doors.

FLOORS

These should be covered with good-quality cork or rubber material with a non-slip surface, so as to make walking as silent as possible. This is particularly important when study tables are provided in the museum.

FITMENTS

The majority of vertebrate material in a teaching museum consists of skeletons and separate skulls. Probably the best way of displaying such material is to arrange the specimens on shelving in glass-fronted cupboards. Material should not be displayed at too great a height, as the shelving will obscure much of the specimens; similarly, if the specimens are too low this again makes if difficult to see them without squatting. The rear of the cupboard may be too far back, in which case a false back should be inserted and placed as close to the specimens as possible. The back should be painted with a flat washable paint of a pleasing colour, preferably a colour which will enhance the appearance of the specimen. Suitable colours are dove grey, pale sea green and pale pastel blue. The shelves, roof and base of the cupboard could be painted with white paint to give a contrast as well as to help make the cupboard interior brighter. If

MUSEUM TECHNIQUES

the outside surfaces of the display cupboards are painted in a dark contrasting colour, this will again help to make the interior appear more brightly illuminated.

Some of the vertebrate material and most of the invertebrate specimens will be preserved in fluid and displayed in glass or plastic museum jars. Although these may be displayed in shallow glass-fronted cupboards in a similar way to that used for skeletal material, a less expensive method is to employ the bay system which is used in many medical museums. This system uses bays which are constructed around the perimeter of the museum, or back to back in a line down the centre of the museum. These bays are fitted with good-quality shelves, and provided that these are strong and rigid, the backing material of the bays can be made of a relatively inexpensive material such as hardboard. This again should be painted with a flat washable paint of a suitable colour. If space permits, each phylum can be displayed in its own bay. The backs of both the bays and the cupboards not only allow the specimens to show up to their best advantage, but afford a convenient place to attach taxonomic labels and any other information. Where small specimens are being exhibited, such as hydroid colonies, it is recommended that a photomicrograph of a portion of the colony should be attached near to each exhibit. It is possible to obtain useful adjustable shelf brackets. These are available in several sizes, and are strong enough for most purposes. When arranging the collection always leave enough room for any possible expansion.

The museum is often used for study classes and should therefore be furnished with suitable tables. If the bay system is used and the bays are of sufficient size, a small table could be placed in each one. These tables should be fitted with 5 amp electric lighting sockets, as it is always necessary to display a large proportion of zoological material under microscopes. Microscopes with built-in illumination are recommended, but alternatively Angle-poise lamps can be used, or, perhaps better still, strip lights fitted along the back of the tables.

LABELLING AND CATALOGUING OF MUSEUM SPECIMENS

LABELS

The labels which are attached to museum jars should be neat in appearance, permanent, and should contain such vital information as the scientific name of the specimen (the vernacular name if desired), the principal taxonomic groups to which the animal belongs, the location, and its individual catalogue number. In the case of an anatomical part of an animal being displayed, the name of the anatomical part should be included on the label. An example of such a label could be similar to that shown below.

Phocaena phocaena *Linnaeus*, 1758.

'Porpoise'

CETACEA.   ONDONTOCETI.

PHOCAENIDAE.

Cornwall.

Bisected head.   Z. 293.

If possible the label should be electrically-typed, or printed, but if this is not possible it should be written clearly using Indian ink. The adhesive used to attach the label must be efficient and long lasting.

Dry specimens, such as bones, etc., should have plastic or metal labels securely attached bearing similar information. Even specimens which are individually placed in their own containers should at least have their catalogue numbers clearly printed on some suitable place. Indian ink may be used, but in the case of fossil material it is better to paint a small rectangle of white paint on the reverse side and, when dry, paint on top of this the catalogue number in black.

CATALOGUING THE SPECIMENS

Each museum probably has its own system of cataloguing its specimens. The following notes are only offered as a general guide, and are not necessarily the best system that could be found. This system has, however, proved adequate for a number of years.

Each major group or groups of animals (i.e., phylum, a group of phyla—say minor phyla—and class if large enough) is given a separate letter of the alphabet. Then each individual specimen is given a number. For example; rana temporaria (skull) could have number W.27.

In practice, it has been found useful to keep three separate lists of the specimens. First, a list in a loose-leaf 'Twin-lock' folder, listing the specimens according to their catalogue numbers (i.e., in numerical order), secondly, a system of filing cards should be kept, again in numerical order, so that all available information (such as name, classification, location, preservative, catalogue number, name of identifier, name of preparator, and the date of entry) can be entered. The third list is less important, but has been found useful in bringing to notice any obvious gaps in the collection. This list is a taxonomically arranged catalogue.

If the general collection is small the slide collection could be included in the same catalogue, but where large it is preferable to compile a separate system of cataloguing. Small self-adhesive numbers, in different colours, could well be employed for cataloguing slides. These numbers are retailed by most photographic dealers.

FLUID-PRESERVED MATERIAL

As has already been mentioned the majority of invertebrate material in a teaching collection is usually preserved in fluid. Suitable preserving fluids are discussed in Chapter 5. Fluid-preserved material which is to be stored should be kept in wide-necked glass jars with a secure lid, which will allow a minimum amount of evaporation. Unless the lids are suitable very frequent 'topping-up' operations are necessary, particularly when the preserving fluid is alcohol. Display material may be exhibited in glass or perspex jars.

Glass jars are ideal when the preserving fluid is alcohol, or contains alcohol or a similar solvent which will attack perspex. The jars should be rectangular in shape, with polished front and back faces, and should be of a size suitable for the particular specimen; i.e., to allow about $\frac{1}{2}$ in. around three sides of the specimen and about $1-1\frac{1}{2}$ in. at the top to allow space for a label to be attached. A glass lid should be cut to fit the top of the jar and two small holes drilled through the lid (a hand drill fitted with a Type B Glazemaster glass drill and lubricated with a mixture of turpentine and camphor is recommended). The other requirement is a backing plate which is cut from glass (or perspex if preserving fluid is not alcoholic). This again must be drilled at one or more suitably placed points so that the specimen can be securely attached. It is only necessary to drill one hole at each point if a small glass bead is used at the rear of each hole, passing one end of the thread through the bead. The thread suitable for most purposes is nylon monofilament (I.C.I.—gauges 3N and 5N are recommended). It should be remembered that when tying a knot with nylon monofilament a double compound knot should always be used—this is similar to a reef-knot but with an extra turn in each half, see *Figure 7.1.* If it should be necessary to attach small labels to the specimen (e.g., to label the various parts of a brain) the labels themselves should be made from good-quality stiff white paper and typed in a clear type-face—preferably that of an electric typewriter. *Morane* plastic skin* is then heat mounted on both sides of the label and the label attached to the specimen with small entomological pins (stainless steel 'minutens'). If other internal labels are required, similarly prepared labels may be attached to the backing plate with gelatin which is then hardened in formalin. Should internal pointers be required these are easily made

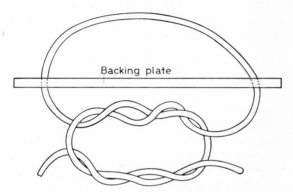

Figure 7.1. Method of tying nylon monofilament (the knot is shown slack for simplification)

by filling thin glass capillary tubing with coloured gelatin. (The best colouring agent is I.C.I. Monolite Fast Scarlet RNVS paste.) The filled capillary is then cut off to the required length when the gelatin has set, and is placed in 5 per cent formalin for a few minutes. The pointers should then be attached in position with strong gelatine solution and the gel made permanent by wetting with formalin.

There are several popular methods for sealing glass lids on to museum jars. A few of these methods are listed below:

(1) *Stockholm Tar–Red Lead Method*

Suitable for sealing jars containing 70 per cent alcohol, formalin, Kaiserling's solution, 1 per cent phenoxetol and other aqueous preservatives.

A quantity of red lead (Pb_3O_4) is mixed with sufficient Stockholm tar (Pix liquida) to form a smooth stiff paste which should be a pale brown colour and free from any unmixed red lead powder. Using a suitable instrument apply a thin even layer to the top of the jar which must be perfectly dry. Then apply the prepared lid to the top of the jar, add a heavy weight (a beaker filled with lead shot is ideal) and

*Adhesive Dry Mounting Co. Ltd., Farringdon St., London, E.C.4.

311

leave to harden for two or three days before disturbing. It should be noted before attaching the lid that sufficient fluid is added to the jar to cover the specimen, but the jar is not completely filled until the sealing mixture has hardened. This is done by means of a fine pipette attached to a funnel, the pipette passing through one of the small holes previously drilled in the lid. The other small hole allows the escape of displaced air. Finally, the holes are covered with glass coverslips which are attached with 'Micrex' or another suitable substance such as 'Vinalak'.

(2) *Bitumen Method*

Suitable for jars containing aqueous preservatives and 70 per cent alcohol.

Before commencing, the prepared lid should be heated in an oven. Melt some bitumen in a metal crucible over a small bunsen flame, and when fluid spread a thin, even layer over the top of the jar. Hold the preheated lid in a hot flame with a pair of forceps until the lid is hot enough to remelt the bitumen which has been applied to the top of the jar. Put the lid in position and press down until the seal is complete. If one or two air gaps remain, it is often possible to remove them by pressing the lid with another hot glass plate. It is, of course, necessary to use a duster to press the plates in position, or a nasty burn may result. Leave the jar for about 30 min to allow the lid to cool and the bitumen to harden. The jar is then ready for topping-up with preserving fluid, and after this has been done the two holes in the lid are covered with coverslips and sealed with Micrex or Vinalak. Any excess bitumen which may have run down the outside should be scraped off with a sharp knife, and the glass cleaned with xylene. This cleaning method is also applicable to the Stockholm tar–red lead mixture.

(3) *Gelatin–glycerol Method*

Suitable for jars containing aqueous preservatives and 70 per cent alcohol. This seal is transparent, and a finishing coat of asphalt varnish is therefore unnecessary.

Soak 15 g of sheet gelatin in cold water for a few minutes until it has swollen. Drain off the water, then transfer the swollen gelatin to a crucible. Heat the crucible on a sand bath until the gelatin is melted, then stir into it 6 ml. of glycerol. This mixture is then added to the rim of the jar and a previously heated glass lid is placed in position. Add a weight and leave until cold.

(4) *Sealing Method for Jars Containing Solvents such as Liquid Paraffin, Methyl Benzoate, Xylene, Methyl Salicylate, etc.*

Warm together until melted:

Gum arabic	50 g
Water glass	2 g
40 per cent formaldehyde solution	30 ml.
Sucrose	50 g

The melted mixture is added to the rim of the jar and a hot lid is placed in position. Add a weight and leave for a few days without disturbing.

(5) *Rubber–wax Method for Sealing Jars Containing Excessively Fatty Specimens*

Heat together in an iron crucible until molten:

Scrap rubber	2 parts
Paraffin wax	1 part

Spread the molten mixture on rim of jar and apply heated lid; add a weight, and allow the mixture to cool thoroughly before moving.

(6) *Araldite Method*

For sealing glass jars containing solvents such as liquid paraffin, methyl benzoate, xylene, methyl salicylate, etc.

This method is far simpler than method (4) and appears to be very satisfactory. Mr. J. Marner (Anatomy Department, University College, London) has tried this method with great success. The jar is filled to within $\frac{1}{4}$ in. of the rim, and Araldite 123B, mixed with an equal quantity of hardener 953B, is spread evenly on to the rim of the jar which must be absolutely dry. The glass lid is gently warmed and is carefully applied to the jar. The jar should be left undisturbed for several days.

(7) *Commercial Sealing Mixtures*

A few commercial sealing mixtures are available, one of the most useful being 'Murrayite' by Flatters & Garnett Ltd.

FINISHING THE PREPARATIONS

In nearly every case the appearance of the museum jar will be improved if the seal is obscured by applying paint to the edges of the lid and the top $\frac{1}{4}$ in. of the jar—a suitable preparation being asphalt varnish. If Sellotape or some other suitable masking tape is applied to the lid and to the near top of the jar, this will result in the painting having clean edges. Any runs which may occur with the varnish are removed when the tape is taken off, and any other excess varnish is readily soluble in xylene or benzene.

A clear label should be affixed to the jar and should contain such information as the generic and specific name of the specimen, its taxonomic position, its original location, the anatomical part being described if the specimen is not the entire animal, and the catalogue number.

Perspex Jars

Museum jars made from clear plastic sheet (perspex) have a much better appearance than glass museum jars. They are, however, unsuitable for specimens preserved in alcoholic solutions (the small alcohol content of Pick-Judah III does not affect plastic), or in solvents such as methyl salicylate, methyl benzoate, etc. Specimens which are to be frequently handled are better displayed in glass jars, as plastic jars are easily scratched.

The main advantage of plastic jars, apart from their actual appearance, is that they can be made to measure, and also that perspex is far easier to drill than glass.

There are two standard methods for making plastic jars. The first is to make the base and sides separately and then to fit on the top, and the second method, which is in every way superior, is to make the sides and top in one piece and then to fit on a front and back, and finally add the base, mounting the specimen in an inverted position. In other words, the lid which is the last to be fitted is actually the base. The former is called a 'box' type museum jar, and the latter a 'bent' type museum jar. The only difficulty with the manufacture of the 'bent' type of jar is that some system for heating the perspex so that it can be bent must be arranged. The actual details of construction of such jars are beyond the scope of this book, but the method is described in the work of Hackett and Norman (1952).

Briefly, the major points in the construction are as follows: measure the specimen and calculate the size of the container so that $\frac{1}{4}$ in. is left around all of the sides and also room for a label. When cutting the pieces of perspex allow $\frac{1}{4}$ in. extra each side for the width and $\frac{1}{2}$ in. at each end (i.e., $\frac{1}{2}$ in. wider and 1 in. longer than required). The piece which is to be bent to form the top and sides should be of $\frac{1}{8}$ in. perspex sheet, and the front and back pieces should be of $\frac{1}{16}$ in. sheet. N.B. If the jar is of large dimensions (over 7 in. high, with a front surface area of more than 28 in.^{2} $\frac{1}{8}$ in. sheet should be used for the front and back. When the height is more than 10 in. high and the front surface more than 60 in.^{2} even thicker perspex must be used. The base is usually made from $\frac{1}{4}$ in. sheet. The bending is done in one of several ways. The earliest method was to use a small gas flame which was moved across under the piece of perspex sheet by means of a slide. An improved method is to correctly locate the strip between two copper rods heated by a current of 350 amp at 0·5 V derived from a suitable transformer. The required temperature is just under 100°C, although the temperature usually recommended for shaping perspex is 130–150°C. Edges of the bent strip are flattened on a sander and then softened by pipetting under the edges, ethylene dichloride. The strip is allowed to rest on a sheet of glass separated from it by a few pieces of 24 S.W.G. wire. Allow 15 min for the solvent to work then attach the bent strip to the back sheet and apply a weight. Leave to set for several hours (preferably overnight). Fix two small perspex stops inside the jar to support the backing plate which is made from $\frac{1}{16}$ in. sheet, and should be $\frac{1}{4}$ in. shorter then the internal height of the jar. Then attach the front surface in a similar manner. When set, the excess sheet should be deeply scratched with a scalpel and then snapped off. This method is only recommended for $\frac{1}{16}$ in. sheet. The base, made from $\frac{1}{4}$ in. sheet perspex, is cut to allow $\frac{1}{2}$ in. all around the jar, and the upper corners are chamfered to make the jar more attractive. Small legs, triangular in shape, made from $\frac{1}{8}$ in. sheet perspex, are fitted at each corner. The attachment of the legs prevents the base from becoming scratched. After the base has been attached and about one minute has elapsed, some of the filling solution is run in through a small hole previously drilled through the base. This is in order to displace any ethylene dichloride vapour and also to wet the specimen. Allow to dry for about 12 h before filling completely. After filling fit a plug which is made from a strip of perspex. A method which employs a perspex screw had been described by Tovee (1960), and has much to recommend it. If any air bubbles form it is a simple matter to withdraw the screw and 'top up' the container.

Cell Mounts

These plastic cells are made in two sizes, $2\frac{3}{4}$ in. × $1\frac{1}{2}$ in. × $\frac{1}{2}$ in. and 5 in. × 3 in. × 1 in., by P. K. Dutt & Co. Ltd., Bromley, Kent, and are suitable for specimens which are preserved in formalin, Kaiserling, or 1 per cent phenoxetol. They may also be used for mounting up dry specimens such as insects. The back or base plates are available in black, white or transparent material. Dry material is best attached by a pin or pins to a strip of cork which is cemented in position on the base plate. Liquid-preserved specimens should be sewn on to drilled pieces of perspex which are cemented on to the base plate. The sewing should be done with nylon monofilament.

These cells mounts are very attractive and relatively inexpensive. Full instructions are supplied by the manufacturer.

EMBEDDING IN BLOCKS OF SOLID PLASTIC

Although blocks of solid plastic containing biological specimens are very attractive and strong, the percentage of failure is so high that the author would not recommend this method of embedding for any rare or valuable specimen. There are a large number of resins available for this purpose, and the formulae for each manufacturer's products vary from one to another, and are also continually changing. For this reason alone it is considered pointless to describe any of these methods in detail. However, some general information concerning this technique is given below.

The casting should be carried out in flexible moulds of silicone-rubber, polythene, P.V.C., neoprene of fully cured Welvic. If such moulds are used, special releasing agents are unnecessary. If casting is carried out in glass vessels (Petri-dishes, etc.), the surface should be smeared with a very thin layer of silicone Releasil fluid.

The manufacturer's formula must be strictly adhered to, and also the details of casting. Generally, the ingredients have been condensed into three separate substances: the polyester resin, a special peroxide hardener, and an accelerator. The first two ingredients can generally be mixed together in sufficient quantity to complete the casting, but the accelerator is only added to measured portions of this mixture just before use. The casting is carried out in stages. First of all, a preliminary layer of the complete mixture is allowed to polymerize in the mould. This layer should not exceed $\frac{1}{4}$ in. depth. The specimen which may be dry, wet, or cleared is then added to the sticky surface of the first layer. Then a thin holding-down layer should be applied and allowed to polymerize before adding further layers (about $\frac{1}{8}$ in. thick) until the specimen has been covered by about $\frac{1}{4}$ in. of clear plastic. Dry specimens should be previously soaked in the plain unmixed resin for several hours or days and placed in a vacuum desiccator for a short time to eliminate any trapped air. Certain substances inhibit the setting of these plastics, among them strong formaldehyde solutions, and alkalis. When the blocks are setting it is not advisable to subject them to strong sunlight as this greatly accelerates the reaction and causes high exothermic acitivity. Particular attention must be paid to cleanliness during the embedding procedure, as any dirt which finds its way into the block will spoil its final appearance.

When polymerization is complete the block is ejected from the mould and the sticky surface removed with a duster wetted with xylene. It is then roughly shaped by means of a linisher, band-saw, emery-wheel or simply by grinding flat on some emery paper pinned to a flat hard surface. Polishing the shaped block is done by means of a wet linisher using grades of emery or silicon carbide cloth down to 400 grit, and finished on a buffing machine using a soft mop, first with polishing soap and then with a clean mop. Manual polishing may also be carried out but is very time consuming. A few of the embedding kits which are on sale are listed below:

(1) CEEMAR Embedding Kit

The kit contains:

1 tin of CEEMAR embedding resin FR.264
1 bottle CEEMAR hardener FR.228
1 bottle CEEMAR accelerator FR.252

At the time of going to press the formula for embedding biological specimens is:

CEEMAR embedding resin FR.264	100 g
CEEMAR hardener FR.228	8 ml.
CEEMAR accelerator FR.252	10 drops

Supplied by:

E. M. Cromwell & Co., Ltd.,
Bishop's Stortford,
Hertfordshire.

(2) MARCO Embedding Kit

The kit contains:

1 tin of MARCO embedding mixture
1 bottle of MARCO hardener

The formula for the embedding mixture is:

MARCO embedding mixture ..	6 parts by weight
MARCO hardener	1 part by weight

Supplied by:

Scott Bader & Co., Ltd.,
Wollaston,
Wellingborough,
Northamptonshire.

(3) BEETLE Polyester Resins

Kits are not obtainable, but the following quantities are sold and will usually be found to be sufficient at any one time.

BEETLE polyester resin 4116	2 lb.
BEETLE polyester resin 4134	$\frac{1}{2}$ lb.
Catalyst 347	1 oz.
Accelerator B	1 oz.

Resin 4116 is a brittle resin when set, while resin 4134 is flexible. A suitable mixture for embedding biological specimens is:

BEETLE polyester resin 4116 ..	80 parts by weight
BEETLE polyester resin 4134 ..	20 parts by weight
Catalyst 347	$\frac{1}{2}$ part by weight
Accelerator B	$\frac{1}{2}$ part by weight

Supplied by:

B.I.P. Chemicals Ltd.,
Popes Lane,
Olbury,
Birmingham.

DRY MATERIAL

The majority of the dry material will almost certainly be osteological specimens, and the preparation and maintenance of such material is discussed in Chapter 8. Other dried material such as echinoderms, crustacea, insects and other arthropods should be kept in individual cases. If they are kept in glass-topped display boxes it is necessary to include a small quantity of a suitable pesticide such as naphthalene, camphor or *p*-dichloro-benzene. Some insect boxes are constructed with a proper camphor cell, but if not the pesticide may be contained in a small muslin bag which can be fixed inside the case with a pin. A periodic check should be made to make sure that the pesticide has not completely evaporated.

Specimens kept in properly sealed cell mounts (P. K. Dutt), do not require any pesticide treatment, and if this is included it will volatilize and cause a mistiness inside the lid.

Taxidermy preparations are also prone to attack by moths and other pests, and to combat them a small container of *p*-dichloro-benzene should be placed under the specimen, and the specimen occasionally sprayed with a small quantity of *p*-dichloro-benzene dissolved in carbon tetrachloride.

Freeze-dried specimens also suffer from attack by insect pests and these too should be protected with some similar pesticide which is placed in the display box with the specimen.

SPECIAL MUSEUM TECHNIQUES

(*1*) *Hochstetter method*

The *exact* details of Hochstetter's method have never been published, but the following prodecure will give results which are only slightly below Hochstetter's standard.

Briefly the specimens are embedded in paraffin wax and the excess wax removed from the specimen, leaving a dry preserved specimen which should have a reasonably lifelike appearance. The technique is carried out in the following way.

(*i*) The selected animal is killed by a recommended method and is carefully positioned on a weighted piece of cork so that it assumes a lifelike posture. With small mammals, such as mice, it is easier to do this when *rigor mortis* has taken place, as otherwise the animal will be too limp.

(*ii*) Fixation is then carried out by first of all injecting the specimen with 5 per cent neutral formalin and then immersing it in the same fluid. Leave to fix for several days, the exact time required depending on the size of the animal.

(*iii*) Gradually transfer the specimen to absolute alcohol by taking it through gradually increasing strengths of alcohol, leaving it for about 1 week in each change.

(*iv*) Transfer the specimen to chloroform and leave for several days to become thoroughly impregnanted. Chloroform is recommended because it does not cause the tissues to become transparent as happens with benzene or xylene.

(*v*) The specimen is then transferred to a container filled with a mixture of chlofororm which has been saturated with 60°C melting point paraffin wax. This is placed in an incubator at about 37°C after being covered with a lid. After several days the lid may be removed and the chloroform allowed to evaporate gradually.

(*vi*) Finally, transfer the specimen to a bath of molten paraffin wax of the same melting point, and allow to thoroughly impregnate in an oven at 61°C.

(*vii*) Remove the specimen from the wax, place on it a filter paper in the oven, and allow the excess wax to drip off the specimen. Care should be taken to remove the specimen and cool it before any of the wax which is in the tissue is removed.

(*viii*) Before the specimen has cooled completely it should be wiped with a cloth moistened with benzene or xylene. In the case of hairy specimens, it may be necessary to brush the hair with a xylene-moistened stiff brush.

This method gives good results with a wide variety of animals. Specimens which the author has tried include, fish, salamanders, frogs, snakes, lizards, terrapins, mice, insect pupae, nereid worms, and a specimen of *Arenicola marina*.

(2) *Spalteholz Preparations*

The original technique, which was intended for the preparation of stained transparencies of osteological specimens, has now been superceded by the Dawson method and its modifications (see page 339).

However, the method is of some importance as it can be used with some slight modifications to produce excellent transparencies of large crustacea. The technique here is as follows:

Fix the specimen in the usual way, and then transfer to 1 per cent hydrochloric acid solution for a few days. Then bleach the specimen in an alkaline solution of hydrogen peroxide. Wash the specimens thoroughly, and slowly bring them up to 90 per cent alcohol, then thoroughly dehydrate in several changes of absolute alcohol and mount in a mixture of:

Methyl salicylate	..	..	..	5 parts w/w
Benzyl benzoate ..	..	..	..	3 parts w/w

An alternative clearing mixture is:

Methyl salicylate	..	..	..	3 parts w/w
Isosafrol (ylang-ylang oil)	..	..		1 part w/w

The original method omitted the treatment with hydrochloric acid, and included staining of bone with a mixture of crystalline alizarin and alizarin cyamin.

If the above technique is followed carefully, omitting the acid treatment, excellent transparencies of starfish can be prepared showing the skeleton. Care should be taken, in this instance, to see that the fixative is neutral.

(3) *Laboratory Method for Curing Animal Skins*

The following method is suitable for the curing of skins of all mammals, and also snake and lizard skins:

(*i*) Remove the skin carefully with a minimum amount of attached subcutaneous tissue.

(*ii*) Fix the skin for 1 week in 5 per cent formalin.

(*iii*) Wash in running water for several hours.

(*iv*) Stretch out and pin to a board with the hair face down.

(*v*) While still wet, rub into the surface of the skin a quantity of Lankroline F.P.4, which is manufactured and sold by Lankro Chemicals, Eccles, Manchester, Lancashire. The Lankroline which does not affect one's own skin should be vigorously rubbed into the selected animal's skin which may be left for a considerable time in this condition without it coming to any harm.

(*vi*) With a blunt instrument (a table knife or back of a scalpel) scrape away all attached fat and subcutaneous connective tissue, taking care not to cut the skin. After each period of scraping apply more Lankroline.

(*viii*) When all of the attached tissue has been removed, rinse the skin in warm detergent solution—Teepol is excellent. Rinse again in clean water and pin out again on the board, this time fur upper-most. Allow to dry at room temperature.

(*viii*) When dry brush the hair thoroughly.

Skins prepared by this method are very soft.

(4) *Cabinet Skin Preparations*

There are internationally recognized methods for these prepara-tions, and the brief essentials of the method are listed below. Before commencing, accurate measurements must be recorded on a strong label which should be finally attached securely to the finished prepar-ation. The required measurements and information are:

Measurements of birds

(*i*) Total length from tip of tail to tip of beak; (*ii*) length of wing from tip to carpal joint; (*iii*) length of beak from tip to feather start; (*iv*) length of tail (longest feather); (*v*) length of tarsus.

Measurements of mammals

(*i*) Length of head and body; (*ii*) length of tail (excluding hairs); (*iii*) length of hind foot (excluding claws); (*iv*) Length of ears from notch to tip.

Other information required on the label

(*i*) Type of country, also longitude and latitude; (*ii*) altitude; (*iii*) colour of iris, leg, foot, and/or beak; (*iv*) sex (determined by dissection after skinning); (*v*) a note should be made of the stomach contents and any other information which may be interesting; (*vi*) date and name of preparator.

Make all the observations in Indian ink.

Method of preparation

(*i*) Plug the throat with cotton-wool.

(*ii*) Dust into the hair or feathers some fine oak sawdust.

(*iii*) Make a small (1–2 in.) incision in the skin of the abdominal region, or in the case of birds beneath the base of the wing, and remove the skin, leaving the carpals, tarsals, phalanges and the front of the skull in position in the skin.

(*iv*) Remove the eyes and the brain.

(*v*) Rub a mixture of potassium aluminium sulphate and potassium nitrate (equal parts) into the inside of the skin. Leave an excess of the mixture inside the skin, plug with tow or cotton wool, and sew up the skin. Arsenical soap (hornadase) may be used as an altern-ative to the alum–nitrate mixture (see also Southern, 1964).

(5) *Freeze-Drying Technique*

In the past few years much research has been carried out into the use of freeze drying as a means of preservation of biological material. The results have been very promising, and it appears likely that this method of preservation for display purposes will become very popular. The following notes are a brief description of the freeze drying process and are taken from the Information Leaflet 324, of the Smithsonian Institution, by R. O. Hower.

The advantages of freeze drying

The value of freeze drying is that it virtually prevents the shrinkage that occurs in other drying methods (in which drying takes place from a liquid phase, allowing surface tension to cause the cell walls to collapse—i.e., shrink). But if tissue is first frozen to give it mechanical rigidity, and the frozen water (ice crystals) is removed by subliming (passing from a solid to a vapour, omitting the liquid state) the ice and the material dries without gross physical change.

The process

The specimen must first be frozen (in a deep freeze) thus changing the original liquids in the tissues to ice crystals. When the ice crystals are sublimed, the cell walls—and therefore the specimen itself—will be rigid. The rigidity will be permanent. To prevent gross shrinkage, the frozen specimen should be kept in a vacuum-tight chamber at a temperature of $-15°C$ to $-20°C$ during the drying process. As the process requires the transfer of water vapour from the ice crystals inside the specimen to the specimen's surface, the water vapour pressure surrounding the surface must be lower than the vapour pressure inside. This difference in pressure encourages the transfer of water vapour out of the specimen.

To maintain a low water vapour pressure outside the specimen—inside the specimen chamber—some of the water vapour which collects in the chamber must continually be removed. A refrigerated surface, called a condenser or cold trap, is the most efficient device for this purpose because the cold surface of the refrigeration unit attracts the water vapour, which then condenses on the cold trap in the form of ice crystals.

Equipment

A specimen chamber, deep freeze, and vacuum pump are necessary. While not absolutely essential, a cold trap or condenser is highly desirable.

The specimen chamber must be vacuum tight and must be refrigerated. Extremely thin or porous specimens dry so fast that they can be freeze dried with very little external refrigeration, but larger specimens—particularly those with thick skins, such as vertebrates—

must be dried in a chamber with a temperature no higher than −10°C, or they will thaw and shrink during drying. However, the lower the temperature, the slower the drying (due to reduction of vapour pressure of the ice in the specimen), so −10°C to −15°C is recommended for most specimens. The easiest way to refrigerate the chamber is to place it inside a deep freeze adjusted to about −15°C.

The cold trap or condenser should be a separate chamber between the specimen chamber and the vacuum pump. (If the condenser is inside the specimen chamber it will tend to reduce the specimen temperature and prolong drying.) Particular care must be taken to keep the cold trap operating properly, otherwise water vapour will get into the pump and probably ruin it.

A glass cold trap, available from most laboratory supply houses, is simply a large glass vessel with two tubes entering at the top—a short tube, and a long tube which extends almost to the bottom of the vessel. The trap should be immersed about halfway into a cold liquid, such as a bath containing dry ice and alcohol or acetone. Vapour coming in from the specimen chamber enters the trap through the short tube and condenses around the sides of the vessel. The long tube is connected to the vacuum pump. (*Note*: Obtain the widest possible tubing for the cold trap. Most commercial cold traps have very narrow tubing which may seriously hamper the flow of water vapour.) To calculate the resistance to flow, use Poiseuille's law (1 g of water occupies a volume of 3 l. at 0·3 mm Hg. The relationship of pressure to volume is linear so that a gramme of water would occupy 300 l. at 3 mm Hg.) The cold trap should be kept 15–20° colder than the specimen chamber.

The only purpose of the vacuum pump, if a cold trap or condenser is used to remove water vapour, is to reduce the total pressure in the specimen chamber to permit more efficient transfer of water vapour from the specimen to the trap. The pump must be capable of evacuating the chamber to operating pressure within a reasonable period of time, handling about 5 per cent of the dissolved gas from the specimen as well as air which leaks into the system.

It is possible to do without a cold trap and pump out the water vapour directly through the vacuum pump, *but only if the pump is equipped with a gas ballast mechanism* which will prevent condensation of water vapour in the pump oil. It is also necessary to have a far larger capacity vacuum pump if water vapour is to be removed in this manner.

The specimen

Specimens must be frozen in their final positions as they will be rigid following drying. Use imagination in posing specimens with wires and other devices. (If glass eyes are involved, insert them before freezing.) Specimens must be completely frozen before being placed in the vacuum chamber. The drying time of intact birds, mammals, fish, and other vertebrates is usually about 2 weeks, but this can be reduced by skinning one side of the specimen or even by drilling holes through the skin after the specimen is frozen. This permits easier passage of water vapour through the skin.

After drying, specimens can be left in ordinary atmosphere without evidence of spoilage. They may, however, attract pests. Presumably, the feathers or fur could be dusted with some suitable poison or the specimen injected with sodium arsenite prior to freezing.

A Word of Warning

This is an extremely oversimplified summary, and anyone attempting to build freeze-drying apparatus should fully understand the process—particularly the concepts of vapour pressure and mean free path, both basic to this process. (A table of water vapour pressure over ice at various temperatures should be obtained.)

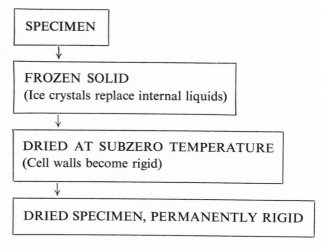

Very simple apparatus will yield satisfactory results if modest specimens are chosen. The student is warned against over-enthusiastic packing of the chamber with squirrels, rabbits, dogs, or other large mammals as the drying time will become excessive and the result inferior. The amount and rate of water evolution from the specimen in the light of the vapour handling capabilities of the system should be carefully calculated and observed throughout the process.

(6) *Staining Thick Sections of Brain*

It is possible to stain the myelinated fibres of the brain, and leave the non-myelinated fibres unstained, in other words stain the grey matter and leave the white matter unstained.

In 1931, Mulligan published a technique involving the soaking of slices of brain in hot phenol solution prior to the staining procedure and this has remained the basis of all techniques involving the differential staining of grey matter. Tompsett (1956) describes an improved method. The procedure is as follows:

(*i*) Cut 1 cm thick sections of a thoroughly fixed brain, and refix them in fresh 10 per cent formalin for 48 h.

(*ii*) Wash for 1 h in running water, then transfer to the following, Mulligan's, solution for 5 min:

Phenol (crystals)	5 g
Copper sulphate (crystals)	0·5 g
Conc. hydrochloric acid .. .. ..0·125 ml.
Distilled water	100 ml.

This solution is maintained during this time at 60°C.

(*iii*) Transfer slices to iced water for 10 sec.

(*iv*) Transfer slices to 2 per cent aqueous ferric chloride for 45 sec to 1 min according to the intensity of staining required. Grey matter will gradually turn brown.

(*v*) Wash in gently running water for 1 min, and then transfer to a 1 per cent aqueous solution of potassium ferrocyanide made up with distilled water. Leave for about 4 min, during which time the ferric chloride retained in the grey matter will be converted to ferric ferrocyanide or Berlin blue. The blue colour is at first milky but it will gradually darken after removal from the solution. Each slice must be given exactly the same time in the solution for consistent staining to result.

(*vi*) Transfer the slice to cold running water overnight, then store for at least a month before mounting in:

Glycerol	25 ml.
Formaldehyde (40 per cent soln.)	10 ml.
Citric acid	0·2 g
Distilled water	75 ml.

Use a large volume of solution (say 5 l. per human brain), and protect the sections from bright light as this causes the blue colour to fade.

(*vii*) After one month's storage, mount in a fresh change of the same solution in specially prepared perspex jars (Kampmeier and Hospodar, 1951).

REFERENCES

Hackett, C. J. and Norman, W. A. (1952). 'The Duguid–Young technique for making plastic specimen containers.' *Med. Biol. Illus.*, **11**, No. 3, 191 (July 1952)

Hochstetter, F. (1927). 'Die paraffindurchtränkung zur Erhaltung von Tieren und Pflanzen in ihrem natürlichen Aussehen.' *Die Umschau*, XXXI, 650–52

Kampmeier, O. F. and Hospodar, E. W. (1951). 'Mounting of stained serial slices of the brain as wet specimens in transparent plastic.' *Anat. Rec.*, **110**, 1–15

Mulligan, J. H. (1931). 'A method of staining brain for macroscopic study.' *J. Anat., Lond.*, **65**, 468–72

Southern, H. N. (1964). Handbook of British Mammals. Oxford; Blackwell

Tompsett, D. H. (1956). *Anatomical Techniques*. Edinburgh; Livingstone

Tovee, J. P. (1960). *J. Inst. Sci. Tech.*, **6**, No. 4

FURTHER READING

Harris, R. H. (1964). 'Vacuum dehydration and freeze drying of entire biological specimens.' *Ann. Mag. nat. Hist.*, ser. 13, VII, 65, Feb.

8

TECHNIQUES FOR THE PREPARATION OF VERTEBRATE SKELETONS

Although all vertebrate skeletons are built up on the same general plan (i.e., skull, vertebral column, rib cage, pectoral and pelvic girdles and limbs), there are so many modifications throughout this large group of animals that it is necessary to examine a few of the major kinds of skeleton which occur.

The following pages include drawings of some important animal skeletons, together with information regarding either the animal in particular or the group of which the skeleton shown is a representative (after Reynolds, 1913).

Where possible the technician who is about to undertake the preparation of any skeleton should examine either the skeleton of a similar animal or read up a description of the skeleton in a suitable textbook. Unless this is done, the inexperienced preparator will frequently lose or damage some of the bones. For example, hyoids, abdominal ribs of crocodiles, and all sesamoid bones are frequently lost because the preparator was ignorant of their existence.

The Skeleton of the Dogfish (*Scylliorhinus caniculus*)

The endoskeleton of the dogfish (*Figure 8.1*) is almost entirely cartilaginous. It may become calcified in places, e.g., the centrum of each vertebra is lined by a layer of calcified tissue.

Vertebral Column

Consists of some 130 vertebrae; the haemal arches differ markedly in the trunk and tail regions. In the trunk region the two halves of the haemal arch diverge from each other as blunt processes, to which the ribs are attached. Further back, at about vertebra 37, the two halves of the haemal arch project downwards and meet forming a complete arch. Near to the end of the tail, the haemal arches bear median haemal spines.

Skull

The skull is an oblong box, with a flattened floor and a more irregular roof. Its sides are expanded in front, owing to the olfactory capsules, and behind owing to the auditory capsules, while in the middle they are deeply hollowed to form the orbits.

Visceral Skeleton

This is by far the most complex part of the skeleton as far as the preparator is concerned. There is a large mandibular arch, and a hyoid arch, and behind these arches are five branchial arches, each of which is a hoop, incomplete above and formed of four or more pieces of cartilage. Some of these cartilages bear gill rays along their posterior borders.

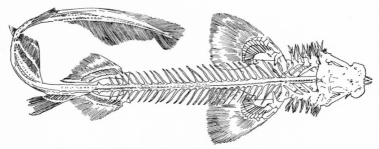

Figure 8.1. Skeleton of a dogfish (Scylliorhinus caniculus)

Pectoral Girdle and Fins

The pectoral girdle forms a crescent-shaped hoop of cartilage, incomplete above and lying just behind the visceral skeleton. Each of the pectoral fins articulates with the pectoral girdle by means of three basalia or basal cartilages. Along the outer borders of the three basalia are arranged a series of close-set cartilaginous pieces, the radialia. Succeeding the radialia are a series of small polygonal pieces of cartilage, and finally the fin is completed by the dermal fin rays which are horny.

Pelvic Girdle and Fins

The pelvic girdle is much smaller than the pectoral, and is formed of a stout, nearly straight bar of cartilage placed transversely across the ventral region of the body. It bears on its posterior surface a pair of facets with which the pelvic fins articulate. Each pelvic fin is much smaller and far more simple in construction than the pectoral fins. Each fin consists of a long, somewhat curved rod, the basi-pterygium, which extends directly backwards on the inner side of the fin and articulates in front with the pelvic girdle. From its outer side arise a series of about 14 parallel cartilaginous radials which bear small polygonal pieces of cartilage. The anterior one of these radials usually articulates with the pelvic girdle. In the adult male dogfish the distal end of the basi-pterygium bears a stout rod nearly as long as itself, and grooved on the dorsal surface. This is the skeleton of the clasper.

The Skeleton of the Codfish (Gadus morrhua)

The only parts of the exoskeleton which are retained in a prepared codfish skeleton are the teeth and the fin rays. The teeth are arranged in groups on the premaxillae, mandible, vomer, and superior and inferior pharyngeal bones. The fin rays are delicate, nearly straight bony rods which support the fins.

The endoskeleton of the codfish (*Figure 8.2*), though partially cartilaginous, is mainly ossified.

Vertebral Column

This consists of a series of some 52 vertebrae, all completely ossified. They can be divided into those of the trunk region which bear movable ribs, and those of the caudal or tail region which do not bear movable ribs. There are 17 trunk vertebrae and some 35 caudal vertebrae.

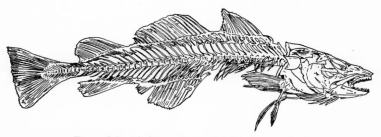

Figure 8.2. Skeleton of a codfish (Gadus morrhua)

The Skull

The skull is very fully ossified, but it is a very complicated structure due to the fact that it is composed of a large number of plate-like bones which overlap or loosely articulate with one another. This makes the skull of the codfish and all teleosts one of the most difficult skeletal structures to prepare. The technician should examine either a good diagram of a codfish skull or another already prepared skull before attempting to prepare one for himself. The cranium itself has a series of bones associated with it, and there are a number of bones in connection with the upper jaw and also the lower jaw. (Part of the lower jaw is cartilaginous, forming Meckel's cartilage, which is not seen in the dried skull.) The hyoid arch, made up of a series of bones, and the five branchial arches complete the major parts of the skull.

The Pectoral Girdle and Fins

In the girdle, the membrane bones are well developed, while the cartilaginous bones, the scapula and coracoid are much reduced. The pectoral fins, each consist of four small irregular bones, bearing a series of about 19 dermal fin rays.

The Pelvic Girdle and Fins

These have a very anomalous position in the codfish, being attached to the throat in front of the pectoral girdle. The girdle is nearly triangular in shape, and the fins are smaller.

The Unpaired or Median Fins

These are six in number, three being dorsal, two anal or ventral, and one caudal. The dorsal and anal fins each consist of two sets of structures, the fin rays and the interspinous bones. The first dorsal fin has 13 rays, the second has 16–19, and the third 17–19. The first anal fin has about 22, and the second anal fin 14. The interspinous bones of the dorsal and anal fins alternate with the neural and haemal spines, respectively, and form short, forwardly projecting bones, each attached proximally to the base of the corresponding fin ray. The caudal fin consists of a series of about 43 rays which radiate from the posterior end of the vertebral column, being connected with the urostyle or hypural bone, and with the posterior neural and haemal spines without the intervention of interspinous bones. The caudal fin of the codfish is homocercal.

The Skeleton of the Frog (*Rana temporaria*)

The only exoskeletal structures found in the frog are the teeth, which are borne on the maxillae, premaxillae, and vomers, and the horny covering of the calcar or prehallux.

The endoskeleton of the adult frog (*Figure 8.3*) consists partly of cartilage, and partly of bone. Some of the cartilage (in the suprascapula, and in the epiphyses of the limb bones) is calcified. To demonstrate the cartilaginous parts of the skeleton a cartilage transparency of a frog should be prepared (see page 340).

The Vertebral Column

This consists of a tube, formed of a series of ten bones which surround and protect the spinal cord. Of these bones, nine are vertebrae and the tenth is a straight rod, the urostyle. The urostyle is almost as long as the rest of the vertebrae put together. The first vertebra is a ring-like structure with a much reduced centrum which is opisthocoelous (concave posterior surface). Vertebrae 2–7 are all procoelous (concave anterior surface). The eighth vertebra is amphicoelous (both anterior and posterior surfaces are concave). The ninth vertebra has very stout transverse processes which are directed backwards and somewhat upwards. These processes articulate with the pelvic girdle, this being the reason why this vertebra is

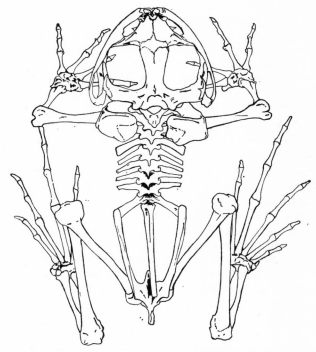

Figure 8.3. Skeleton of a frog (Rana temporaria)

sometimes called the sacrum. The anterior end of the urostyle is expanded and bears two concave articular surfaces by means of which it articulates with the sacrum.

The Skull

This consists of a cranium proper, which remains partially cartilaginous, sense capsules which are bony or cartilaginous structures, and the jaws. The upper jaw is of cartilage which is almost completely overlain with bone. The lower jaw consists of a pair of cartilaginous bones, in connection with each there are developed

331

two membrane bones and one cartilage bone. The lower jaw is devoid of teeth.

The Hyoid

This consists of a broad thin plate of cartilage, drawn out into two pairs of long processes.

The Pectoral Girdle and Sternum

The pectoral girdle is formed of two half-rings of cartilage which encircles the sides of the body a short way behind the head. These two halves meet each other in the ventral mid-line, and separate the anterior elements of the sternum from the posterior ones. Some parts of the girdle are bony while others are cartilaginous. The sternum is made up of four parts arranged in two groups, the most anterior and posterior elements remaining cartilaginous.

The Fore-limbs

These consist of a humerus, a united radius and ulna (the radio-ulna), and the manus consisting of a carpus of six small bones arranged in two rows, and five digits, the first of which has no phalanges. (Phalangeal formula is 0, 2, 2, 3, 3.)

The Pelvic Girdle

The pelvic girdle is a V-shaped structure consisting of two halves which are fused together in the mid-line posteriorly, while in front they are attached to the ends of the transverse processes of the ninth or sacral vertebra. Each half bears at its posterior end a deep cup, the acetabulum, with which the head of the femur articulates. The ventral portion of the girdle never ossifies, but calcifies in old animals.

The Hind-limbs

These consist of a femur, a long united tibia and fibula (the tibio-fibula), and a pes consisting of two parts, the tarsus and the foot. The tarsus consists of two rows of structures, the proximal row of the long astragulus and calcaneum, and a distal row of three very small pieces of calcified cartilage. The foot consists of five complete digits as well as a supplementary toe, the prehallux or calcar. (The phalangeal formula is 2, 2, 3, 4, 3.)

The Skeleton of Lacertilia

The following is a general account of the skeleton of lacertilia.

The body is elongated, and as a rule four pentadactyl limbs are present, but sometimes the limbs are vestigial (e.g. some skinks) or absent (e.g. *Anguis*, slow-worm). An exoskeleton in the form of horny plates, spines or scales is present. The vertebrae are procoelous (concave surface of centrum is anterior), or rarely as in the geckos amphicoelous. The sacral vertebrae of living forms are not ankylosed together, and the caudal vertebrae usually have well-developed chevron bones.

In the skull the orbits are separated only by an imperfectly developed interorbital septum. (N.B. Take care of this structure when preparing the skull.) Teeth are always present, and may be confined to the jaws or may be developed also on the pterygoids and rarely on the palatines. They are either acrodont or pleurodont. The rami of the mandibles are joined together by a suture.

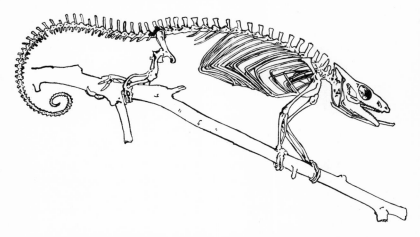

Figure 8.4. Skeleton of a chameleon (Chameleo melleri)

A pectoral girdle is always present, and generally also a sternum. Clavicles and an interclavicle are commonly present, but are absent in the chameleons.

Sternal ribs are present in chameleons and skinks. Usually the limbs are pentadactylate and the digits are clawed. Sometimes, one or both pairs of limbs are wanting. When the posterior limbs are absent, the pelvic girdle is also absent, but the loss of the fore-limbs does not lead to a corresponding loss of the pectoral girdle. Phalangeal formula is usually 2, 3, 4, 5, 3 (4).

The Skeleton of Crocodilia

The following is a general account of the skeleton of Crocodilia.

The skull is usually sculptured externally, and is more or less elongated with the external nares situated near the extremity. There is a secondary palate formed by the meeting in the mid-line of the maxillae and palatines, and the pterygoids also, the posterior nares opening far back. The teeth are inserted into deep sockets, and are confined to the maxillae, premaxillae and dentaries. The vertebrae in all recent forms are procoelous, except that the second sacral is biconcave and the first caudal biconvex. The ribs are double-headed, articulating with the centrum and arch anteriorly, and with the transverse processes only, posteriorly. Both sternal and abdominal ribs occur, also cervical ribs.

Both the scapula and coracoid are elongated. There is no precoracoid, the sternum remains cartilaginous, and there are no clavicles. There are two sacral vertebrae; the large ilium is directed backwards, and the ischia meet in a ventral symphysis. The epipubes are flat and spatulate, and are directed forward in the abdominal wall.

Figure 8.5. Skeleton of a crocodilian (Tomistoma schlegeli)

There are five digits in the manus (phalangeal formula = 2, 3, 4, 4, 3). The pes has five digits, but the fifth is much reduced, consisting only of a short metatarsal (phalangeal formula = 2, 3, 4, 5, 0). The calcaneum is elongated, such as is almost unknown elsewhere except in mammals.

In all crocodilians there is a more or less complete exoskeleton formed of rows of bony scutes overlain by epidermal scales; these bony scutes are especially well developed on the dorsal side, but may also occur on the ventral side. It is possible to prepare these scutes and arrange them on a sheet of perspex which can be supported above the skeleton, but this is usually not necessary.

The Skeleton of Chelonia

The following is a general account of the skeleton of Chelonia.

The chelonians are characterized by the imperforate temporal roof of the skull, the entire absence of teeth (jaws are covered with horny plates), an interparietal foramen, and by the presence of a more or less well-developed osseous carapace. There is a single external naris.

There are eight cervical vertebrae, with variously convexoconcave centra. There are ten thoracic vertebrae fused with each other and with the ribs, and except in *Dermochelys* with the dermal carapace.

334

THE SKELETON OF AVES

The thoracic ribs are attached intercentrally, at least anteriorly, and are overlain by dermal plates corresponding in number to them. External to the ribs and dermal plates there is usually a series of marginal plates. The plastron is composed of two clavicles, an interclavicle and three other pairs of dermal bones.

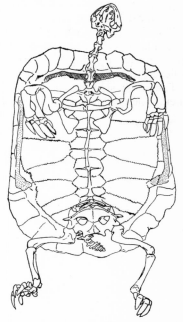

Figure 8.6. Skeleton of a tortoise (Testudo graeca) with plastron removed

The pectoral girdle, enclosed within the carapace, is composed of a more or less rod-like bifurcated scapula, and an elongated coracoid; the precoracoid is absent. The digits have the phalangeal formula of 2, 3, 3, 3, 3, except in the Trionychoidea, in which the fourth digit has an additional phalanx.

The ilium is directed forward from the sacrum; the pubes and ischia meet in a firm symphysis and there is a large puboischiatic vacuity. The tail is always short, and the body broad and relatively short.

The Skeleton of Aves

The following is a general account of the skeleton of birds.

The important epidermal exoskeleton of bird, i.e., feathers, can be ignored as far as skeletal preparation is concerned. The horny covering of the jaw extremities (the beaks) may be left in position if desired. The toes and tarso-metatarsus are usually featherless and covered either with granular structures or with well-formed scales. This covering may be left in position on one foot provided that it is injected with a small quantity of embalming fluid or some other preservative. Claws are sometimes found on the manus. Claws are present on some or all of the digits of the pes. Spurs also occur, and are conical horny structures developed on bony outgrowths of the radial side of the carpus, metacarpus, or metatarsus. They are particularly well developed in some of the gallinaceous birds, which use them for fighting. Teeth do not occur in living birds, but are believed to have been present in some extinct forms.

The most striking thing about the endoskeleton of birds is its pneumaticity. In the embryos all the bones contain marrow, but as

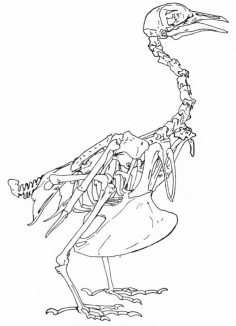

Figure 8.7. Skeleton of a pigeon (Columba livia)

growth proceeds this becomes replaced by air to a variable extent in different forms. Always some part of the skeleton is pneumatic.

The vertebral column is readily divisible into a very mobile cervical region, and an extremely rigid postcervical region. The cervical vertebrae in all living forms have heterocoelous centra (saddle shaped). Cervical ribs are often present. The thoracic vertebrae bear ribs which articulate with sternal ribs. There are two true sacral vertebrae, but as development proceeds a number of other vertebrae become fused with the true sacrals to form a large synsacrum. These pseudosacral vertebrae usually include the lumbar, and some of the thoracic and caudal vertebrae. In all recent birds the tail is short, and in the great majority of cases the posterior vertebrae are fused together to form a pygostyle.

The skulls of birds are relatively easy to prepare due to the fact that most of the bones fuse together. In most birds the upper beak is immovably fixed, but in some birds an elastic joint is established (e.g., parrots, geese and *Opisthocomus*). The dentaries of the two rami are always fused together. The hyoid apparatus is very variable, and consists of a median portion composed of three pieces placed end to end, and a pair of cornua. In woodpeckers the cornua are enormously long, and curve over the skull, extending as far forwards as the anterior nares.

The sternum is greatly developed in birds, and is generally keeled, though the development of the keel varies greatly. The pectoral girdle is well developed in all the Carinatae, but much reduced in the Ratitae. Clavicles are generally present.

In the wing of all living birds the ulna is thicker than the radius, and the digits are modified, the metacarpals being completely fused, and the phalanges reduced in number. In a few birds the metacarpus bears a bony outgrowth, which is sometimes sheathed in horn to form a spur.

Birds have a very large pelvis and its characters are constant throughout the whole group. The ilium is very large, and is united along its whole length with the sacral and pseudosacral vertebrae. The ischium is broad and extends back parallel to the ilium with which in most birds it fuses posteriorly. The pubis forms a long slender rod lying parallel to the ischium. The acetabulum in birds is always perforate.

In the posterior limb the tibia is always well developed. The proximal tarsals are fused with its distal end, forming a tibio-tarsus. There is frequently an oblique bar of bone crossing the anterior face of the tibio-tarsus at the distal end, just above the articular surface of the tarso-metatarsus. The fibula is always imperfectly developed, usually with its distal end atrophied. The distal tarsals fuse with the second, third and fourth metatarsals, forming the tarso-metatarsus. The first metatarsus is nearly always free. No adult bird has more than four digits in the pes. In penguins the metatarsals are separate.

In most birds the third metatarsal is curved so as not to lie in the same plane as the others. In most birds the first four toes are present while the fifth is always absent. The first toe commonly has two phalanges, the second three, the third four and the fourth five.

The Skeleton of Mammalia

The following is a general account of the skeleton of mammals.

As well as hair, which is always present in mammals, the exoskeleton is often represented by the presence of scales, spines, hoofs, nails, claws, and horns.

In the endoskeleton the vertebral centra have terminal epiphyses except in the Prototheria and some Sirenia. The cranial region of the skull is greatly developed, and in the adult all the skull bones apart from the mandible, hyoid, and auditory ossicles are firmly united together. The teeth are always attached to the maxillae, premaxillae and mandibles, and never to any other bones. They are nearly always implanted in distinct sockets. The teeth are generally markedly heterodont, four forms—incisors, canines, premolars and molars—being commonly distinguishable. Some mammals are monophyodont, having only a single set of teeth, but the majority are diphyodont, having two sets, a deciduous or milk dentition, and a permanent dentition.

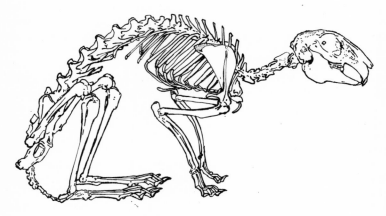

Figure 8.8. Skeleton of a rabbit (Oryctolagus cuniculus)

In the shoulder girdle the coracoid is greatly reduced (except in the Prototheria), generally forming only a small process on the scapula. In the pelvic girdle the pubes meet in a ventral symphysis, except in some Insectivora and Chiroptera. In many mammals a fourth pelvic element, the acetabular bone, is distinguishable.

A bacculum (os penis) is present in males of the following orders: Carnivora, Chiroptera, Rodentia, and Primates (except Man).

TRANSPARENCY TECHNIQUES

(1) *The Alizarine Technique for Bone and Other Tissues Containing Calcium*

There are numerous and varied ways of carrying out this technique, but the following method has stood the test of time. It is of importance to remember that all solutions must be prepared with distilled water. Prior to fixation it is sometimes necessary in the case of vertebrates to skin and eviscerate the animal concerned, and in some cases it is also helpful to remove excess muscular tissue. However, it is possible to prepare quite satisfactory specimens in an entire state. The method is as follows:

(*i*) Fix in 70 per cent alcohol for 1–3 days, according to size.

(*ii*) Defat for 1 day in acetone.

(*iii*) The partial maceration should now be carried out: Fish should be transferred to 1 per cent ammonium hydroxide solution, until the posterior part of the vertebral column is visible. Vertebrate embryos should be transferred to 0·5 per cent sodium or potassium hydroxide solution, until the terminal digits are clear. Specimens of frog–sparrow–mouse size should be transferred to 1 per cent hydroxide solution, while larger specimens of snake–pigeon–rat size may require 1·5–2 per cent hydroxide solution. In all cases leave until the terminal digits are clear.

(*iv*) Transfer to fresh hydroxide solution and then add a few drops of a saturated solution of alizarine red S in absolute alcohol to the hydroxide solution, until the mixture is a pale red colour. The part of the animal containing calcium gradually takes up the stain. If the skeleton, etc., is insufficiently stained when all of the colour has been removed from the solution, then a few more drops of alizarine solution should be added. The total staining time should not normally exceed 24 h.

(*v*) Transfer to the appropriate hydroxide solution for 1 h.

(*vi*) Transfer to a mixture of 1 part glycerol and 9 parts hydroxide for a few days.

(*vii*) Transfer to a mixture of equal parts of glycerol and hydroxide solution for a few days.

(*viii*) Transfer to a 70 per cent aqueous solution of glycerol for a few days.

(*ix*) Transfer to an 80 per cent solution of glycerol for a few days.

(*x*) Transfer to a 90 per cent aqueous solution of glycerol for a few days.

(*xi*) Transfer to pure glycerol. Change the glycerol after a few days and store in the fresh glycerol.

The most common alternative method of clearing is to dehydrate via graded alcohols, then clear in benzyl alcohol. The alizarine technique is most useful in genetics and embryology, the earliest ossification being demonstrated with great accuracy. Small specimens which are difficult to prepare as dry osteological mounts, in particular amphibia and reptiles, are well demonstrated by this method. It will display the internal calcareous shell of certain cephalopod molluscs, and such things as the 'gastric mill' of certain decapod crustacea.

(2) *The Victoria Blue Technique for Demonstrating Cartilage*

This transparency technique requires more skill than the alizarine method. The reason for this being that the staining process is regressive, where the specimen is grossly overstained and then gradually differentiated. It requires some experience to know when the required degree of differentiation has been reached, as at this stage the animal has not been cleared. The original technique employed methylene blue or toluidine blue, but more satisfactory results are obtainable with victoria blue.

The method is as follows: (*i*) If desired, skin and eviscerate the animal. Fix in 5 per cent formaldehyde solution for 1–3 days according to size; (*ii*) Transfer to acid alcohol (1 per cent hydrochloric acid in 70 per cent alcohol), for 24 h; (*iii*) Stain for 1 week in 1 per cent victoria blue in acid alcohol; (*iv*) Differentiate with several changes of acid alcohol. This may take several days or even weeks; (*v*) When differentiation is considered complete, transfer to 90 per cent alcohol for about 12 h; (*vi*) Dehydrate thoroughly in several changes of absolute alcohol for a few hours; (*vii*) When completely dehydrated, clear the specimen in methyl benzoate. When cleared, store in a fresh change of methyl benzoate.

This technique gives excellent results with cartilaginous fish, and larval amphibians.

PREPARATION OF CARTILAGINOUS SKELETONS

The preparation of the skeleton of a dogfish is described. A similar method will give good results with all other cartilaginous skeletons.

Method

Eviscerate the fish, taking care not to cut either of the limb girdles. Place the dogfish into a large bowl of hot (not boiling) water and leave it immersed for 2 or 3 min. Remove from the water and place the fish on a tray. Using the fingers pull away as much of the flesh as possible, then immerse the fish in cold water for 1 min. Replace in hot water for a further few minutes and again remove as much flesh as possible. Transfer the fish to cold water, and if any of the skeleton is exposed soak the animal for a few minutes in 70 per cent alcohol. By the repeated transference of the fish from hot water to cold water and to 70 per cent alcohol, gradually expose all of the skeleton. Before all of the skeleton appears it is advisable for it to be partly dismembered. The pectoral girdle and fins should be pulled away, also the pelvic girdle and fins. The vertebral column should be separated from the skull and branchial 'basket'. Any remaining flesh is easily removed by gently brushing it with a nylon toothbrush dipped into bleaching powder (calcium hypochlorite). The branchial basket and the ribs must be treated with extreme care as they are particularly fragile. The cleaned portions of skeleton should be hardened by immersion in formol–alcohol (5 per cent formalin in 70 per cent alcohol) for 24 h. Transfer to 70 per cent alcohol in which it should be stored.

If the specimen is to be mounted in a perspex jar the skeleton may be transferred to 10 per cent formalin, in which it should remain for several days before being mounted in a fresh change of solution.

THE PREPARATION OF BONY SKELETONS

The method chosen for the preparation will depend upon several factors: whether the skeleton is required in an articulated or disarticulated condition, and whether the animal is received in a fresh, unpreserved state or has been preserved in alcohol, formalin or similar preservative. If the preparator has any choice in the matter, it is better to choose an unpreserved specimen, which may be stored in a deep freeze until it is prepared.

For convenience, the following techniques are subdivided into (1) those suitably employed with fresh material, and (2) those suitably employed with preserved material.

(1) TECHNIQUES FOR FRESH MATERIAL

Fresh material in this case means animals which have been freshly killed, or preserved in a deep freeze, or those which have been roughly fleshed and dried in the sun. For the preparation of articulated skeletons from fresh material, one of the two following methods should be used.

(a) Dermestes Vulpinus 'Leather Beetles'

These will eat the flesh of unpreserved animals until only the skeleton is left. The method is as follows: obtain a culture of *Dermestes* beetles and larvae, and put these into a layer of sawdust, below a piece of perforated zinc gauze, and in an escape-proof container of a suitable size. As this method gives the best results with small vertebrates, the container need only be small. One can easily be constructed from $\frac{1}{8}$ in. perspex sheet. The specimen should be skinned and eviscerated and partly dried before it is placed on the zinc gauze, after which the lid is carefully replaced and the whole container kept in a warm place. Inspect periodically to ensure that the larvae and beetles are eating the flesh, and that the skeleton is not beginning to fall apart. When sufficiently cleaned, remove from the container, taking care not to lift out any beetles or larvae. If necessary the skeleton may be bleached and defatted. The culture is easily maintained by feeding with a small dead animal, such as a mouse. Rags should be placed over the specimen while it is being cleaned by the beetles. Larger dermestaria are easily built.

(b) Hot Water Maceration

This is probably the best method of preparation. Skin and eviscerate the animal. Then divide the animal into several pieces of a manageable size. For example, with an average size dog it would be advisable to divide it into the following portions: head, neck; rib-cage; lumbar-sacral region with pelvic girdle attached; tail; both scapulae; separate limbs. Search for the clavicles which are suspended in the muscles between the scapulae and sternum. The hyoid apparatus should be carefully removed, and if the dog is male, the os penis should be removed.

With a sharp knife remove as much flesh as possible, taking care not to damage the bones. Put each piece of the animal into a separate container of warm water, containing a small quantity of washing soda. Allow the solution to simmer (not boil) until the flesh can be easily removed with a scalpel or other suitable instrument. Great care must be taken to ensure that the surface of bone is not cut. Return the cleaned bones to the simmering bath for a few minutes and then brush away any remaining flesh, using a nylon toothbrush which is dipped into bleaching powder (calcium hypochlorite). All ligaments should be left in place so that the majority of the bones will be correctly articulated. When clean, rinse the bones in running water, and bleach for 24 h. Then dry the bones in an incubator, and if they require defatting this should be the next and final treatment. Many of the smaller bones will not require defatting as the addition of washing soda to the water emulsifies most of the fat. It may be necessary to drill a small hole at each end of the long bones, through into the marrow cavity, to allow the fat to escape into the defatting mixture (see page 345).

For the preparation of disarticulated skeletons from fresh material, one of the following three methods should be employed:

(i) Prolonged Hot-water Maceration

This is suitable for all large vertebrates and all teleost fish. The technique is similar to that just described, but the simmering is prolonged, so that the bones readily separate from one another. Methods (ii) and (iii) are enzymic maceration methods:

(ii) Trypsin Technique

Skin and eviscerate the animal, then incubate at 37°C in a 1 per cent solution of trypsin in 0·5 per cent aqueous sodium carbonate. The flesh should be completely digested after 48 h of incubation, when the supernatant fluid should be decanted, and the bones carefully transferred to a beaker. Rinse the bones several times with warm water, then bleach for 24 h.

(iii) Papaine Technique

Skin and eviscerate the animal, then incubate at 37–45°C in a vessel nearly filled with tap-water to which has been added a small quantity of papaine powder. The papaine should be sprinkled on to the surface of the water and allowed to dissolve slowly. Cover the vessel with a close-fitting lid. The flesh will be completely digested away after two or three days. Some batches of papaine take longer to act than others, and it is worth activating each batch with a few drops of some filtered papaine solution which has been recovered from a previous time.

When the flesh has been completely digested the supernatant fluid should be decanted and the bones carefully transferred to a beaker, where they must be rinsed several times in warm water. The bones should then be bleached for 24 h.

Maceration methods are always accompanied by an unpleasant smell, and they are therefore only suitable for small animals, which may be completely sealed in a container. When decanting the supernatant fluid great care must be taken to ensure that no bones are lost, and to prevent this happening the fluid should be poured through a fine metal sieve.

The papaine method is of great use when one needs to completely disarticulate skulls, but of course this is only possible where the individual bones have not become ankylosed. Another use of the papaine method is to separate the bones contained in 'owl pellets' which often provide a source of shrew and vole skulls, and various bones.

(2) TECHNIQUES FOR PRESERVED MATERIAL

As previously stated the technician will in most cases find it far better to avoid using preserved material if at all possible. However, if preserved material has to be used, alcohol-preserved specimens are far easier to deal with than formalin-preserved animals. For alcohol-preserved material the following technique using antiformin has proved very successful, and some excellent skulls of small snakes have been prepared.

Antiformin Technique (*Johan, 1924*)

The skinned and eviscerated specimen is put into a hot (not boiling) 2 per cent solution of antiformin for 1 h, after which time it should be possible to pick off most of the flesh without much difficulty. Any stubborn flesh may be removed by brushing the bones with a nylon toothbrush moistened with a cream of bleaching powder and water. The stock solution of antiformin is prepared as follows:

Sodium carbonate	..	..	..	..	150 g
Bleaching powder	..	..	..	..	100 g
Water ..	..	..	..	..	..	1 l.

Dissolve the sodium carbonate in 250 ml. of the water and the bleaching powder in the remaining 750 ml. Mix the two solutions, and shake occasionally for 3–4 h. Filter. To the filtrate add an equal volume of 15 per cent aqueous sodium hydroxide solution.

H. L. H. Green describes another method, using antiformin for both fresh and preserved material. He simmers fresh material in a mixture of 1 part antiformin to 8–10 parts water, and preserved material in 1 part antiformin with 5 parts water. The author confirms that this method gives good results.

For formalin-preserved material another method which often gives good results is one which employes pancreatin. Care must be taken to remove any lead shot from the animal before commencing the process, as this will cause the bones to become blackened.

Pancreatin Technique

The animal should be skinned and eviscerated, then left in running water for several days to remove all traces of preservative. As much flesh as possible should then be removed taking great care not to damage the bones. The carcass is then immersed in a simmering bath of Rowle's fluid. Inspect every few minutes, and when the remaining flesh has become sufficiently digested remove the animal from the fluid and rinse it under a tap. Any stubborn pieces of flesh may be brushed off by using a nylon toothbrush moistened with a cream of bleaching powder and water. Rowle's fluid is prepared as follows:

Pancreatin powder	..	..	..	2 g
Sodium sulphide	..	..	..	1 g
Normal saline ..	..	..	..	1,900 ml.

The simmering should be carried out in a fume cupboard or in a well-ventilated room.

DEFATTING OF BONES

Whichever method has been used to prepare the bones, it will usually be necessary to treat the bones with a suitable fat solvent to remove the fat which is generally present in large quantities. The bones must be dried thoroughly before the defatting process is commenced. Large long-bones should have a small hole drilled through into the marrow cavity from each end of the bone. This allows better penetration of the solvent and an easy exit for the fat.

The defatting may be carried out by immersing the bones in a large quantity of trichloroethylene, or in a mixture of benzene and chloroform. By far the best method is to reflux the trichloroethylene and to place the bones in the vapour, allowing the fat to drip away into the reservoir of liquid solvent. But to carry this out a degreaser such as that used in garages must be used. Special attention must be paid to the special safety precautions which apply to the use of this solvent, and any degreaser must be airtight and the process carried out in the open air or in a large well-ventilated room. The best grade of trichloroethylene is 'Triklone' N (trichloroethylene, Grade 7) from I.C.I. Limited. This grade can be repeatedly distilled without any deterioration in its properties, and it contains no materials which will stain or discolour the material being degreased. The author has been given to understand that I.C.I. will advise users of the suitability of their apparatus before it is used.

BLEACHING OF BONES

All skeletal material is enhanced by the process of bleaching. The best bleaching solution is prepared by diluting 20 volume hydrogen peroxide with an equal quantity of warm tap-water and adding a few drops of strong ammonium hydroxide solution to catalyse the reaction. However, this is a relatively expensive bleach, and when large quantities are required a less expensive bleach, which will usually give satisfactory results, may be prepared by diluting 20 volume hydrogen peroxide with water to the proportion of 1 part peroxide to 5 parts water, then a few drops of strong ammonium hydroxide are added and the surface of the solution covered with a thin layer of bleaching powder, which should be allowed to dissolve slowly. In both cases bleaching should be complete in about 24 h, although small bones will only require a few hours.

When the bleaching is complete, the bones are removed from the solution, rinsed in water, then placed on a filter paper and dried in an incubator. To speed up the drying process, small bones may be rinsed in acetone before being dried in the incubator.

After-treatment of Bones

The bones of skeletons which are to be mounted or put on display may be impregnated with a plastic, which makes them far easier to clean. The plastic should on no account obscure any of the surface detail of the bones and should impart little or no gloss. A plastic which provides these needs is polyvinyl acetal alvar. It should be dissolved in a mixture of 3 parts absolute alcohol to 1 part amyl acetate until a thin varnish is obtained. The bones should be dipped into the varnish or they may be painted. Fragile bones such as those which are obtained from animals which have suffered from calcium deficiency, or from specimens which have been stored for a long time in a slightly acid formalin solution, should be immersed in the alvar for several days so that they become thoroughly impregnated with the plastic. The varnish dries very rapidly in a warm atmosphere.

All osteological material should be kept covered at all times, to prevent dust from settling on the bones. Mounted specimens should be covered with perspex or glass covers, and separate bones or collections of bones should·be kept in glass-topped cardboard boxes or in plastic containers.

The Articulation and Mounting of Skeletons

It is most important that the final posture of the skeleton should be as natural as possible. A good photograph of the animal will help you to decide on a good stance. For example, in the case of an arboreal animal such as a chameleon (*Figure 8.4*) it may be advisable to mount the animal clinging to a branch. In the case of a large skeleton it is recommended that the prepared portions are arranged on a blackboard which is laid flat on the floor. These pieces of skeleton are placed in a suitable position, and their outline drawn on to the blackboard with chalk. From this drawing it is an easy matter to determine the length of the main supports which will be required, and also the dimensions of the baseboard.

Although the individual bones of each portion of the skeleton should not have been separated, it is inevitable that some of the bones will have become detached. The method selected for attaching these bones to the skeleton, and also the various portions of the skeleton to each other, will depend on several factors, namely the size of the bones and the purpose for which the skeleton is intended. By far the strongest method for joining bones together is to use wire, but no matter how neatly this is done it is always disfiguring and is not always suitable for specimens which are only intended for display. In such a case it is better to use a strong transparent glue.

Wiring Bones Together

Bones which do not naturally move freely against each other must be so wired that they are completely rigid. But on the other hand, bones which articulate together at a joint should be wired so that they will move in the correct plane. For example, the ends of two phalanges should be drilled from side to side, and not from top to bottom.

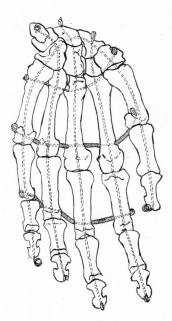

Figure 8.9. The wiring of bones

The drilling should be carried out with a high-speed twist drill (foot operated if possible), using as fine a drill as possible for a particular wire.

The commonest method of fastening the wire is to twist the two ends together using a fine pair of pliers. but for large osteological preparations which are to be handled a great deal a curl joint is employed. This method enables a thicker wire to be employed. The bones are drilled in a suitable fashion and a piece of wire is passed through the hole in the two bones. Both ends in turn are curled (twisted into a spring). (See *Figure 8.9*.) For articulated hands and feet which are to be handled a great deal it is recommended that spacing springs be employed to keep the digits at a regular distance from one another.

Springs are easily made from suitable wire by the following method: fit a metal rod (3/32 in. diameter) into the chuck of a motorized drill (a hand drill will suffice if held by another person). A fine hole, just large enough to take the spring wire, is drilled into the rod about $\frac{1}{4}$ in. away from the end. The wire to be made into a spring is put into this hole and the end of the wire is bent. Holding the coil of wire slightly towards the motor or drill, switch on the motor. Be ready to switch off as soon as the spring fills the rod. The spring is removed from the rod and can be cut into suitable lengths. Each digit is then spaced by one of these springs, the springs being placed over a wire which runs through the hand or foot from one digit to the next, a curl joint being made at each end of the wire (see *Figure 8.9*).

It is not possible to give a list of the various gauges of wire which will be required for articulating the assortment of skeletons dealt with in a zoology department, but the following list will serve as a guide:

> 21 S.W.G., strong enough for most jobs.
> 25 S.W.G., a wide variety of uses.
> 32 S.W.G., a wide variety of uses.
> 36 S.W.G., suitable for the finest bones.

Suitable wires are 80/20 Vacrom wire from *Vactite Wire Co. Ltd., Bootle 20, Lancashire*, and Temco 18/8/Mo from *Temco Ltd., Lydbrook, Gloucestershire* (Spence, 1961).

Although tinned copper wire is less expensive, it should be avoided in all cases where there is a possibility that the bones will at some time require bleaching.

Articulation of Bones by Means of Glue

Except in the case of small skeletons, glues should not be used to attach bones unless they are to be used solely for display purposes. Glues should be avoided at any movable joints, for unless the joints are made movable it will be extremely difficult to obtain a lifelike posture in the finished skeleton. Suitable glues for osteological work are:

Vinalak VH/09, from *P. K. Dutt & Co. Ltd., Clan Works, Howard Rd., Bromley, Kent.* This may be thinned or redissolved with toluene.

Casco Contact clear instant adhesive, from most hardware stores, manufactured by *Leicester, Lovell & Co. Ltd.* This may be redissolved with ethyl methyl ketone, benzene or acetone. It is supplied in handy collapsible tubes.

Very strong glues for which there is no solvent are the Araldites, supplied from the manufacturers. Araldite 123B/953B is a useful gap-filling adhesive. It dries white, and it is cold setting. Araldite (two tube pack) is another very strong adhesive. It is transparent and practically colourless when dry. This is obtainable from most hardware stores. The manufacturers of all the Araldites are *CIBA (A.R.L.) Limited, Duxford, Cambridge*, who also supply a useful leaflet on their products (see Mahoney and Ferguson, 1965).

In all cases the adhesive should be spread across both of the faces to be joined. In the case of Casco contact adhesive, it should be allowed to become tacky before the surfaces are pressed together.

The Construction of the Base Board and Supports

The method of estimating the dimensions of the base board and the length of the supports has already been described. Wood is by far the best material for a base board. Brass tubing of a suitable size is a good material for the supports. The actual shape of the supports will vary with each particular animal, but generally mammals require two main supports, each bearing two side supports for the limbs. Birds generally only require a single support which runs vertically up to the synsacrum and then forwards below the vertebral column to a position near to the anterior end of the rib cage. Large reptiles such as crocodiles, require short supports, but do not usually need side supports for the limbs.

The lower end of each of the main supports should be tapped to take a countersunk bolt. At the appropriate position the base board should be drilled to half its depth to accommodate the support, and the hole continued to just allow the passage of the bolt. The underside of the hole should be countersunk to house the head of the bolt. It may be necessary to use a washer in order to give more rigidity, in which case this too should be countersunk.

The side supports may be made from brass tubing of a smaller diameter to that of the main support. It is advisable to make them a little longer than is thought necessary, as it is not always easy to estimate the angle at which they will be required, and it is a simple matter to cut them off to the required length when the time comes. One end of each of the side supports should be compressed in a vice until flat. This flat portion should be drilled to accommodate two small brass bolts. The main support is also drilled so that the bolts pass through the first side support, through the main support, then continue through the opposite side support. The side supports are then tightened in position with two nuts. It is then a simple matter to bend the supports to the required angle. Another method of attaching the side arms is to braze them into position. For very heavy skeletons it may be necessary to use supports of mild steel, and the side arms are then attached by welding.

Support for the Vertebral Column

With the majority of skeletons it is necessary to pass a strong support through the entire length of the neural canal. Various gauges of galvanized wire have proved very useful for this purpose. The wire should be sufficiently long to allow it to support the skull by passing through the foramen magnum to the skull roof. At the rear end of the vertebral column it may be necessary to file the wire until it is tapered and so fits firmly into a vertebra. The wire should be of a large enough diameter to prevent the vertebral column from rotating, but should this still occur it may be remedied by glueing the wire at a few places with Araldite. Getting the vertebral column firmly in position and bent to a correct shape is probably the most important part of the process. Mild steel should be used for heavy skeletons.

Attachment of the Finished Skeleton to the Supports

When the skeleton has been completely prepared, and the supports have been made and attached to the base board, which by now should have been painted black, marks are made on the underside of the vertebrae which connect with the supports. Two holes are drilled through each marked centrum into the neural canal, and a length of wire is passed through these holes so that the two ends of the wire are protruding from the ventral end of the holes. The two ends of the wire are twisted together so forming a support which is passed into the upper end of the main support. If side supports have been provided, the humerus and femur of each side are similarly drilled and fitted with a twisted wire which will sit in position in the side supports.

It may be thought necessary to attach the feet to the base board. A simple way to do this is to drill one or two of the digits of each foot and pass a short stainless steel pin through this hole and into the base board. The pin should be inserted at an angle.

REFERENCES

SOURCE OF SUPPLY

Polyvinyl acetal alvar: *Shawinigan Ltd., Marlow House, Lloyd's Avenue, London, E.C.3*

REFERENCES

Green, H. L. H. H. (1934). 'A rapid method of preparing clean bone specimens from fresh or fixed material.' *Anat. Rec.*, **61**, No. 1

Johan, B. (1924). 'A simple and rapid method for preparing (macerating) macroscopic bone specimens.' *Bull. No. X. Internat. Assoc. Med. Mus*, pp. 22–24

Mahoney, R. and Ferguson, J. (1965). 'The use of Araldite 123B, a cold-setting adhesive, in the repair of sub-fossil and recent skulls.' *J. Sci. Tech.*, **11**, No. 3, pp. 114–118

Reynolds, S. H. (1913). *The Vertebrate Skeleton.* London; Cambridge University Press

Spence, T. F. (1961). (a) 'Maceration of skeletons of man, apes and monkeys.' *J. Sci. Tech.*, 8, No. 1; (b) 'The repair of bones in monkeys, apes and man.' *J. Sci. Tech.*, **8**, No. 2

FURTHER READING

Crosbie, J. (1959). 'Preparation for the mounting of the skeleton of a small mammal.' *J. Sci. Tech.*, **5**, No. 1

Harris, R. H. (1951). 'The use of enzymes in the osteological preparation of the Emperor Penguin.' *Mus. J. Lond.*, **57**, No. 12

Harris, R. H. (1960). 'Alizarine Transparencies.' *Mus. J. Lond.*, **60**, No. 4

Tompsett, D. H. (1958). 'The preparation of skeletons.' *Mus. J. Lond.*, **57**, No. 12

9

PHYSIOLOGICAL TECHNIQUES

OSMOSIS

Animal or vegetable membranes may be of different degrees of permeability, according to the dimensions of their pores, so that some small molecules of solute may be let through but not others of larger molecular size. When only the solvent can pass through, and the solutes are held back, the membrane is known as a *semi-permeable membrane*.

Osmosis is the process which occurs when two solutions of different concentrations are separated by a semi-permeable membrane. The solvent of the less concentrated solution will pass through the membrane until the concentration of the two solutions is equal. If the volumes of the two solutions are fixed, the transfer of solvent molecules (usually water) will increase the pressure in the more concentrated solution. It is this increase in pressure which is known as *osmotic pressure*.

It has been shown that it is possible to measure osmotic pressure of certain solutions by forming a semi-permeable membrane of copper ferrocyanide in a porous pot. The pot is then filled with the required solution after it has been fitted with a cork and a closed mercury manometer. It is then immersed in distilled water. The distilled water passes into the pot until the pressure within the pot is equal to the osmotic pressure of the dissolved substances. This type of experiment, and others, show that the same laws apply to the osmotic pressure of substances in solution as to the pressure of gases in their free state. By Avogadro's hypothesis, equal volumes of gases at the same temperature contain equal numbers of molecules. As the same laws apply, it is therefore possible to calculate the osmotic pressure of a solution (say 1 per cent cane sugar) in solution at a given temperature.

One gramme molecule of any gas at 0°C and 760 mm Hg has a volume of 22·4 l.; therefore 342 g of cane sugar (1 mol.), if it could be converted to a gas at 0°C and 760 mm Hg, would have a volume of 22·4 l. In 1 per cent cane sugar solution, 1 g of cane sugar is dissolved in 100 g of water making a total volume 100·6 cm.[3] at

0°C. The osmotic pressure of the sugar molecules in this solution will therefore amount to

$$\frac{22,400}{342 \times 100 \cdot 6} = 0 \cdot 651 \text{ atm.}$$

A biological method for determination of the osmotic pressure of certain solutions is the blood corpuscle method.

The outside layer of erythroctes is impermeable to a number of dissolved substances, and if erythrocytes are placed in a solution of such a substance of smaller osmotic pressure than their own contents they will swell up. As the erythrocytes have no supporting cell wall, this swelling may continue until the erythrocytes burst. The bursting naturally results in the haemoglobin being liberated into the surrounding solution. If the mixture is allowed to settle, or it may be centrifuged, the fact that bursting has occurred (haemolysis) is shown by the red colour of the supernatant clear fluid. To use this method for determining the osmotic pressure of a solution such as cane sugar, this is added in various dilutions to erythrocytes until a dilution is found where haemolysis only just occurs. Such a solution is known as an *isotonic solution*. A more concentrated solution is referred to as a *hypertonic solution*, and a less concentrated solution as a *hypotonic solution*. A more accurate determination can be made by finding the concentration of the given substance at which the erythrocytes show no change in dimensions or volume.

Osmotic Pressure of Electrolytes

We might expect to find that a 0·58 per cent solution of NaCl (mol. wt. = 58·5) would be isotonic with a 1·8 per cent solution of glucose (mol. wt. = 180). This, however, is not the case, because salt solutions as well as solutions of acids and alkalis are electrolytes, i.e., they ionize. Since each individual ion acts as a complete molecule, as regards osmotic pressure, the osmotic pressure of a dilute solution of NaCl will be double that of an equimolecular solution of a non-electrolyte such as glucose. For example, 0·58 per cent NaCl is isosmotic with 3·5 per cent glucose and not with the molecular equivalent of 1·8 per cent. With a solution such as that of sodium sulphate, the osmotic pressure is increased three-fold, since this salt dissociates into two Na^+ ions and one SO_4^{--} ion.

'NORMAL' PHYSIOLOGICAL SOLUTIONS

Using the blood corpuscle method, already described, it is possible to find a concentration of salt solution which will cause no change in the dimensions or volume of the erythrocytes. It will be found that the concentration will vary according to the animal from which the corpuscles were obtained. 0·65 per cent NaCl solution is isotonic with frog's blood corpuscles, and 0·9 per cent NaCl solution is isotonic with mammalian corpuscles. Since the osmotic concentration is equal in all the cells of the body and is also the same as that of the blood, it is convenient to refer to these isotonic solutions as *'normal' solutions*; 0·65 per cent NaCl being called 'normal' frog saline, and 0·9 per cent saline being called 'normal' mammalian saline. For short-term experiments it may be sufficient to use such a simple 'normal' solution, but Ringer showed that it was necessary to add both calcium and potassium salts to the sodium chloride to make a solution which would keep a heart alive and beating. Therefore, the functioning of a cell is not only dependent on its contents and on the osmotic pressure of the surrounding medium, but also on the nature of the ions which are in contact with its external surface. When

Table 9.1

	Ringer (frog)	Ringer-Locke	Ringer-Tyrode	Ringer-Dale
Water	100·0	100·0	100·0	100·0
NaCl	0·65	0·9	0·8	0·9
KCl	0·014	0·042	0·02	0·042
$CaCl_2$	0·012	0·024	0·02	0·024
$NaHCO_3$	0·02	0·01–0·03	0·1	0·05
NaH_2PO_4	0·001	—	0·005	—
$MgCl_2$	—	—	0·01	0·0005
Glucose	(0·2)	(0·1–0·25)	0·1	0·05

an experiment is to be carried out in which a tissue or organ is to be kept alive for some time, therefore, a special 'Ringer's fluid' is employed containing sodium, calcium and potassium ions in the correct amounts. As well as these salts, sodium bicarbonate and sometimes sodium phosphate are added so as to imitate the reaction of normal body fluids and to provide a means of neutralizing any small amounts of acid which may be produced by the tissue while the experiment is in progress.

Table 9·1 shows the composition of some of the more commonly employed physiological saline solutions. Where sea-water is available, an excellent physiological solution for terrestrial and freshwater invertebrates is easily made by mixing two parts of sea-water with nine parts of distilled water. This gives a solution which is equivalent to 0·62–0·64 per cent saline. If sea-water cannot be obtained frog saline will usually suffice. For parasites of marine invertebrates, sea-water should be used.

Because frog Ringer solution is used so frequently in most physiological sections of zoology departments, it is convenient to have a constant supply. To save the trouble of carrying out frequent weighing of small amounts of the ingredients, it is better to keep a quantity of concentrated stock solutions. The following system has been adopted in the author's department with great success.

Primary stock solutions

(1) $NaHCO_3$ .. .. .. $\frac{M}{2}$ ($\frac{1}{2}$ molar) solution

(2) KCl .. .. 2M solution

(3) $CaCl_2$ .. .. $\frac{4M}{3}$ solution

(4) NaCl .. .. 2M solution

(5) (Buffer solution) $NaHCO_3$ .. $\frac{M}{400}$ solution

(This itself is prepared by adding 5 ml. of $\frac{M}{2}$ $NaHCO_3$ solution to each litre of glass distilled water, after which the solution is aerated for 2–3 h.)

Secondary stock solutions (buffered)

(6) Buffered 0·11 M potassium chloride.
Prepared as follows: Solution (2) .. 50 ml.
Solution (5) to 900 ml.

(7) Buffered 0·075 M calcium chloride.
Prepared as follows: Solution (3) .. 50 ml.
Solution (5) to 900 ml.

(8) Buffered 0·11 M sodium chloride.
Prepared as follows: Solution (4) .. 100 ml.
Solution (5) to 1,800 ml.

The actual frog Ringer solution is prepared from solutions (6), (7) and (8).

Solution (6) .. .. 15 ml.
Solution (7) .. .. 15 ml.
Solution (8) .. .. to 1 l.

pH

Because most animal tissues contain about 80 per cent of water, it is easy to see that water must play a very important part in every reaction which takes place within the animal. It is known that 1 l. of pure distilled water at 22°C contains 10^{-7} gramme ions of hydrogen, and the same number of hydroxyl ions. The temperature coefficient of the dissociation of water is rather high, so that at 18°C the hydrogen ion concentration in pure distilled water is only $0·78 \times 10^{-7}$, while at 37°C it is $1·76 \times 10^{-7}$.

Should a strong acid (e.g., hydrochloric acid, HCl) be added to a strong base (e.g., sodium hydroxide, NaOH), the hydrogen ions and hydroxyl ions combine to form molecules of water, leaving behind only sodium and chloride ions. The same union occurs whatever strong acid and strong base are used, i.e., a combination of hydrogen and hydroxyl ions to form molecules of water. In a solution containing hydrogen (H) and hydroxyl (OH) ions, the active mass in any reaction which may occur is equal to the product of the two concentrations, i.e., H × OH. This product is a constant in an aqueous solution at any given temperature and is, in fact, at 22°C, 10^{-14}. This increases with rises in temperature (e.g., at 37°C it is $3 \cdot 1 \times 10^{-14}$). So it follows that the more hydrogen ions there are present in a solution the fewer will be the number of hydroxyl ions.

It is the actual concentration or activity of the hydrogen ions in the solution which bathes the living cell that will affect its behaviour, and not the titratable acid or base. It is for this reason that the reactions of body fluids is always expressed in terms of the hydrogen ion concentration, denoted by cH, or of H ion activity, caH.

Because it is inconvenient to use such expressions as $1 \cdot 05 \times 10^{-7}$, etc., it has become common practice to use, not the cH figure directly, but the negative exponent of 10 as a positive number, calling it the hydrogen exponent or pH. For example, 5×10^{-6} is the same as $10^{-5 \cdot 3}$, and a solution containing this quantity of hydrogen ions is said to have a pH of 5·3. It should be noted that as the acidity increases so the pH falls. The actual change from one pH to another is far greater than is at first apparent; for example, it is easy to see that the hydrogen ion concentration cH of 4×10^{-6} is double that of 2×10^{-6}, but it is far more difficult to appreciate that a pH of 5·398 signifies an acidity which is double that of pH 5·699.

Because hydrogen ions and hydroxyl ions are present in all chemical processes occurring in living cells, it will be obvious that any difference in pH will affect any cellular function.

BUFFERS

As various cellular activities take place, so minute amounts of acid or alkali are produced, affecting the pH. This is minimized by certain substances (buffers) being present in the protoplasm and fluids of the body in which the cells are bathed. In a similar way, these substances which act as buffers are added to normal physiological solutions in which experimental tissues are bathed, so that they will take up acid or alkali without greatly affecting the pH of the fluid.

An example of a good buffer system is that afforded by sodium bicarbonate, $NaHCO_3$, when a solution of this salt is maintained in equilibrium with an atmosphere containing a constant proportion of carbon dioxide, CO_2. Due to dissociation such a solution will contain the following ions:

$$NaHCO_3 = Na^+ + HCO_3^-$$
$$H_2CO_3 = H^+ + HCO_3^-$$
$$H_2O = H^+ + OH^-$$
$$HCO_3^- + H_2O = H_2CO_3 + OH^-$$

H_2CO_3 is a weak acid (one that dissociates only slightly in solution) so that only a few hydrogen ions are produced. Therefore, if an acid is added to the solution, a certain amount of $NaHCO_3$ is decomposed with the formation of CO_2 and a neutral salt. But the CO_2 escapes from the solution, so that the only result is a decrease in the concentration of the $NaHCO_3$.

The salts of weak acids, e.g., boric, acetic, etc., or weak bases (alkalis), e.g., ammonia, may also act as buffers, and these buffer solutions are of great value in physiological work because by mixing two such buffer substances in known proportions solutions of definite pH may be prepared. Such solutions will only change their pH when acids or alkalies are added to them.

In Chapter 11 several useful tables of buffer solutions are given.

TWO PHYSIOLOGICAL EXPERIMENTS INVOLVING THE USE OF A KYMOGRAPH

Before describing these two experiments a few notes on kymographs would be appropriate.

A kymograph is an instrument carrying a drum which revolves at a chosen speed, the drum being covered with a smoked paper on which physiological tracings may be made.

There are two main types of kymographs: those with a built-in motor fitted with gears and those which are belt driven from a separate motor. In this latter type the speed is controlled by attaching the belt to wheels of varying diameters. The kymograph with the built-in motor has many advantages over the other type, the main one being that it takes up far less bench space.

Before using any particular kymograph, check the positions of the clutch, the fast and slow switch (if present), the electrical contacts which can be adjusted to act as a switch linked to the rotation of the drum, and if the kymograph is belt driven check that these have been so fitted that the drum will revolve in a clockwise direction. If it does not, this may be remedied by putting a single twist into the belt.

Also, adjust the kymograph so that it is revolving at a suitable speed for the particular experiment which is to be carried out.

Preparing the Smoked Kymograph Paper

The kymograph paper is of a special type, one side of it being shiny and so prepared that it readily accepts soot. The paper may be purchased in a roll, but it is more convenient to purchase it in ready prepared lengths, one end of each length being covered with an adhesive. The length of paper should be fitted on to the drum so that it is tight enough to prevent it slipping down on the drum. It should also be fitted so that the overlap will not cause an obstruction to the writing points.

The paper is smoked by means of an ignited mixture of coal gas and benzene vapour. A special smoker is used for this purpose, and the smoky flame is held a few inches from the drum which is kept rotating at a moderate speed in a horizontal position. Care should be taken to ensure that the paper does not ignite. The smoking should be continued until the paper is completely black, but the deposit must not be too thick. A fume cupboard must always be used.

The special smoker is fitted at the base of the handle with a small container for the benzene, and the coal gas which enters immediately above this container draws up some of the benzene vapour. However, if large numbers of papers are to be smoked it is more convenient to bubble the coal gas through a Dreschel bottle filled with benzene.

The Preparation of Writing Points

It is important that the writing points be of the correct type for the particular job which they have to perform. For example, those attached to the lever of a time marker may be rigid, and their weight is of little importance, but a writing point fitted to a lever which may be attached to a delicate organ should be carefully balanced and as light as possible. Again, writing points attached to levers which will move through large vertical distances must be designed so that they remain in contact with the smoked paper throughout the length of their movement. *Figure 9.1* shows three types of writing points.

In *Figure 9.1* (*a*) is a rigid type, made from a celluloid writing point attached to a straw with sealing wax. The tip of the celluloid is bent at 45 degrees. A writing point of this sort is used for recording muscle twitches, and for use on time markers.

Figure 9.1 (*b*) shows a flexible type made from two pieces of folded sticky paper, with a hinge of cigarette paper fastened between the folds. The lever is again made from a straw, and the actual writing point is made from drawn glass and attached with sealing wax. Useful for recording heartbeats.

Figure 9.1 (*c*) illustrates a flexible type, probably the most sensitive type of writing point. The writing point of drawn glass is counter-balanced at the top end with solid glass or with sealing wax. The hinged portion is made in the same way as that in *Figure 9.1* (*b*). It is useful for recording heartbeats, and gut and uterus contractions.

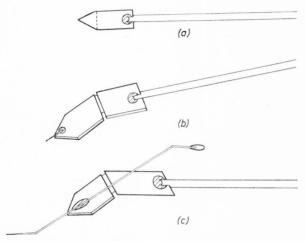

Figure 9.1. Three types of writing points: (a) a rigid type; (b) a flexible type; (c) a very sensitive flexible type

Varnishing the Finished Tracings

In order that the tracings may be kept for permanent record the paper should be varnished. Some workers varnish the paper while it is still attached to the drum, but this results in the drums becoming coated with varnish, which is often difficult to remove. There is always a short length of the paper which is of no importance, and it is better to cut the paper through at such a point and to carefully dip the tracing (smoked side uppermost) into a dish of varnish, making sure that the varnish flows steadily and evenly from one end to the other. The paper should then be hung up to dry over a tray kept for that purpose, weighting the lower end of the paper with a heavy spring paperclip. The varnish should then be filtered back into its stock bottle. There are several varnishes which are used, but they should always have a matt finish so that the tracings are easy to photograph. The following formulae are all satisfactory varnishes.

(1) Vinalak VH/09 (polybutyl methacrylate in

toluene)	..	..	..	..	..	1 part
Acetone	..	..	..	..	..	3 parts

This is an extremely good varnish, which dries rapidly.

(2) White hard varnish ..   .. 500 ml.
     Absolute alcohol   ..   ..1,500 ml.
     Castor oil   ..   .. 10 ml.
(3) Colophony resin   ..   .. 100 g
     Absolute alcohol   ..   ..2,000 ml.
     Propylene glycol   ..   .. 200 ml.
     Castor oil   ..   .. 5 ml.

Add the other reagents to the resin, and warm on a steam or water bath until the resin is dissolved. Filter through glass wool before use.

In each case, increasing the quantity of castor oil will increase the gloss of the finish.

(1) RECORDING THE NORMAL HEARTBEAT OF A FROG

Requirements

1 pithed frog (the pithing must be carried out by a competent person).
1 dissecting mat, and some pins.
1 kymograph, complete with smoked paper.
2 adjustable stands.
1 straw holder plus straw or 1 Starling heart lever.
1 writing point attached to straw or heart lever.
1 bent, fine entomology pin, attached to a 12 in. length of cotton.
1 time clock or metronome timer.
1 time marker.
1 mercury key (or any other type of switch), and some mercury.
Sufficient flex for time marker circuit.
a.c. mains supply or accumulators.
Reasonable quantity of frog Ringer solution, in a beaker.
1 glass pipette with rubber teat.
A small quantity of plasticine.
1 glass writing point (for writing on the smoked paper).
Dissecting instruments.

Procedure

Set up the kymograph so that the drum will rotate at about 1 cm/sec. Fit the lever on to the adjustable stand and test the writing point. Then assemble the time marking circuit (*Figure 9.2*) and arrange it so that it will record a time trace of 1 sec intervals. Some workers find it convenient to make a complete time trace around the drum before commencing the actual experiment. If this is done the apparatus can be removed, and it will leave more room for the remainder of the equipment. Write the time interval on the smoked paper at the beginning of the time trace, using the glass writing point.

Pin out the pithed frog, ventral side up, and expose the heart by cutting through the abdominal wall and then severing the pectoral girdle on both sides of the sternum and removing the flap of tissue containing the sternum and attached pieces of the girdle. Open up

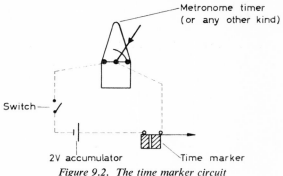

Figure 9.2. The time marker circuit

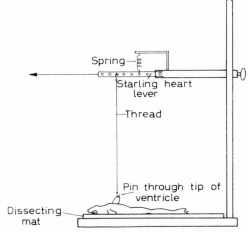

Figure 9.3. Method of attachment of a frog's heart to a Starling heart lever

the pericardium with a fine pair of scissors taking care not to touch the heart itself. Insert the bent pin with the attached thread into the tip of the ventricle. Flood the heart with frog Ringer solution, and attach the thread to the heart lever.

Arrange the heart lever so that the writing point is making proper contact with the drum, and attach the thread from the pin which is inserted into the tip of the ventricle. The lever must be adjusted, and possibly counterbalanced with small pieces of plasticine so that the thread is taut when the lever is itself in a nearly horizontal position, but not so taut that the heart will be unable to contract. The writing point should move rhythmically up and down with the beating of the heart, and when the lever has been properly adjusted so that this movement is as great as possible, the drum should be started. Try to analyse the visible form of the repeated cardiac movements with respect to the movements of the different parts of the heart (*Figures 9.3* and *9.4*).

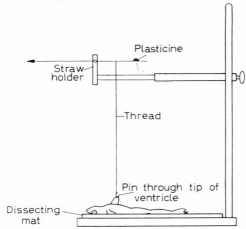

Figure 9.4. Method of attachment of a frog's heart to a straw holder

OTHER SIMPLE EXPERIMENTS WHICH MAY BE CARRIED OUT WITH THIS PREPARATION

(a) Differential Temperature Effects

Warm a glass rod to about 30°C and hold it near to the ventricle and then near to the sinus. Record the two effects, remembering to make an arrow on the tracing where the treatment commenced and finished, and also a short description of the experiment.

(b) Effect of Acetylcholine and Adrenaline

With the drum rotating at about $\frac{1}{2}$ cm/sec run a single drop of the solution of acetylcholine (concentration 1:500,000) over the heart. Wash off with frog Ringer solution as soon as the effect has been recorded.

When the heartbeat has finally returned to normal, apply a single drop of adrenaline solution (concentration 1:2,000) to the heart and record the effect. Wash off with frog Ringer solution as soon as the effect has been properly recorded.

(c) *Excitability Wave of the Ventricle*

Place the nerve of a frog nerve-muscle preparation across the ventricle so that it touches both tip and base. Before doing this, it may be necessary to temporarily detach the thread from the lever. Record the effect of this on the normal heartbeat.

(2) EXPERIMENTS WITH THE SKELETAL MUSCLE AND NERVE OF A FROG

Requirements

1 pithed frog (the pithing must be carried out by a competent person).
1 dissecting mat, and some pins.
1 kymograph, complete with smoked paper.
2 adjustable stands.
1 muscle chamber complete with 2 silver electrodes.
A short piece of thread.
1 straw fitted with a firm writing point.
1 induction coil.
1 or 2 accumulators.
1 mercury key (or other type).
1 morse key.
Some mercury.
Sufficient wire flex for both stimulating and time marker circuits.
1 time clock and metronome timer (the latter for stimulating).
1 time marker.
1 electrical stimulator, if possible (if this is available there will be no need to use the induction coil and the metronome as a stimulator).
A large quantity of frog Ringer solution.
1 glass pipette with rubber teat.
Dissecting instruments.
1 glass writing point (for writing on the smoked paper).

Procedure

Cut through the skin around the 'waist' of the pithed frog. Take hold of the skin of the hind quarters and pull vigorously until it is peeled off both legs like a pair of trousers. Keep the limbs moist with frog Ringer solution throughout the dissection. Identify the following muscles (*Figure 9.5*):

(*i*) Sartorius—strip-shaped, runs along the middle of the ventral surface of the thigh.

(*ii*) Ilio-fibularis—narrow, runs along the middle of the dorsal surface of the thigh.

(*iii*) Gastrocnemius—calf muscle, attached to the knee above and ends below in the tendon of Achilles, which runs around the heel and is inserted into the toes.

Carefully remove the ilio-fibularis muscle and note the sciatic nerve immediately ventral to it. Isolate the nerve throughout the thigh by cutting and tearing away the surrounding tissue without

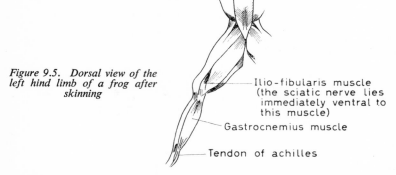

Figure 9.5. Dorsal view of the left hind limb of a frog after skinning

Ilio-fibularis muscle (the sciatic nerve lies immediately ventral to this muscle)
Gastrocnemius muscle
Tendon of achilles

touching the nerve itself. Cut through the vertebral column just anterior to the sciatic nerve, sever the ilio-sacral joints, and cut through the proximal end of the tibio-fibula. Also cut through the tendon of Achilles just below the foot, and through the femur just above the knee joint. Then carefully remove, in one piece, a piece of vertebra attached to the sciatic nerve, the knee joint, the gastrocnemius muscle and a short length of the tendon of Achilles. Repeat this on the other side of the animal, so acquiring two gastrocnemius

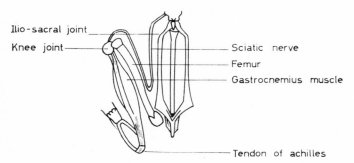

Ilio-sacral joint
Knee joint
Sciatic nerve
Femur
Gastrocnemius muscle
Tendon of achilles

Figure 9.6. The left hind limb of a frog, showing the relative positions of the gastrocnemius muscle and sciatic nerve

muscle-sciatic nerve preparations (*Figures 9.6* and *9.7*). Tie a short length of thread into a loop attached to each Achilles tendon. Place both of the preparations into a clean dish containing frog Ringer solution.

TWO EXPERIMENTS INVOLVING USE OF A KYMOGRAPH

A FEW EXPERIMENTS THAT MAY BE CARRIED OUT WITH THE NERVE-MUSCLE PREPARATION ALONE

(1) Pinch the upper end of the sciatic nerve of one preparation with fine forceps and note the contraction of the gastrocnemius muscle. Repeat this two or three times, each time about 1 mm below the previous position. Then pinch the uppermost point again, and note that there is no response. This emphasizes that the nerve must never be handled with forceps, and the preparation should be picked up at the knee joint.

(2) Touch the nerve, just below the damaged region, with a hot wire. Note the response due to this thermal stimulation.

(3) Place a crystal of NaCl on the lowest part of the nerve, and note the response to this chemical stimulation.

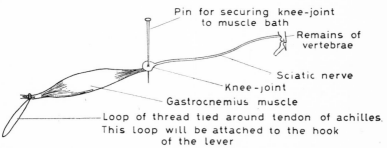

Figure 9.7. *A complete nerve-muscle preparation, ready for putting into the muscle bath*

The above three experiments may be carried out as soon as one of the sciatic nerves has been exposed and before the actual dissection has been completed.

(4) It is also interesting to remove one of the sartorius muscles and to place it in a dish of 0·6 per cent NaCl. The spontaneous twitches which develop after a short time are due to a lack of calcium.

KYMOGRAPHIC EXPERIMENTS TO BE CARRIED OUT WITH THE NERVE-MUSCLE PREPARATION

For all the following experiments the nerve-muscle preparation must be arranged in the muscle bath as shown in *Figure 9.8*. It is important that when the actual experiment is not in progress, the nerve be removed from the electrodes and submerged in the Ringer solution. While the actual experiment is in progress, the sciatic nerve must be kept moist with regular washing of Ringer solution, using the pipette.

Before the experiments can be carried out, the stimulating circuit must be arranged. Wire up the primary of the induction coil to an accumulator with a mercury switch in the circuit. Wire up the terminals of the secondary coil to the electrodes of the muscle bath.

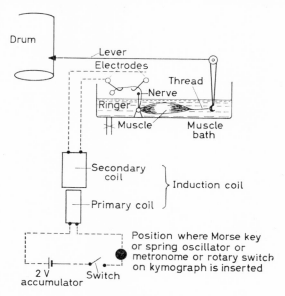

Figure 9.8. The stimulating circuit

With the secondary coil at various positions from, and angles to, the primary coil, study the characteristics of the shocks produced when the current in the primary is switched on and off. Do this by placing electrodes on the lips or tongue and by wiring an ammeter/voltmeter into the circuit. Write up observations as a basis for applying shocks in the following experiments. Put the electrodes under the sciatic nerve which should be lifted above the level of the Ringer solution. Then apply shocks, varying the position of the secondary coil until the muscle contracts only on the 'break', and not on the 'make'. This is the position at which all of the experiments will be carried out.

NOTE: If a stimulating unit is being used, it eliminates the use of the induction coil, and the 'strength' switch is adjusted until the muscle will only contract on the 'break'.

As each of the following experiments should be recorded in triplicate each experiment is best carried out on a separate drum. It is recommended that about 3 or 4 smoked drums are prepared ready for use. A time trace must be made for each experiment (*Figure 9.2*, page 361). During the time that the correct impulse is being determined the drum should be operated manually so that each impulse or contraction is shown by a straight vertical tracing. Care should be taken to ensure that the 'break' shock is strong enough to cause a full contraction of the muscle (i.e., all the fibres must contract). Unless the contraction is maximal the results will be affected.

Experiment 1. Successive Stimuli from Frequencies of about 1 Sec to about 50 Per Sec (see Figure 9.8)

Shocks can be given once or twice per second by hand with the Morse key. More frequent shocks can be given by using the metronome timer. By altering the connections on the primary coil to bring in the vibrator, higher frequencies can be obtained. The tracings should show all stages between a series of isolated twitches and the fusion of separate twitches into a smooth maintained 'tetanus' contraction.

N.B. For this experiment the drum should be rotating at about 2·5 cm/sec. If a stimulator unit is used, the various frequencies may be given with this instrument.

Experiment 2. Single Break Stimuli Delivered Via the Rotary Contact on the Kymograph (see Figure 9.8)

Replace the hand switch in the primary circuit by the rotary switch of the kymograph. If a stimulator unit is being used, connect the terminals of the external trigger of this unit to the rotary switch. Set the kymograph so that the drum will rotate at about 10 cm/sec, or even faster. Make sure that the muscle is only contracting on the 'break' by rotating the drum by hand until the rotary switch operates, so making a vertical line on the tracing. When adjusted, record the muscle twitch with the drum in motion, and the distance between the vertical line and the recorded twitch will be a measure of the latent period. On fresh paper repeat the above experiment, but allow the drum to rotate many times until the muscle shows obvious signs of fatigue in an increased latent period and an incomplete and slow relaxation. This fatigue is clearly demonstrated in the superimposed series of twitches.

TO MEASURE THE OXYGEN CONSUMPTION OF ANIMALS IN RELATION TO TEMPERATURE

The effect of temperature upon the metabolic rate of 'cold-blooded' (poikilothermic) animals is well known. The metabolic rate is very conveniently measured in terms of oxygen consumption, and many methods have been devised for obtaining this measurement. That given below is a method by Welsh and Smith (1960) and will be found to be simple and efficient, providing a rough direct measurement of the amount of oxygen consumed by an animal in air or in a small amount of water in a closed vessel at a known temperature. Carry out the experiment at two or three well separated temperatures in water baths which are large enough to stabilize temperatures against minor fluctuations during the course of the experiment, or in baths which are provided with thermostatic controls.

Select rectangular wide-mouthed bottles of a suitable size, and provide each with a rubber stopper through which projects a 1 ml. graduated pipette, as shown in *Figure 9.9.* For air-breathing animals, each bottle is provided with a CO_2 absorbent chemical. This chemical, dry soda-lime, is placed at the bottom of the bottle, and is separated from the animal by a screen of guane. The dry soda-lime may be loosely wrapped in muslin before being introduced.

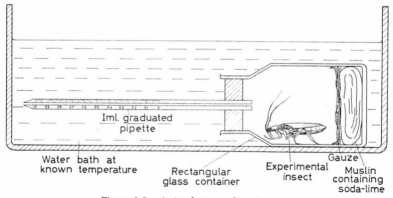

Water bath at known temperature   1ml. graduated pipette   Rectangular glass container   Experimental insect   Gauze   Muslin containing soda-lime

Figure 9.9. A simple type of respirometer

The containers with animals, plus control vessels containing no animals, are placed horizontally into the baths at known temperatures. The bottles are supported and kept submerged by means of racks. Each bath should contain one experimental bottle plus one control bottle. The water of the bath which enters the pipettes serves as a manometer fluid, and as oxygen is consumed by the animals the position of the menicus is recorded at regular intervals. The apparatus is sensitive to changes of pressure, and the indicated oxygen consumption must be corrected for any changes of volume shown by the control vessel.

Some precautions must be taken: allow about half an hour for the respirometers to come to temperature equilibrium in the baths before recording observations. Respirometers placed in a bath below room temperature should be cooled in the bath for a few minutes, before the open ends of the pipettes are submerged, to prevent the water from being drawn in and so fill the pipette.

With animals such as crabs, it may be desirable to study them in shallow water. This is done by securing the CO_2 absorbent chemical to one side of the vessel so that it is above the animals and the water when the respirometer is in the horizontal position. A strip of filter paper soaked in 15 per cent KOH may be laid along the side of the bottle (Teal, 1959).

The results may be expressed in cubic millimetres of oxygen at standard temperature and pressure consumed per gramme wet weight of animal per hour at each temperature.

Suggested animals for this experiment are large insects, such as cockroaches, small crabs, and terrestrial snails.

REFERENCES

Teal, J. M. (1959). 'Respiration of crabs in Georgia salt marshes and its relation to their ecology.' *Physiol. Zool.*, **32,** 1–14

Welsh, J. H. and Smith, R. I. (1960). *Laboratory Exercises in Invertebrate Physiology*. Philadelphia; Burgess Pub. Co.

10

PALAEONTOLOGICAL TECHNIQUES

Palaeontology is the study of fossils. A fossil may be defined as the remains of an organism, or direct evidence of its presence preserved in rocks. Generally only hard parts are preserved, which are usually partly or wholly replaced by minerals deposited from circulating water, as impressions or casts.

It was William Smith 1769–1839 (the maker of some of the earliest geological maps) who showed that each rock group is characterized by the fossils which it contains, and that the rocks above and below it contain different fossils. One is therefore able to correlate the equivalent rock groups in different areas, even when the rocks themselves are different in character. Also, one can determine the characters of the organisms living in each period. These conceptions have since led to the division of geological time into a number of Eras and Periods; the rocks belonging to each Period are said to constitute a System (*Table 10.1*).

PREPARATIVE METHODS

These vary according to the size and condition of the fossil and the type of matrix.

(1) LARGE WELL-PRESERVED BONES IN SOFT MATRIX (E.G., WET CLAY, SHALES)

Transport in a damp condition. If affected by seawater, wash in running water, testing occasionally with silver nitrate until all the chlorides have been removed. Careful scrubbing should remove the matrix. Then dry the bones slowly. If porous they should be strengthened by soaking in polyvinyl alcohol paste diluted down by 1 to 3 parts of distilled water. The paste is a saturated solution in water.

(2) SMALL BONES IN SOFT MATRIX

Transport in a damp condition. These small bones should be dried, and the matrix removed mechanically with needles. Any cracks or gaps in the bones should be filled with Fibrenyle. Very small cracks are better filled with Vinalak 5909. The solvent for Fibrenyle is toluene, and Vinalak may be thinned with toluene.

370

TABLE 10.1

No. of Years Ago (millions)	Era	Period		Events
	CAENOZOIC	*Quaternary*	RECENT or HOLOCENE	This present post-glacial age
0·01			PLEISTOCENE	Includes the Great Ice-age. *Deinotherium* and *Hipparion* became extinct. *Equus*, *Elephas* and *Bos* appeared. Man appeared
1		*Tertiary*	PLIOCENE	Marine fauna similar to that at present. Ginkgo tree in Europe. Anthropoid apes on the up-grade
15			MIOCENE	*Deinotherium* appeared. Sharks very abundant. Grasses established
35			OLIGOCENE	Grasses appeared. Termites appeared. Other insects already exist. *Palaeotherium* present early on
45			EOCENE	Bats appeared. *Nummulites* abundant. Large fish fauna. Early whales and sirenia. Most Eutheria present
60			PALAEOCENE	Mammals rapidly attaining dominance on land
70	MESOZOIC	*Upper*	CRETACEOUS	First appearance of urodeles, snakes, marsupials, insectivores and modern-type flowering plants. Dinosaurs, pterosaurs, plesiosaurs, ichthyosaurs, ammonites became extinct

Table 10.1—*continued*

No. of Years Ago (millions)	Era		Period	Events
140	MESOZOIC—*cont.*		JURASSIC	First appearance of plesiosaurs, pterosaurs, ornithischian dinosaurs, birds, anurans and flowering plants
170		*Lower*	TRIASSIC	First appearance of saurischian dinosaurs, ichthyosaurs, chelonians, crocodiles, lizards and rhynchocephalians. At end of period the mammals appeared. First moss appeared, and hexacorals and lamellibranchs prominent in marine fauna. Cotylosaurs and labyrinthodonts became extinct
195	PALAEOZOIC		PERMIAN	First appearance of true ammonites, holostean fish, true cycads and primitive ginkgoes. Trilobites and rugose corals became extinct, also acanthodeans. Endopterygote insects appeared early in this period
220		*Upper*	CARBONIFEROUS	First appearance of reptiles and conifers; Dendroid graptolites died out. Foraminifera abundant
275			DEVONIAN	Brachiopods the most common marine invertebrate; early ammonoids appeared. Graptolites (except dendroids) became extinct. Ostracoderms abounded; Many true fish appeared

Table 10.1—*continued*

No. of Years Ago (millions)	Era	Period	Events
320	PALAEOZOIC —*cont.*	SILURIAN	Seaweeds with limy skeletons abundant; earliest land plants well adapted by end of this period. Corals, crinoids common. Blastoids appeared. Brachiopods most abundant. Trilobites common. Eurypterids became abundant at end of period. *Jamoytius* (similar in many ways to *Amphioxus*) appeared. Ostracoderms and a few fish present
350	*Lower*	ORDOVICIAN	Seaweeds with limy skeletons present. Corals appeared. Brachiopods abundant, including *Lingula*. Cephalopods became abundant. Some gastropods but very few lamellibranchs. Trilobites numerous also ostracods. Graptolites abundant. Fragments of ostracoderms have been found in U.S.A.
420 520		CAMBRIAN	Earliest rocks containing fossils which are well preserved. Dendroid graptolites present, also Archaeocyathines (coralline sponges). Trilobites, brachiopods and some molluscs present

(3) FOSSILS IN CALCIUM CARBONATE MATRIX (E.G., CHALK, LIMESTONE)

The commonest method used with a matrix of this type is the acid technique. Acetic and formic acids are used in strengths from 15 per cent downwards. Formic acid is unpleasant to use, and is usually reserved for dolomitic matrix, as cold acetic acid will not react with this. The procedure is as follows: a chip of the matrix is put into 15 per cent acetic acid to observe the speed of reaction. If this is too rapid the acid is diluted until the reaction is gentle. All of the exposed bone or fossil surface is lacquered with Vinalak and left to dry. Then the specimen is put into the acid bath and left for 10 min. After this time it is removed and examined. If the rock has split open along any soft layers it must be washed in running water for 4–6 h, and then dried. If this is not done the fossil surface will become coated with a white mass of reaction products. If the acid is formic, the washing time may be reduced to 2 h. When dry, any new bone should be lacquered, and the whole procedure repeated continuously until the bone is free. If the bones are long and thin they should be splinted with strips of bamboo glued, along the length of the bone, with Vinalak. Skulls in particular are very fragile and should always be splinted.

N.B. In some cases acid treatment should not be used, for example when the bones are very small. Mechanical preparation is then used. An exception to this are two-dimensional skeletons of specimens such as fish. One surface of the fossil is cleaned by the acid technique and then the removed matrix replaced by an artificial one. The one usually employed is Marco Resin SB 26C which is transparent and is not affected by acid treatment. Consequently when the matrix on the other side is removed with acid, both sides of the fossil become visible.

(4) FOSSILS IN SILICA MATRIX

A silicious matrix is the most difficult one to deal with. It gives no reaction with mineral acids. If the lie of the fossil is clear the matrix may be ground away (using a dental drill), and if the surface of the fossil is smooth the last flakes of matrix can often be removed with the tip of a knife. If the bone is rough a Stensio's hammer should be used.

(5) POORLY PRESERVED BONE

The impression left by a poorly preserved bone will often show more detail than the bone itself. If the matrix is soft any remaining bone should be removed mechanically, but if the matrix is silicious the bone may be removed with acid treatment. Many vertebrate fossils only occur as natural moulds. Casts are easily prepared from these moulds by using one of the following methods.

(a) Squeeze Methods

'Squeezes' are only possible with impressions which have no under-cuts. Temporary squeezes may be prepared by brushing the fossil surface with talc and then pressing a piece of plasticine on to this talced surface. Lift the plasticine squeeze from the fossil, taking care to avoid any distortion. Permanent squeezes are prepared in a similar fashion using Vinagel 116/Red. When the Vinagel squeeze is removed it must be heated in an oven for 10 min at 150°C. Allow to cool before disturbing. Vinagel is unsuitable for making squeezes of large specimens. Other substances suitable for the preparation of squeezes include some of the dental impression compounds.

(b) Moulding Methods

Three methods are in common use. These are, in order of the author's preference:

(i) Silicone rubber—The type employed is Cold-cure Silastomer 9161. This substance will reproduce the finest detail, and results always merit the cost, which is considerable. The impression should be washed and dried and then a dam built around the limit of the fossil. This dam is easily constructed from plasticine, potter's clay, or simply by placing the fossil into a cardboard box of a suitable size. Just before pouring the compound, the fossil surface should be painted with a dilute solution of detergent, but avoid the formation of bubbles. Sufficient silicone-rubber is then poured into a disposable container and mixed thoroughly with 6 per cent of Catalyst N 9162. Pour the mixed silicone-rubber on to the fossil, allowing it to slowly spread over the entire surface, so avoiding the trapping of air. Add sufficient rubber to cover the highest point of the fossil by $\frac{1}{4}$ in. Tap gently to release any air, and set aside to polymerize; this should take from 1–2 h. When set, remove the dam and then carefully peel off the mould. Silicone-rubber is flexible but tears more readily than rubber latex. It is white in colour. It is possible to make a silicone-rubber cast from a silicone-rubber mould, but liquid soap must be used as a separator.

(ii) Rubber latex—The most satisfactory type is Revultex. If desired the rubber latex is coloured by adding the chosen pigment to 10 per cent ammonium hydroxide solution and then adding this solution to the latex. The best pigments are burnt umber (brown) and cadmium red (red). The set rubber will be darker in colour than the fluid latex and this must be taken into account when adding the pigment. A

dam is constructed as previously described. The releasing agent in this case is 2 per cent releasil silicone-fluid in carbon tetrachloride. This should be allowed to evaporate before adding the latex. Set aside to solidify. This may take as long as 24 h.

(*iii*) *Polyvinyl chloride*—The most reliable type is Welvic M 11/4. This method of casting should only be used when it is certain that the fossil will be able to withstand the necessary heat treatment. There are several methods of using Welvic, but the one given here, the pre-gel method, is probably the most reliable: place the specimen in an oven at 80°C and leave for 1 h. A plasticine retaining wall is then built around the fossil. Brush the fossil with 2 per cent releasil silicone fluid in carbon tetrachloride, and allow it to dry.

To prepare the paste, thin sufficient Welvic with a small quantity of dibutyl phthalate. If a pigment is required, mix a small amount of burnt umber into a cream with a few drops of dibutyl phthalate, strain through a nylon stocking, and stir this into the paste. Leave to stand for several hours to eliminate air bubbles.

When pouring the paste make sure that no air is trapped and when completed, tap gently. Leave to stand for about 5 min, then put into an oven to set at 100°C. When the Welvic has attained this temperature, the pre-gelling occurs; i.e., it becomes solid but is still very soft. It is possible to remove the plasticine dam at this stage but this must be done carefully.

It should then be returned to the oven which is now set at 150°C. The final gelation then occurs. This is determined by the fact that the surface becomes glossy, and does not tear easily when scratched with a needle. When removed from the oven, allow to cool slowly before removing the mould. Do not store Welvic casts in plastic boxes.

It is possible to make a Welvic cast of a Welvic mould, but neat silicone releasil fluid must be used as a separator (see Rixon and Mead, 1956).

The Preparation of Two-part Moulds and Plaster Casts

Once the technician has mastered the technique for the preparation of two-part moulds it is an easy step to the production of more complex moulds, such as are required for casting skulls.

The method described employs a vinyl resin hot melt compound, but silicone-rubber may be used as an alternative. The vinyl resin used is Vinamold HMC 1028 (red) or HMC 2036 (yellow). A cardboard box of a suitable size is filled with potter's clay to such a depth that the specimen to be cast can be pressed into it until only its top half is visible. Three depressions are made in the clay outside the limit of the specimen, and then the exposed surface of specimen and clay is painted with a thin film of Vinamold sealing oil.

Meanwhile the Vinamold should have been melted. This is done by cutting up the purchased Vinamold into small cubes and placing these into a pyrex beaker. This is then heated in an oven to 130–140°C. Stir before pouring. The pouring is carried out as rapidly as possible taking care to avoid the trapping of air bubbles. Allow to cool before removing the mould. If it is satisfactory the mould is put into a suitable box, the fossil replaced in the mould and after small notches have been cut in three of the sides and the surface painted with the sealing oil, the second part of the mould is poured. When cool, the two parts are separated and the specimen removed. The cold Vinamold is easily removed from the beaker. When sufficient plaster casts have been prepared from the mould, it can be remelted time and time again—it is therefore economical.

To Produce Plaster Casts

Accurate reproduction of the finest detail is essential with this kind of work, and for this the best plaster to use is hydrocal plaster (superfine dental plaster). Alternatively, fine industrial plaster of paris may be used. It is important that the plaster is mixed in the following manner: pour some water into a dish and shake the plaster evenly into this water until it is covered by only a thin film of water. Stir slowly and evenly with a spoon. Avoid the introduction of air bubbles, and allow the mixture to stand as long as possible before pouring. With hydrocal plaster the mixture must be poured immediately after preparing. Knock the dish to assist the rise of any bubbles and then pour slowly from one point until the cast is at least $\frac{1}{2}$ in. thick. Knock gently and put aside to set. As the plaster sets, heat is evolved, but the cast should not be removed from the mould until this heat has been dissipated.

When preparing casts from two-part moulds, the plaster must be poured into both halves and any surplus plaster removed. Just before the plaster sets the two halves are brought together and placed on a level table. When set, the cast is removed from the mould, and any 'flash' (a thin projection of plaster at the junction of the two halves of the mould) is carefully removed with a scalpel. A good cast has no flash.

Pyritized Fossils

Some fossils are impregnated with ferric sulphide (FeS). This is stable for long periods, but sometimes it becomes converted to sulphuric acid which tends to act on shales to give a soft, deliquescent product. If the fossil is decomposing in this manner it must be treated with ammonia in a fume cupboard. A white film appears and the fossil should then be painted with a thin solution of Bedacryl No. 122X in toluene. This treatment is not always successful.

Colouring the Casts

Both plaster of paris and silicone-rubber casts are white in colour. It is advisable to use side lighting when examining such casts, but if well done colouring the casts will reveal the finest detail. Silicone-rubber casts are easily coloured by dusting the surface with powdered graphite and then wiping it with a clean cloth. This leaves the depressions coloured.

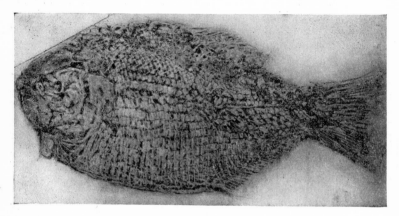

Figure 10.1. A plaster cast of Dapedius, coloured by the 'dip technique'

There are many methods for colouring plaster casts. It should be borne in mind that unless the cast is to be used for exhibition purposes there is no need to reproduce the original colour of the fossil. The only reason for colouring is to show up the detail in the cast. Two useful methods are:

(1) *'Dip technique'*—sufficient raw umber solution is prepared to enable the cast to be completely immersed. Do not leave in the water-colour but immediately lift it out of the dish and place it on edge. With a piece of cotton wool wipe the colour from the matrix. After this is done place the cast face upwards on the table and allow to dry. This method works particularly well with casts of fish (*Figure 10.1*).

(2) *'Painting technique'*—the reproduced fossil on the cast is

378

painted with burnt umber to the desired shade of brown, and then this painted area is lacquered with thin Vinalak solution in ethyl methyl ketone taking great care to avoid lacquering the unpainted area of matrix. Set aside to dry for 10 min, and then dip the entire cast into a dilute solution of Indian ink. The matrix area should be light grey in colour when dry (*Figure 10.2*).

Figure 10.2. A plaster cast of Lepidotus, coloured by the 'painting technique'

The Preparation of Casts in Other Materials

Plaster casts are very brittle, and if they are to be handled a great deal they will soon get damaged. In such a case it may be considered worth the extra cost of making the cast of plastic. By far the easiest plastic to use is N.H.P. Metallurgical Mounting Plastic. However, it can only be used with moulds which are open. The plastic is obtainable in the following colours: brown, ivory, and white.

To prepare a cast a little of the powder is mixed with a small quantity of the liquid and stirred into a smooth solution. This is then poured into the mould. It is important at this stage to make sure that the entire surface of the mould is wetted with the solution. More powder is added to the mould until it is gradually filled. It should then be set aside until the plastic has polymerized. This usually takes about 30 min, and the reaction is exothermic. When hard, the cast is easily removed from the mould. This plastic is remarkably strong and will withstand the roughest treatment. If the casts are to be painted it is necessary to use oil-paints.

The Preparation of Casts in Glass Fibre Resin

Plaster casts have the disadvantage that they are very easily chipped and broken. By preparing casts of glass fibre resin, they can be made so strong that it would be possible to send them through the post unparcelled. The method was devised and described by Rixon and Meade (1960). Below is a brief description of the method:

A mould of the fossil is made from I.C.I.'s Welvic paste, Vinamold HMC 1028, Revultex rubber latex or silicone-rubber, in the manner previously described. The surface of the mould is now painted over with undiluted silicone fluid M.S. 200/350cs, and the excess is carefully wiped off.

An estimate is made of how much resin will be required to cover the surface of the mould with a thin layer. The required amount is prepared in the following way:

Crystic 189	94 ml.
Accelerator E.	4 ml.

(This can be prepared in bulk and will keep for months at a cool temperature.) To each 64 g add 40 g of Pregel 17. Then add 4 ml. of Catalyst M to every 100 g of Pregel + resin mixture. Titanium dioxide is added to the mixture (about 3 per cent), and is thoroughly stirred in. It is recommended that the titanium dioxide be mixed in with a small quantity of the resin before being added to the main part of the mixture. Tap the vessel containing the mixture so that any trapped air bubbles will rise to the surface. The mixture is now painted into the mould so that the complete surface is covered with a thin layer. The mould is then set aside until the resin has set (30 min or longer). Brushes and glassware should be cleaned immediately with acetone, followed by hot water, a detergent, and a scouring powder.

During the setting time of the resin, chopped stranded glass mat is cut into convenient lengths. The best type of glass fibre is surfacing mat—glass fibre Tissue Type G.T. If the mould is small and complicated, lengths of $1\frac{1}{2}$ in. and $\frac{1}{2}$ in. wide are suitable; for less complex shapes, larger pieces can be used.

A further batch of resin is now prepared in a slightly different way:

Crystic 189	92 ml.
Accelerator E.	2 ml.

(This can be mixed in bulk and stored.)
To each 100 g mixture, add 4 ml. of Catalyst M.
No Pregel is added to this impregnation coat.

Place some of the strips of glass mat in a dish and cover them with some of the impregnation mixture, pressing it well into the glass strips with a palette knife. (If large pieces of mat are used the resin will have to be painted on to them and then rolled in between two pieces of cellophane.) Using a palette knife the resin-soaked fibre glass is placed in the mould over the pregel coat which by this time should have set hard. The whole surface of the glass mat should not come in contact with the mould at once, but should be pressed on gradually to avoid trapping air. The mat is then pushed down into the mould with a stiff brush making sure that it is worked into all hollows and that it is flat to the mould at all places. When completely covered it is left to set for 2 h. If a greater thickness is required, another application can be made within a few hours. A smoother backing can be made to the cast by finishing with a layer of surgical cellulose soaked in resin.

Basic colours other than white can be obtained by using burnt sienna, burnt umber, and raw umber in powder form, instead of titanium dioxide. If silicone rubber or Vinamold HMC 1028 moulds are used, lubricating is not necessary.

Glass fibre chopped strand mat Type H.P.A. is obtainable from *Messrs. Fibreglass Ltd., St. Helens, Lancs*; Glass Fibre Tissue Type G.T. is obtainable in small quantities from *Tiranti*; The Crystic Resin 189, Accelerator E., Catalyst M, and Pregel 17 is obtainable from *Scott Bader Ltd., 109 Kingsway, London, W.C.2*; Silicone fluid M.S. 200/350cs is obtainable from *Messrs. Hopkins and Williams, Chadwell Heath, Essex*.

SOURCES OF SUPPLY FOR OTHER MATERIALS MENTIONED IN THIS CHAPTER

Bedacryl No. 122X and Welvic M 11/4: *Imperial Chemical Industries, Plastics Division, Welwyn Garden City, Herts.*

Cold-cure Silastomer 9161: *Midland Silicones Ltd., 68 Knightsbridge, London S.W.1.*

Fibrenyle: *Pelham Puppets Ltd., Marlborough, Wilts.*

Marco Resin SB 26C (embedding kit): *Scott Bader Ltd., 109 Kingsway, London W.C.2.*

N.H.P. Metallurgical Mounting Plastic (brown, ivory, or white): *North Hill Plastics Ltd., Manley Court, Stoke Newington High Street, London N.16.*

Vinalak 5909 (now sold as VH/09): *P. K. Dutt & Co. Ltd., Clan Works, Howard Road, Bromley, Kent.*

Vinagel 116/Red: *Vinyl Products Ltd., Butter Hill, Carshalton, Surrey.*

Vinamold HMC 1028 (red) or HMC 2036 (yellow): *Vinatex Ltd.,
Devonshire Road (off Butter Hill), Carshalton, Surrey.*

REFERENCES

Rixon, A. E. and Meade, M. J. (1956). 'Casting techniques.' *Mus. J.
Lond.*, **56,** No. 1, April
Rixon, A. E. and Meade, M. J. (1960). 'Glass fibre resin casts of fossils.'
Palaeontology, **3,** pt 1, 124–26

FURTHER READING

Rowland, E. O. (1961). 'A rapid method for making plaster casts for
geological work.' *Proc. geol. Ass.*, **72,** pt 4, 461–66
Spence, T. F. (1960). 'A technique of plaster casting for museum
specimens.' *J. Inst. Sci. Tech.*, **6**

USEFUL DATA

EQUIVALENT WEIGHT

The equivalent weight of an element is that weight of the element which will combine with or replace 1 of hydrogen, 8 of oxygen, or 35·5 of chlorine (parts by weight). The relationship between the equivalent of an element, its atomic weight, and valency, may be expressed as follows:

$$\text{Equivalent} = \frac{\text{Atomic weight}}{\text{Valency}}$$

VALENCY

The valency is a number indicating how many atoms of hydrogen one atom of an element can combine with or replace.

$$\text{Valency} = \frac{\text{Atomic weight}}{\text{Equivalent}}$$

VAPOUR DENSITY

A number representing the relative weight of a known volume of a gas as compared with the weight of the same volume of hydrogen, at the same temperature and pressure.

NORMAL SOLUTION

Denoted by the symbol N or N/1 a normal solution is one which contains 1 gram-equivalent of the solute in 1 l. of solution. Therefore a decinormal solution (N/10) contains one-tenth of a gram-equivalent in 1 l. One litre of a normal solution of any acid will require for neutralization 1 l. of a normal solution of any alkali.

MOLAR SOLUTION

Denoted by the symbol M or M/1 a molar solution is one which contains the molecular weight of the solute in grammes in 1 l. of solution.

TEMPERATURE

To convert degrees Centigrade into degrees Fahrenheit, multiply by $\frac{9}{5}$ and add 32

$$\text{i.e., } °F = \left(°C \times \frac{9}{5}\right) + 32$$

USEFUL DATA

To convert degrees Fahrenheit into degrees Centigrade, subtract 32 and multiply by $\frac{5}{9}$

$$\text{i.e., } °C = (°F - 32) \times \frac{5}{9}$$

PRESSURE

The standard pressure of 1 atm. is 760 mm Hg. at $0°C = 14·7$ lb/in.

CONVERSION FACTORS FOR IMPERIAL AND METRIC WEIGHTS AND MEASURES

MASS

1 kilogramme (kg)	= 35·274 oz.
	= 2·2046 lb.
1 gramme (g)	= 0·0353 oz.
1 milligramme (mg)	= 0·0000353 oz.
1 pound (lb.)	= 453·59 g
1 ounce (oz.)	= 28·350 g

FLUID MEASURE

Imperial	Metric
1 minim	0·0592 millilitre (ml.)
1 fluid ounce (fl. oz.)	28·412 ml.
1 pint (20 fl. oz.)	568·25 ml.
35·196 fl. oz.	1,000 ml.
1 gallon (gal.)	4,546 ml.

LENGTH

1 kilometre (km)	= 0·62137 mile
1 metre (m)	= 39·370 inches (in.)
1 centimetre (cm)	= 0·39370 in.
1 millimetre (mm)	= 0·039370 in.
1 micron (μ)	= 0·000039370 in.
1 inch (in.)	= 25·400 mm
1 foot (ft. = 12 in.)	= 30·480 cm
1 yard (yd. = 3 ft.)	= 91·440 cm
1 mile (1,760 yd.)	= 1,609·34 m

SUPERFICIAL MEASURE

1 in.^{2}	= 6·4516 cm^2
1 ft.^{2} (144 in.^{2})	= 929·03 cm^2
1 yd.^{2}	= 8,361·26 cm^2
1 cm^2	= 0·15500 in.^{2}
1 m^2	= 1,550·0 in.^{2}

CONVERSION FACTORS

CUBICAL MEASURE

1 in.³	= 16·387 cm³
1 ft.³ (1,728 in.³)	= 28,317 cm³
1 cm³	= 0·061023 in.³

CALCULATING CAPACITIES

Rectangular containers: Capacity in gallons = Volume (ft.³) × 6¼.
Circular containers: Depth (ft.) × diameter² (ft.) × 4·9 = capacity in gallons.

THE PREPARATION OF 5N DILUTE ACIDS AND AMMONIUM HYDROXIDE SOLUTION

5N acetic acid: 285 ml. glacial acetic + water to 1 litre
5N ammonium hydroxide: 280 ml. conc. solution + water to 1 litre
5N hydrochloric acid: 430 ml. conc. solution* + water to 1 litre
5N nitric acid: 320 ml. conc. solution* + water to 1 litre
5N sulphuric acid: 136 ml. conc. solution* + water to 1 litre

Caution—The acid (particularly sulphuric) should be added slowly, with stirring, to the water.

ATOMIC WEIGHTS OF SOME COMMON ELEMENTS

Element	Symbol	Atomic Weight	Element	Symbol	Atomic Weight
Aluminium	Al	26·97	Manganese	Mn	54·93
Antimony	Sb	121·76	Mercury	Hg	200·61
Arsenic	As	74·91	Molybdenum	Mo	96·0
Barium	Ba	137·36	Nickel	Ni	58·69
Bismuth	Bi	209·00	Nitrogen	N	14·008
Boron	B	10·82	Osmium	Os	191·5
Bromine	Br	79·916	Oxygen	O	16·0000
Cadmium	Cd	112·41	Palladium	Pd	106·7
Calcium	Ca	40·08	Phosphorus	P	31·02
Carbon	C	12·01	Platinum	Pt	195·23
Chlorine	Cl	35·457	Potassium	K	39·096
Chromium	Cr	52·01	Radium	Ra	225·97
Cobalt	Co	58·94	Silicon	Si	28·06
Copper (Cuprum)	Cu	63·57	Silver (Argentum)	Ag	107·880
Fluorine	F	19·00	Sodium	Na	22·997
Gold (Aurum)	Au	197·2	Strontium	Sr	87·63
Hydrogen	H	1·0078	Sulphur	S	32·06
Iodine	I	126·92	Tin (Stannum)	Sn	118·70
Iron (Ferrum)	Fe	55·84	Titanium	Ti	47·90
Lead (Plumbum)	Pb	207·21	Tungsten (Wolfram)	W	184·0
Lithium	Li	6·940	Uranium	U	238·07
Magnesium	Mg	24·32	Zinc	Zn	65·38

BUFFER SOLUTIONS
(from *Histochemistry*, by A. G. Everson Pearse, by courtesy of J. & A. Churchill Ltd.)

pH 0·65 to 5·20
Walpole, 1914. 50 ml. N sodium acetate $+ x$ ml. N HCl, made up to 250 ml.

pH	x ml. HCl	pH	x ml. HCl	pH	x ml. HCl
0·65	100	1·99	52·5	3·79	42·5
0·75	90	2·32	51·0	3·95	40·0
0·91	80	2·64	50·0	4·19	35·0
1·09	70	2·72	49·75	4·39	30·0
1·24	65	3·09	48·5	4·58	25·0
1·42	60	3·29	47·5	4·76	20·0
1·71	55	3·49	46·25	4·92	15·0
1·85	53·5	3·61	45·0	5·20	10·0

pH 2·2 to 8·0
McIlvaine, 1921. 200 ml. mixtures of x ml. 0·2 M Na_2HPO_4 with y ml. 0·1 M citric acid

x ml. Na_2HPO_4	y ml. citric acid	pH	x ml. Na_2HPO_4	y ml. citric acid	pH
4·0	196	2·2	107·2	92·8	5·2
12·4	187·6	2·4	111·5	88·6	5·4
21·8	178·2	2·6	116·0	84·0	5·6
31·7	168·3	2·8	120·9	79·1	5·8
41·1	158·9	3·0	126·3	73·7	6·0
49·4	150·6	3·2	132·2	67·8	6·2
57·0	143·0	3·4	138·5	61·5	6·4
64·4	135·6	3·6	145·5	54·5	6·6
71·0	129·0	3·8	154·5	45·5	6·8
77·1	122·9	4·0	164·7	35·3	7·0
82·8	117·2	4·2	173·9	26·1	7·2
88·2	111·8	4·4	181·7	18·3	7·4
93·5	106·5	4·6	187·3	12·7	7·6
98·6	101·4	4·8	191·5	8·5	7·8
103·0	97·0	5·0	194·5	5·5	8·0

pH 3·6 to 5·6
Walpole, 1914. 200 ml. mixtures of 0·1 N acetic acid and 0·1 N sodium acetate

pH	0·1 N acetic acid (ml.)	0·1 N sodium acetate (ml.)	pH	0·1 N acetic acid (ml.)	0·1 N sodium acetate (ml.)
3·6	185	15	4·8	80	120
3·8	176	24	5·0	59	141
4·0	164	36	5·2	42	158
4·2	147	53	5·4	29	171
4·4	126	74	5·6	19	181
4·6	102	98			

pH 2·62 to 9·16

Michaelis, 1931. Stock solution: 9·714 g sodium acetate $3H_2O$ + 14·714 g sodium barbiturate in CO_2 free distilled water, made up to 500 ml. 5 ml. of this solution + 2 ml. of 8·5 per cent NaCl (may be omitted) treated with x ml. of 0·1 N HCl and $(18 - x)$ ml. water

x ml. 0·1 N HCl	pH	x ml. 0·1 N HCl	pH	x ml. 0·1 N HCl	pH
16·0	2·62	9·0	4·93	4·0	7·66
15·0	3·20	8·0	5·32	3·0	7·90
14·0	3·62	7·0	6·12	2·0	8·18
13·0	3·88	6·5	6·75	1·0	8·55
12·0	4·13	6·0	6·99	0·75	8·68
11·0	4·33	5·5	7·25	0·5	8·9
10·0	4·66	5·0	7·42	0·25	9·16

pH 7·4 to 9·0

Holmes. Mixtures of M/5 boric acid with M/20 sodium tetraborate

pH	M/5 H_3BO_3 (ml.)	M/20 $Na_2B_4O_7$ 10 H_2O (ml.)	pH	M/5H_3BO_3 (ml.)	M/20 $Na_2B_4O_7$ 10 H_2O (ml.)
7·4	18	2	8·2	13	7
7·6	17	3	8·4	11	9
7·8	16	4	8·7	8	12
8·0	14	6	9·0	4	16

This buffer is recommended by Burtner and Lillie, 1949, for making up Gomori's hexamine-silver solution

pH 7·19 to 9·10

Gomori. 25 ml. of 0·2 M tri(hydroxymethyl)aminomethane, Eastman-Kodak (M.W. 121·18), + x ml. 0·1 N HCl and distilled water up to 100 ml.

pH	x ml. 0·1 N HCl	pH	x ml. 0·1 N HCl
7·19	45·0	8·23	22·5
7·36	42·5	8·32	20·0
7·54	40·0	8·41	17·5
7·66	37·5	8·51	15·0
7·77	35·0	8·62	12·5
7·87	32·5	8·74	10·0
7·96	30·0	8·92	7·5
8·05	27·5	9·10	5·0
8·14	25·0		

pH 5·29 to 8·04

Sörensen, 1909–12. 100 ml. mixtures of M/15 Na_2HPO_4 and M/15 KH_2PO_4

pH	M/15 Na_2HPO_4 (ml.)	M/15 KH_2PO_4 (ml.)	pH	M/15 Na_2HPO_4 (ml.)	M/15 KH_2PO_4 (ml.)
5·29	2·5	97·5	6·81	50	50
5·59	5	95	6·98	60	40
5·91	10	90	7·17	70	30
6·24	20	80	7·38	80	20
6·47	30	70	7·73	90	10
6·64	40	60	8·04	95	5

pH 7·8 to 10·0

Clark and Lubs, 1916. 50 ml. 0·2 M H_3BO_3 + 0·2 M KCl + x ml. 0·2 M NaOH, diluted to 200 ml.

pH	x ml. 0·2 M NaOH	pH	x ml. 0·2 M NaOH
7·8	2·65	9·0	21·40
8·0	4·00	9·2	26·70
8·2	5·90	9·4	32·00
8·4	8·55	9·6	36·85
8·6	12·0	9·8	40·80
8·8	16·40	10·0	43·90

pH 8.45 to 12·77

Sörensen-Walbum, 1920. 100 ml. mixtures of 0·1 M glycine and 0·1 M NaCl with 0·1 M NaOH

pH	x ml. glycine-NaCl	y ml. NaOH	pH	x ml. glycine-NaCl	y ml. NaOH
8·45	95	5	11·14	50	50
8·79	90	10	11·39	49	51
9·22	80	20	11·92	45	55
9·56	70	30	12·21	40	60
9·98	60	40	12·48	30	70
10·32	55	45	12·66	20	80
10·9	51	49	12·77	10	90

INDEX

A page number in bold type gives the main position to which reference should be made.

Bos, 371
Botryllus, 124, 143
Bouganvillea, 22, 26
Bouin's fluid, 192
Bovoidea, 142
Bowerbankia, 55
Brachiopoda, 5, **59**
    culture, of, 61
    exposing loop of, 61
    killing and preservation of, 61
Brachiosaurus, 133
Brachyura, 80
Brain, staining thick sections of, 325
Branchiopoda, 80, 95
Branchiostoma, see Amphioxus
Branchiura, 95
Brechites, 63
Brontosaurus, 133
Brontotherioidea, 141
Bryozoa, see Ectoprocta
Buffers, 356, 386
Bufo, 129
Bugula, 56, 58

Cabinet-skin preparations, 321
Caenolestoidea, 136
Caenozoic, 371
Calcarea, 19
Calculating capacities, 385
Caligus, 109
Callavia, 106
Callianira, 27, 29
Calliostoma, 64
Callorhynchus, 127
Cambrian, 373
Camptosaurus, 133
Cancer diagnosis, Papanicolaou's
    stains for, 258
Candling of fowl eggs, 274
Cannula, method of inserting, 290
Canoidea, 139
Caprimulgiformes, 134
Carboniferous, 372
Carchesium, 6
Carcinus, 95, 109
Cardium, 63, 66
Carinatae, 134, 337
Carmine, 235
Carmine-gelatin, 292
Carnivora, 138, 339
Carnoy's fluid, 193
Cartilage transparencies, 340
Cartilaginous skeletons, preparation
    of, 340
Casco contact adhesive, 349
Casting methods used in Palaeon-
    tology, 375
Castolite, 301
Casuarius, 134

Cataloguing museum specimens, 309
Catharistes, 132
Caudata, 129
    culture of, 175
Ceboidea, 137
Celestine blue, 243
Cell
    mounts for museum specimens, 315
    walls, impregnation of, 256
Cellepora, 56
Celloidin technique, 208
    attachment of sections to slides, 212
    block making, 211
    creosote method, 212
    dry method, 211
    embedding, 208
    section cutting, 210
    wet method, 211
CEEMAR embedding kit, 317
Central nervous system, staining of,
    260
Centrurus, 106
Cephalochordata, 124,
    culture of, 143
    killing and preservation of, 143
Cephalodiscida, 121
Cephalodiscus, 121, 122
Cephalopoda, 63
Cephalaspis, 125
Ceratium, 5
Ceratomorpha, 141
Ceratopsia, 133
Cercopithecoidea, 137
Ceriantharia, 23
Cerianthus, 23
Cervoidea, 142
Cestoda, 29,
    fixation of, 33
    staining of, 35
Cestodaria, 30
Cestoidea, 30
Cestum, 27–29
Cetacea, 138
Chaetognatha, 5, **119**
Chaetonotoidea, 43
Chaetonotus, 43, 44
Chaetopterus, 70
Chalicotherioidea, 141
Chalkley's medium, 6
Chameleo, 130, 131, 346
    skeleton of, 333
Champy–Kull technique for mito-
    chondria, 257
Champy's fluid, 193
Charadriiformes, 134
Chatton–Lwoff technique (modified),
    14
Cheilostomata, 56
Cheirolepis, 127